Exciting and accessible science captivates students and makes them eager to learn.

ScottForesman Science

Discover the Wonder

Complete science coverage? Of course!
But *Discover the Wonder* offers you much more…

Easy and manageable to teach, *Discover the Wonder* puts you in complete control at every step.

Complete and manageable assessment features a unique blend of content, portfolio, and performance assessment opportunities.

Program Components

Varied resources meet all your needs

Student Text

Available as a single volume edition or individual modules.

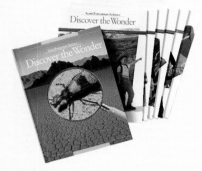

Flip Charts (Grades 1 and 2)

Enlarged student text pages are provided in a sturdy spiralbound flip chart that's ideal for teaching. You can write on it too! (22"x 34")

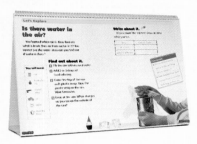

Teacher's Edition

Available as a single volume edition or individual modules.

Teacher's Resource Package

Teacher's Assessment Package

Flexible and effective! Assessment opportunities help you assess your students.

- chapter and module tests, Forms A and B
- performance-based assessment
- portfolio assessment suggestions
- activity-specific scoring rubrics for all formal student activities

Interactive Transparencies

Transparencies help students grasp major concepts. Especially useful for students who learn best through visuals, or for students who are second-language learners.

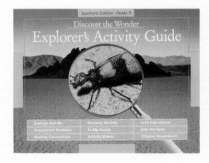

Science Study Sheets (Grades 3-6)

Great for review! These blackline masters are based on the **KWL** pattern. Includes:

- vocabulary support
- concept map for each lesson
- concept development and review

Explorer's Activity Guide

(Student Text and Teacher's Edition) Includes:

- take-home projects that emphasize the home/school connection
- opportunities to extend text activities and collect data
- *plus* unique portfolio assessment opportunities

Hands-On

Equipment Kits

The right stuff for science activities!

- *Modular Kits* include equipment for all Student Text activities. Provided by module, each kit comes in a sturdy plastic bin.
- *Economy Kits* offer the same materials as grade-level kits, without all the plastic bins and duplication of material. Perfect when funds are limited.

ExploraCenter

A mini-science museum for the classroom! Includes:

- seven inviting science tools
- 30 activities per grade
- Color Activity Cards at grades 1-2
- Teacher's Guide

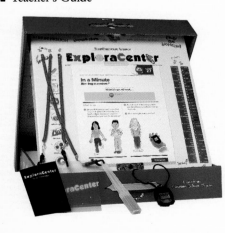

Technology

Videodisc/Videotape

Bring the world of science right into your classroom!

- Special video "field trips" to exciting places set the stage for each module.
- Animation, archival clips, photos, art, and other footage on the videodisc support and enhance module content.

CD-ROM Software (Macintosh/Windows)

Software and videodisc make a terrific team!

- Call up images from the videodisc.
- Explore topics via maps, charts, graphics, information screens, and motion sequences on the CD-ROM.
- Create special multimedia presentations from the videodisc and software with the Journal feature.

ScottForesman Online

Access exciting educational materials on the World Wide Web!

- *Young America* electronic field trip follows PACT 95 designers and crew as they design and race a boat to defend the America's Cup. Updated each school year!
- References in *Discover the Wonder* Teacher's Editions to the *Young America* electronic field trip help you enhance math-science connections.
- To come—more electronic field trips, teacher and student support, E-mail, and bulletin boards will continually update your *Discover the Wonder* program.

Literature Library

Award-winning books and authors connect science with literature!

- At grades 1-2, 16 literature selections per grade connect with the text via the Teacher's Edition.
- At grades 3-6, 12 books per grade connect with the help of a separate Teacher's Guide.

Real science for the real world!

ExploraCenter
Classroom mini-museum! Inviting display box includes:
- 7 tools for exploring
- Activity Cards
- Teacher's Guide

ScottForesman Online
Access exciting educational material from ScottForesman Online on the World Wide Web! See page 3.

Explorer's Activity Wallchart
Activities on display—to help children observe, explore, and discover. It's a neat way to collect and interpret data, too!

Big Books
Colorful and inviting! Photos, lively activities, and a child-friendly style introduce young students to science.

Literature Library
Twelve award-winning books highlight the science-literature connection.

Videotape
Management help on tape! See real classroom teachers model *Discover the Wonder* activities and provide management tips.

Audio Cassettes
Engaging tapes introduce Literature Library books.

Teacher's Assessment Package
Options for flexibility! Choose among three:
- content (traditional)
- portfolio
- performance

Teacher's Edition
Keeps teaching manageable! This practical guide organizes the entire Learning System for you.

Equipment Kit
Convenient Kit provides all the materials you need to do the Kindergarten System activities.

Connections across the curriculum

Why teach science in isolation? Scientific concepts are much more meaningful when they're related to topics beyond the classroom. You'll find cross-curricular connections throughout *Discover the Wonder!*

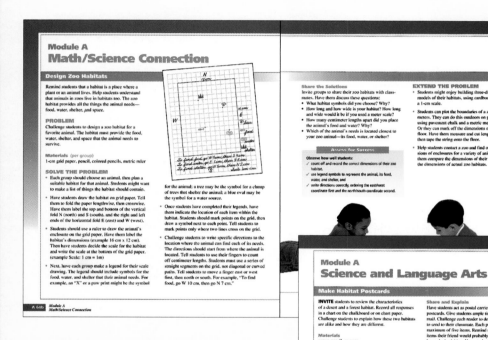

Math/Science Connections

A two-page section in every module of the Teacher's Edition provides you with activities to connect science to mathematics.

Cross-curricular Activities

Every module of the Teacher's Edition connects science to language arts or other subject areas.

Activities suggest a wealth of subject-area connections!

- Math
- Language Arts
- Writing
- Social Studies
- Literature
- Home Connections
- Multicultural Connections
- Technology
- Health
- Science Library
- Art
- Music

Trade Book Libraries connect science to literature

What an enjoyable way to learn science! Exciting books by award-winning authors and illustrators invite students to explore science concepts.

Complete Science

K-6

All the traditional content you need is organized for relevance and understanding.

Module A	Module B	Module C

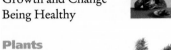  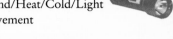

K

All About You
Senses
Growth and Change
Being Healthy

Life Around You
Living/Nonliving Things
Animals
Plants

Changes All Around
Matter
Sound/Heat/Cold/Light
Movement

1

Plants
Characteristics of Trees
Plant Characteristics
Plant Products

Growing and Changing
Human Growth/Nutrition
Animal Growth/Change
Changing the Earth

Sound and Light
Hearing and Seeing
Properties of Sound
Properties of Light

2

Living Things
Animal and Plant Adaptations
Habitats
Grouping Living Things

Changes Over Time
Dinosaur Characteristics
Fossils
Extinct/Endangered Animals

Making Things Move
Forces/Motion
Magnetism
Machines and Work

3

Habitats
Climates and Adaptations
Desert Life
Desert/Climates
Forest/Habitats

Gardening
Plants, Food Chains, and Nutrition
Photosynthesis
Soil/Water Cycle
Nutrition/Digestion

Finding Shelter
Natural Resources and Simple Machines
Building Materials
Heat and Insulation
Simple Machines/Work

4

Earth and Other Planets
The Solar System
Earth/Sun/Moon
Solar System
Earth's Biosphere

Water
Water Cycle, Erosion, and Oceans
Properties of Water
Weathering/Erosion
Water Adaptations/Habitats

Volcanoes and Earthquakes
Changes in Earth's Crust
Earth's Structure
Volcano Eruption/Recovery
Mountains/Earthquakes

5

Take a Closer Look
Minerals, Atoms, and Cells
Scale and Magnification
Atoms/Compounds
Cell Structure/Function

Pedaling Uphill
Force, Work, and Machines
Simple Machines
Compound Machines
Bicycles/Safety

Fun in Motion
Laws of Motion, Body Movements, and Gravity
Laws of Motion
Body Systems/Movement
Gravity/Friction

6

Stargazing
Galaxies, the Universe, and Astronomy
Star Life Cycle
Electromagnetic Spectrum
History of Astronomy

The Living Planet
Cells, Genes, and Heredity
Chemicals of Life
Heredity/Genetics
Reproduction and Change

Digging for Clues
Earth's Geologic Past and Evolution
Geologic Time Scale/ Evolution
Fossil Evidence of the Past
Plate Tectonics

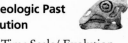

For more information call toll-free

1-800-554-4411

ScottForesman *Health for Life* K-8 is also available!

Module D

The Earth and You

Using Land and Water
Earth and Sky
Weather

Weather

Kinds of Weather
Water Cycle
Seasons

The Earth and Sky

The Sun and Earth
Stars/Constellations/Moon
The Earth: Land, Water, Air

Moving

Energy, Animal Movement, and Transportation

Seeds/Animal Movement
Survival/Migration
Transportation

Flying

Adaptations and Flight

Atmosphere/Air Pressure
Birds/Flight
Flight Technology

Running on Sunlight

Solar Energy and Its Uses

Forms of Energy
Electromagnetic Radiation
Photosynthesis/Digestion

Adaptations

Surviving in Different Habitats

Diversity of Light/Color
Adaptations to Habitats
Ocean Adaptations

Module E

Grades K-2 have 4 modules

Sounds All Around

Sound Energy and Hearing

Energy/Sound Waves
Hearing/Using Sound
Sound Technology

The Weather Report

Weather, Climate, and Seasons

Weather Patterns
Seasons/Climates
Predicting Weather

Electricity

Electrical, Nerve, and Broadcasting Signals

Magnetism/Electricity
Nervous System
Radio/TV Signals

High-Tech, Low-Tech

Water, Electrical, and Manufacturing Systems

Water Purification Treatment
Electrical Supply System
Manufacturing System

Module F

Protecting the Earth

People, Pollution, and Recycling

Water Pollution
Trash/Recycling
Endangered/Extinct Species

Rainforests

Diversity of Life in an Ecosystem

Life in the Rainforest
Rainforest Destruction
Protecting Rainforests

Living Off the Land

Plant Growth, Genetics, and Farming

Plant Signals/Pest Control
Plant Growth and Reproduction
Improved Farming Techniques

Wetlands: Making Decisions

Maintaining a Balanced Ecosystem

Balanced Ecosystem
Wetland Ecosystem
Ecosystem Management

ScottForesman Science
Discover the Wonder

Enjoy complete, flexible science coverage, *plus*

- **Exciting and accessible science for all students**
- **Easy and manageable ways to teach science**
- **Complete and manageable assessment**

For more information call toll-free
1-800-554-4411

 **ScottForesman**

A Division of HarperCollins*Publishers*
Glenview, IL   Oakland, NJ   Atlanta, GA   Carrollton, TX   Sunnyvale, CA

ScottForesman Science

Discover the Wonder

Series Consulting Author

David Heil
Associate Director,
Oregon Museum of Science & Industry
Portland, Oregon

Consulting Authors

Maureen Allen
Science Resource Teacher/Specialist
Irvine Unified School District
Irvine, California

Dr. Timothy Cooney
Professor of Earth Science & Science Education
Earth Science Department
University of Northern Iowa
Cedar Falls, Iowa

Dr. Angie L. Matamoros
Science Curriculum Specialist K–12
Broward County Schools
Ft. Lauderdale, Florida

Dr. Manuel Perry
Manager, Educational Programs
Lawrence Livermore National Laboratory
Livermore, California

Dr. Irwin Slesnick
Professor of Biology
Biology Department
Western Washington University
Bellingham, Washington

ScottForesman

A Division of HarperCollins*Publishers*

Editorial Offices: Glenview, Illinois
Regional Offices: Sunnyvale, California • Tucker, Georgia
Glenview, Illinois • Oakland, New Jersey • Dallas, Texas

Content Consultants

Dr. Linda Berne
Department of Health Promotion
and Kinesiology
University of North Carolina
Charlotte, North Carolina

Dr. Bonnie J. Buratti
Jet Propulsion Laboratory
California Institute of Technology
Pasadena, California

Dr. Norman M. Gelfand
Physicist
Fermi National Accelerator Laboratory
Accelerator Division
Batavia, Illinois

Dr. Roger A. Pielke
Professor
Department of Atmospheric Science
Colorado State University
Fort Collins, Colorado

Dr. Harrison H. Schmitt
*Former Astronaut (Apollo 17) and
United States Senator
Geologist and Science and
Technology Consultant*
Albuquerque, New Mexico

Dr. Lisa K. Wagner
Department of Biology
Georgia Southern University
Statesboro, Georgia

Multicultural Consultants

Dr. Frank Dukepoo
Department of Biology
Northern Arizona University
Flagstaff, Arizona

Dr. Deborah A. Fortune
Department of Health Promotion
and Kinesiology
University of North Carolina
Charlotte, North Carolina

Dr. Amram Gamliel
*Educational Consultant/
Professional Writer*
Newton Center, Massachusetts

Dr. Luis A. Martinez-Perez
College of Education
Florida International University
Miami, Florida

Dr. Anthony R. Sancho
*Director of Hispanic Health
Education Center*
Southwest Regional Laboratory
Los Alamitos, California

Math/Science Consultant

Catherine R. Ney
Teacher
Blacksburg, Virginia
1994–95 Christa McAuliffe Fellow,
State of Virginia

Acknowledgments

Photographs Unless otherwise acknowledged, all photographs are the property of ScottForesman. Page abbreviations are as follows: (T)top, (C)center, (B)bottom, (L)left, (R)right, (INS)inset.

Cover Design Sheldon Cotler + Associates

Cover Background: Karen Tweedy-Homes/Earth Scenes   Magnifying Glass: Richard Chesnut   Inset: John Gerlach/Animals Animals

Page v(T) Esao Hashimoto/Animals Animals   **vi(T)** David M. Dennis/Tom Stack & Associates   **viii(T)** Phil Degginger   **ix(B)** Gerald & Buff Corsi/Tom Stack & Associates   **xiii(L)** Lawrence Migdale/Stock Boston   **xiii(R)** Mike J. Howell/Stock Boston   **xiv(T)** E. R. Degginger   **xiv(B)** NASA

Illustrations Unless otherwise acknowledged, all computer graphics by The Quarasan Group, Inc.   **Page vii** Cecile Duray-Bito   **ix** Roberta Polfus

Acknowledgments continue on page 47.

About the Cover

Furry red squirrels are the most commonly seen mammal of the Great North Woods. However, they can also be found throughout the hardwood forests of the Appalachian region, such as that shown by the fall foliage of the background photograph.

Module A

Living Things

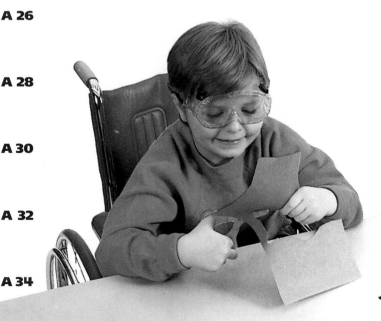

Module B

Changes Over Time

Chapter 2
Dinosaur Detectives B 20

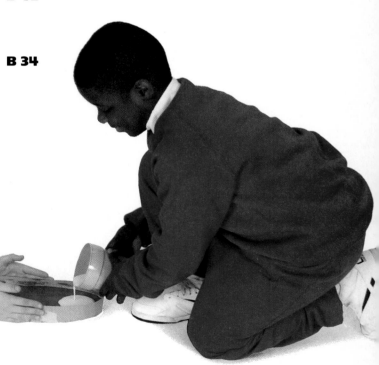

Chapter 3
A Changing World B 42

Making Things Move

The Earth and Sky

Chapter 2
The Moon and Stars D 24

Your Ideas

Living Things

Module A

A 1

Module A Planning Guide
Living Things

Module At-a-Glance

Lessons/Concepts

Chapter 1 Plants and Animals p. A4

CONCEPT: There are certain characteristics and behaviors that enable living things to survive.

STRANDS: Physical, Life

1. What body parts do animals have? p. A5 *(animal and human similarities)*
2. How do body parts help animals live? p. A6 *(butterfly body parts)*
3. What actions help animals stay alive? p. A8 *(animal behaviors)*
4. How can color make things hard to see? p. A10 *(color and survival)*
5. How do color and shape help animals? p. A12 *(animal camouflage)*
6. What parts help plants live? p. A14 *(plant parts)*
7. How do some plants store water? p. A16 *(water storage)*
8. What helps plants grow in new places? p. A18 *(scattering plant seeds)*
9. How are seeds scattered? p. A20 *(seed shapes and scattering)*
10. What did you learn? p. A22 *(plant and animal survival)*

Chapter 2 Where Things Live? p. A24

CONCEPT: A habitat is the place in which a plant or animal lives. A habitat meets all the needs of the plant or animal that lives there.

STRANDS: Life, History

1. Where do you see plants and animals? p. A25 *(habitats)*
2. Where do plants and animals live? p. A26 *(kinds of habitats)*
3. What lives in a water habitat? p. A28 *(water habitats)*
4. How does a habitat help living things? p. A30 *(survival)*
5. How can you make a habitat? p. A32 *(providing habitats)*
6. What habitats are in a zoo? p. A34 *(zoo habitats)*
7. What habitat can you plan for a zoo? p. A36 *(tree habitats)*
8. How many red wolves live in wildlife parks? p. A38 *(red wolf habitat)*
9. What did you learn? p. A40 *(plant and animal habitats)*

Chapter 3 Grouping Living Things p. A42

CONCEPT: Living things, such as plants and animals, can be further classified according to similar characteristics.

STRAND: Life

1. How can you group things? p. A43 *(classifying shoes)*
2. Is it living? p. A44 *(living and nonliving things)*
3. How are living things grouped? p. A46 *(classifying living things)*
4. What are some groups of animals? p. A48 *(classifying animals)*
5. What are some kinds of body coverings? p. A50 *(body coverings on animals)*
6. What are some other groups of animals? p. A52 *(worms, spiders, insects)*
7. How can you make a model of an insect? p. A54 *(insect characteristics)*
8. How do you group plants? p. A56 *(classifying plants)*
9. What did you learn? p. A58 *(living and nonliving things)*

People at Work pp. A60–A61
Module Review pp. A62–A63
Kids Did It pp. 2–3
Study Guide pp. 10–13
Experiment Skills pp. 30–31

Themes: *Scale and Structure, Systems and Interactions, Diversity*

In this module, children discover that animals and plants have characteristics that help them survive. Children learn that living and nonliving things interact in their habitat. They also learn that the diversity of life can be classified by certain characteristics.

Activity Opportunities

Pupil's Edition	Teacher's Edition/Ancillaries

Discover Activity p. A5
Let's Explore pp. A10–A11
Activity p. A17
Activity p. A19
Let's Solve It! pp. A20–A21
Chapter Review pp. A22–A23
	Explorer's Activity Guide
	  pp. 1–13
	ExploraCenter Teacher's Guide
	  pp. 6, 7, 13, 15, 17, 28, 29,
	  30, 32
	Videodisc Classroom
	  Guide pp. 9–16
	Interactive Transparency
	  Guide pp. 6–9
	Interactive Videodisc Software
	  Teacher's Guide pp. 44–52

Discover Activity p. A25
Activity p. A27
Let's Explore pp. A32–A33
Activity p. A37
Let's Solve It! pp. A38–A39
Chapter Review pp. A40–A41
	Explorer's Activity Guide
	  pp. 14–26
	ExploraCenter Teacher's Guide
	  pp. 13, 17, 28
	Videodisc Classroom
	  Guide pp. 9–16
	Interactive Transparency
	  Guide pp. 10–13
	Interactive Videodisc Software
	  Teacher's Guide pp. 44–52

Discover Activity p. A43
Activity p. A45
Activity p. A51
Let's Explore pp. A54–A55
Let's Solve It! pp. A56–A57
Chapter Review pp. A58–A59
	Explorer's Activity Guide
	  pp. 27–38
	ExploraCenter Teacher's Guide
	  pp. 12, 13, 15, 17, 28, 29,
	  30, 32
	Videodisc Classroom
	  Guide pp. 9–16
	Interactive Transparency Guide
	  pp. 14–15
	Interactive Videodisc Software
	  Teacher's Guide pp. 44–52

	Explorer's Activity Guide
	  • Family letter pp. 39–40
	Teacher's Edition
	  • Math/Science Connection
	    pp. A63a–A63b

Assessment Opportunities
(CONTENT • PORTFOLIO • PERFORMANCE)

Pupil's Edition	Teacher's Edition/Ancillaries

Checkpoint pp. A7, A8, A11,
  A12, A15, A17, A19, A21
Chapter Review
  Performance Assessment
  Activity pp. A22–A23
	Teacher's Edition
	  • Check for Understanding
	    pp. A5, A7, A9, A11, A13,
	    A15, A17, A19, A21, A23
	Teacher's Assessment Package
	  • Activity Rubrics p. 3
	  • Chapter Test pp. 5–6
	Explorer's Activity Guide
	  • Chapter Review p. 13

Checkpoint pp. A27, A28,
  A31, A33, A34, A37, A39
Chapter Review
  Performance Assessment
  Activity pp. A40–A41
	Teacher's Edition
	  • Check for Understanding
	    pp. A25, A27, A29, A31,
	    A33, A35, A37, A39, A41
	Teacher's Assessment Package
	  • Activity Rubrics p. 9
	  • Chapter Test pp. 11–12
	Explorer's Activity Guide
	  • Chapter Review pp. 25–26

Checkpoint pp. A45, A47,
  A48, A51, A53, A55, A57
Chapter Review
  Performance Assessment
  Activity pp. A58–A59
	Teacher's Edition
	  • Check for Understanding
	    pp. A43, A45, A47, A49,
	    A51, A53, A55, A57, A59
	Teacher's Assessment Package
	  • Activity Rubrics p. 15
	  • Chapter Test pp. 17–18
	Explorer's Activity Guide
	  • Chapter Review pp. 37–38

Module Review
  pp. A62–A63
	Teacher's Assessment
	Package
	  • Performance Assessment
	    Test pp. 21–22

Module A Event
A Visit to the Rainforest

Planning the Visit

A model of a rainforest can be an imaginative performance assessment of this module. The model rainforest may be built to accommodate visitors. It can be open to children and families on a day that can also serve as an occasion for ecological awareness.

Getting Started

Respect for conservation of plant and animal life comes through an awareness of how these living things are equipped to function in their native habitats. The chapters in this module give children exposure to plant and animal adaptations, as well as the relationship among these plants and animals. Include in the exhibit any pictures children have drawn or models they have made during the chapter activities. Also, photographs of actual rainforest plants and animals will make the model rainforest more colorful and inviting. Some varieties of orchids, tropical ferns, or palms, readily available as houseplants, will make good additions to the model rainforest.

Activity Options

Multicultural Connection

If possible, present a video to help expand children's interest in the people living in the South American rainforest. One such video, available in U.S. libraries, is *The Rain Forest (Selva Verde): The Green Jungle* (Partridge Film Video). After viewing this video (or any similar feature), children can discuss what their life might be like if they lived among the plants and animals of the South American rainforest.

Art Connection

Obtain pictures of a rainforest from magazines and books. Have children choose plants to represent in cutouts, using cardboard, construction paper, glue, and markers. Have them make clay models of some forest animals. Use folded cardboard to make stands for the plants. Install the clay animals among them as part of the rainforest.

Social Studies Connection

Earth's remaining humid tropical rainforests are in the Amazon Basin, in the Congo Basin, and on the islands of Indonesia (Borneo being the largest), Malaysia, and New Guinea. Supply a simple map and several colored-paper pieces matching the sizes and shapes of the rainforest areas. Help children find the locations of the rainforests and cover the location with the appropriate paper pieces. Help children realize that a very small portion of the earth remains rainforest.

Using Multiple Intelligences (See page T5.)

The activities presented on these pages provide the opportunity for students to show their understanding of concepts using their strongest individual problem-solving abilities, or intelligences. The chart shows which of the seven intelligences are developed within each activity option. In addition, all students can develop interpersonal intelligence as they participate in the Module Event, A Visit to the Rainforest.

A Visit to the Rainforest

Activity	Intelligences
Multicultural Connection	interpersonal
Art Connection	visual/spatial
Social Studies Connection	visual/spatial
Language Arts Connection	musical/rhythmic

Language Arts Connection

Supplement the rainforest exhibit with recordings of sounds of the forest. Have children write descriptions of the forest sounds they hear and describe what could be making the sounds.

Let Parents Try It

Provide some pictures of fruit trees and herb and spice plants that grow in rainforests. Allow visitors to sample bits of banana or coconut dipped in spices such as nutmeg, cinnamon, or cardamom that are found in the rainforest.

The Big Event

Set up tables, booths, or areas in your room to fit the choices you have made from the Activity Options. One table can hold the model of the rainforest, complete with painted cardboard plants on stands, clay animals, and a few live plants. Another table can hold the activities, such as the fruit and spice tasting, in which visitors may participate.

Appoint children to act as monitors and assistants at the displays. Children can draw attention to the food-sampling table and encourage parents and guardians to participate. The sound display could include bird or animal sounds, the sound of gentle rain, or the music and rhythms of native people of the forest. Encourage children to take turns guiding visitors from one feature to another.

Module A
Across the Curriculum

Science Background

Animal Adaptions

An adaptation is a trait that helps a species survive. An adaptation can help an animal get food, help protect it from predators, or help it find a mate. Four types of adaptions are: structural, or change in arrangement or shape; color; physiological, or change in vital life processes; behavioral.

The green anole, a lizard, has a structural adaption. When a green anole is caught by the tail, the tail breaks off so that the lizard survives the attack.

Color can help an animal survive. Some fish have black spots near their tails that confuse predators. Camouflage enables some animals to blend with their surroundings. This adaptation helps animals escape predators or hide when they are hunting.

Some seals have a physiological adaptation that helps them conserve oxygen. The circulation in their outer layers and limbs can shut off, and they can hold their breath for long periods. This adaptation helps them hunt for food at great depths.

Opossums exhibit a behavioral adaption when threatened. They can "play possum," or curl up in a ball and pretend to be dead until they are safe.

Classification

Scientists classify organisms into five groups, or kingdoms. Two of the main kingdoms are plants and animals. Scientists subdivide each of the five kingdoms into smaller groups called phyla. More than thirty animal phyla have been named. Vertebrates are members of the chordate phylum because they have backbones. The next smaller group is the class. Mammals, birds, reptiles, amphibians, and three classes of fish are the classes of vertebrates. Classes are further divided into order, family, genus, and species.

Science Across Cultures

Medicines from Plants and Animals

People often think that all medicines are developed in modern laboratories. However, some remedies have their origins in ancient folk medicine. For centuries, people have used the plants and animals around them to produce remedies for human ailments. In some cases, modern researchers have found a basis for the effectiveness of this folk medicine.

Ancient Egyptians believed a diet rich in onions and garlic would protect a person against many diseases. Modern studies have confirmed that onions and garlic contain an ingredient that might help prevent infections.

The early Chinese used seaweed to treat throat problems. Seaweed has a high iodine content. Today, physicians know that iodine reduces problems with the thyroid gland, a gland located in the throat. The Chinese also used poisons found in some fish for sciatica (sī at'ə kə), severe pains in the thigh nerves. After years of study and experiments, biologists and physicians have confirmed that many fish poisons contain a chemical that can help relax muscles.

As time passes, modern medical studies continue to confirm the usefulness of many simple plant and animal medicines used by ancient cultures. Among the most common is the cinchona tree. Native South American peoples used part of this tree to treat fever. Today the active substance in cinchona is refined into quinine and used to treat malaria.

Some native North American peoples chewed the inner bark of the juniper tree to prevent a condition called scurvy. Modern medical research has discovered that scurvy is caused by a lack of vitamin C; juniper contains vitamin C.

Cross-curricular Activities

The activities in this module provide many opportunities to make connections between science and other areas of the elementary curriculum.

In addition, the wide variety of cross-curricular activities helps make learning both interesting and fun!

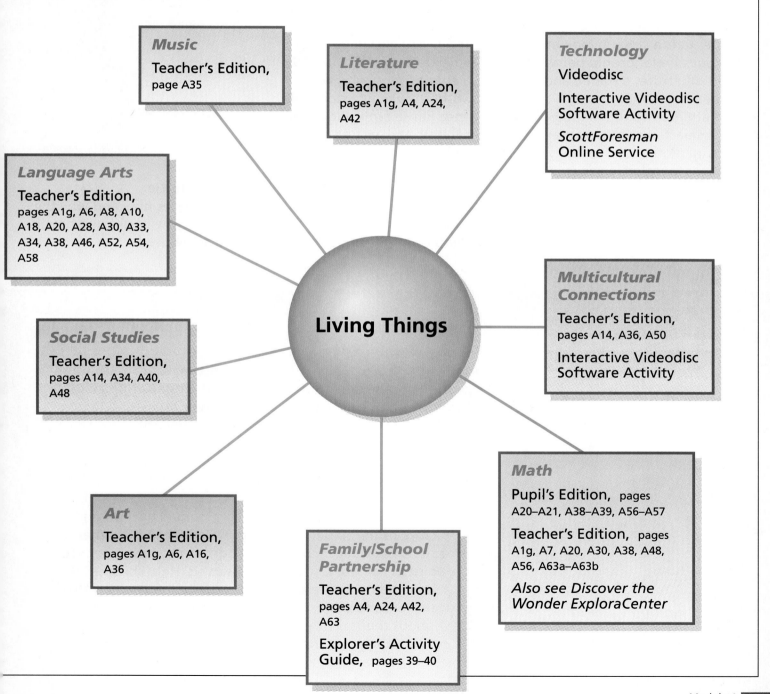

Music
Teacher's Edition, page A35

Literature
Teacher's Edition, pages A1g, A4, A24, A42

Technology
Videodisc

Interactive Videodisc Software Activity

ScottForesman Online Service

Language Arts
Teacher's Edition, pages A1g, A6, A8, A10, A18, A20, A28, A30, A33, A34, A38, A46, A52, A54, A58

Living Things

Multicultural Connections
Teacher's Edition, pages A14, A36, A50

Interactive Videodisc Software Activity

Social Studies
Teacher's Edition, pages A14, A34, A40, A48

Art
Teacher's Edition, pages A1g, A6, A16, A36

Family/School Partnership
Teacher's Edition, pages A4, A24, A42, A63

Explorer's Activity Guide, pages 39–40

Math
Pupil's Edition, pages A20–A21, A38–A39, A56–A57

Teacher's Edition, pages A1g, A7, A20, A30, A38, A48, A56, A63a–A63b

Also see Discover the Wonder ExploraCenter

Module A
Links to Literature

The Lady and the Spider
by Faith McNulty/illustrated by Bob Marstall

Introducing the Literature Library Selection

The literature library selection for this module is *The Lady and the Spider* by Faith McNulty, illustrated by Bob Marstall (Harper & Row, 1986). In this story, the reader gets a closeup look at the ecological relationship between a head of lettuce, a spider, and a gardener.

In addition to the module literature selection, each chapter has a companion book. You may use the chapter selection to invite learning, assess prior knowledge, or reinforce concepts presented in the lessons.

- *An Octopus Is Amazing* by Patricia Lauber (Crowell, 1990) introduces the octopus and tells about the amazing adaptations that help it survive.
- *Little Frog's Song* by Alice Schertle (HarperCollins, 1992) is about a frog who was washed away in a storm. He finds himself in a variety of habitats and isn't happy until he's back home.
- In *Fireflies in the Night* by Judy Hawes (Harper Trophy, 1991), a boy tells about the fireflies at his grandparents' home. He compares fireflies to other insects. He describes how and why they make their light and how it can be used.

Activity Corner

Cross-Curricular Activities

Language Arts
- **Retelling a Story** Review important vocabulary words in the story; then have children retell the story in their own words.

Art
- **Drawing a Picture** Have children draw a picture of the spider and its habitat at some point in the story. Have them dictate a sentence to you about their picture. Write their sentence on the drawing.

Math
- **Collecting Data** Have children identify insect habitats near their home or school. For example, they may see a colony of ants building an ant hill and carrying leaf particles to it. Encourage children to visit the habitat accompanied by a parent or guardian. Then have them report to the class what they observed. Help children record the information they learned on a class chart or bar graph.

Beginning with the Bulletin Board

Making Connections

Have children sort and discuss pictures showing different insects and animals in their natural habitat. Then have children make their own related drawings or models. Include some reproductions of images from the module literature selection *The Lady and the Spider* by Faith McNulty, illustrated by Bob Marstall.

You will need:

 magazine pictures

 drawing paper

 construction paper

 safety scissors

 crayons

 pushpins

 markers

 envelope

 tape

Preparing the Bulletin Board

At the top of the bulletin board, post a card labeled *Habitats.* Divide the board into sections labeled *Gardens, Forests, Zoos,*

and *Water.* Next to each label, place a picture representing that habitat.

Attach a large envelope to the bottom of the board. In it, place magazine pictures, children's drawings, and construction-paper cutouts showing diverse life forms. You may include flowers, trees, a variety of insects, and animals, including people.

Bulletin Board Activity

Have children take a picture from the envelope, identify the image, and attach it to the appropriate area of the bulletin board. Have children explain their choice.

Guide children in discussing the similarities among plants and animals, while helping children decide which habitat is right for a given plant or animal image. If a plant or an animal can be placed in more than one section, discuss the placements with children. As pictures are added to the bulletin board, you may want to help children group the life forms.

Extend the Activity

Move some of the pictures to alternate locations. For instance, a frog could live in water, but might visit a nearby garden. Encourage children to discuss the habitat options available to a specific plant or animal.

Living Things

How can an animal be like a plant? Animals and plants look different. But animals and plants are alike in an important way. They are living things.

Chapter 1

Plants and Animals

It can be fun to learn about different kinds of animals and plants! How do animals and plants get the things they need to stay alive? Page **A 4**

A 2

Chapter 2

Where Things Live

Each animal and plant lives in its own special place. Where do some animals and plants you know about live? Page **A 24**

Chapter 3

Grouping Living Things

You can sort objects into groups by color or shape or size. Can you sort animals and plants into groups too?

Page **A 42**

Chapter 1 Planning Guide
Plants and Animals

Lessons / *Skills*

Lesson 1
Discover Activity: **What body parts do animals have?** pp. A4–A5
(observing, naming, comparing)

Lesson 2
How do body parts help animals live? pp. A6–A7
(observing, describing)

Lesson 3
What actions help animals stay alive? pp. A8–A9
(comparing, drawing conclusions)

Lesson 4
Let's Explore: **How can color make things hard to see?**
pp. A10–A11
(recording, interpreting data, applying information)

Lesson 5
How do color and shape help animals? pp. A12–A13
(observing, interpreting data)

Lesson 6
What parts help plants live? pp. A14–A15
(describing, organizing information)

Lesson 7
How do some plants store water? pp. A16–A17
(recognizing cause and effect, drawing conclusions)

Lesson 8
What helps plants grow in new places? pp. A18–A19
(making analogies, drawing conclusions)

Lesson 9
Let's Solve It!: **How are seeds scattered?** pp. A20–A21
(organizing information, solving problems)

Lesson 10
Chapter Review: **What did you learn?** pp. A22–A23
(communicating, naming, judging and evaluating)

Materials (per group)

Lesson 1 Activity: *What body parts do animals have?*
Module Kit Items: none
School Supplied Items: book with pictures of animals; crayons; drawing paper *(1 sheet/child)*

Lesson 4 Activity: *How can color make things hard to see?*
Module Kit Items: brown construction paper; white construction paper
School Supplied Items: timer; brown wrapping paper *(optional)*
Advance Prep: Cut paper circles about the size of a quarter.

Lesson 7 Activity: *Observe how plants store water.*
Module Kit Items: none
School Supplied Items: jade plant; fern plant; water in watering can; measuring cup *(optional)*

Lesson 8 Activity: *Show how seeds are scattered.*
Module Kit Items: cotton balls *(1/child)*; construction paper, assorted colors *(1 sheet/child)*
School Supplied Items: none

Lesson 10 Activity: *Play a guessing game.*
Module Kit Items: none
School Supplied Items: 6 sheets of paper *(1 sheet/group, then 1 sheet/child)*; pencils *(1/child)*

Assessment Options

	Content	Performance	Portfolio
Teacher's Assessment Package			
Chapter Test, pp. 5–6	✓		✓
Group Interview Assessment, p. 7	✓	✓	✓
Performance Strategies, p. 8	✓	✓	✓
Explorer's Activity Guide			
Activity worksheets, pp. 1–12		✓	✓
Chapter Review, p. 13	✓		✓
Interactive Transparency Package			
Transparency 1 and 2 and BLMs	✓	✓	✓
Teacher's Guide, pp. 6–9	✓	✓	
Activity for second-language learners	✓	✓	✓
Hands-on activity for second-language learners	✓	✓	✓
Science Literature Library			
An Octopus Is Amazing		✓	✓
Interactive Videodisc Software			
Teacher's Guide, pp. 44–52			
Computer-based Activity	✓	✓	
Journal Presentations	✓	✓	✓
Videodisc Classroom Guide, pp. 9–16, or			
Video Reader			
Hands-on activity	✓	✓	✓
ExploraCenter Teacher's Guide,			
pp. 6, 7, 13, 15, 17, 28, 29, 30, 32			
ExploraCenter			
Science activity cards 1, 2, 8, 10, 12, 23, 24, 25, 27	✓	✓	✓
ScottForesman Online Service			
Online field trips	✓	✓	✓

Chapter Overview

Children begin this chapter by thinking about other animals. They learn that animal adaptations such as body parts, actions, color, and shape help animals stay alive. Children also discover that plants have special parts that help them grow. As a culminating activity, children play a plant and animal guessing game.

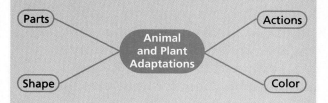

Lesson 1

Chapter 1

Lesson Objective

Children use prior knowledge and visual clues to compare themselves to another animal.

Introduce

Invite Learning

Show the videodisc or videotape segment for this chapter. Bar codes and a description of this segment are given below on page A5.

Make Connections

To **assess prior knowledge,** have each child in a group act out the different kind of animal he or she would like to be. Other group members try to guess the animal. Children should then tell how they are like the animal. Record their comments to use as a **baseline assessment** in Check for Understanding.

Teach

Discover Activity

Children look at an animal in a picture and draw what they see.
Skills: Observing, comparing

Materials (per group)
Module Kit Items: none
School Supplied Items: book with pictures of animals; crayons; sheets of drawing paper

Plants and Animals

Did you ever wish that you could be a different animal for a day? You might like to be a bird. What kind of bird would you be?

How would you look if you were a bird? You might have bright blue feathers. Or you could have webbed feet.

What other special body parts might you have? What things could you do that you can't do now?

A 4

Science Idea Exchange

Managing Groups

Assign specific children to gather and clean up materials. All children in the Discover Activity group should choose an animal picture, draw the body parts of that animal, and share their drawings.

Science and Literature

Read the chapter literature selection *An Octopus Is Amazing* by Patricia Lauber (Crowell, 1990).  Then help children identify the various parts of an octopus that help it survive. Challenge children to compare the octopus to themselves and list the body parts that are different.

Family/School Partnership: Family Support

Encourage families to be active partners in learning by suggesting that they and their children:
● observe an animal or its picture,
● describe the parts of the animal, and
● observe and describe a plant.

Helpful Hints
- Allow groups to share their drawings.
- *See Equipment Kit Teacher's Guide for additional hints.*

What to Expect
Children may **describe** the animal's size, shape, or color and identify its head, tail, legs, paws, claws, beak, or wings.

Close

Check for Understanding
- As a follow-up to the **baseline assessment,** ask children which of the animals' body parts are like their own. Have them compare their comments with those from Make Connections.
- **Answers to Tell about it** Children might say that they and the animals have some similar body parts, such as eyes and legs. They may note differences in body covering (hair rather than feathers).

What Else Do You Want to Find Out?
Using a **constructivist** approach, ask: *What else do you want to know about animals? How could we find the answers to your questions?* Record children's questions on chart paper.

Connecting Lessons
In the next lesson, children will learn how body parts help an animal stay alive. ▶

Discover Activity

What body parts do animals have?

1. Find a picture of an animal in a book.
2. Look at the animal in your picture. Tell what you see.
3. Draw what you see.
4. **Tell about it.** Tell how you and the animal are alike. Tell how you and the animal are different.

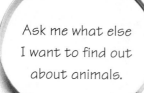

Ask me what else I want to find out about animals.

A 5

Explorer's Activity Guide
The **Discovery Activity recording sheets** on pages 3–4 of the Explorer's Activity Guide can be used by children to record their activity results.

Visual Literacy
Discover the Wonder Videotape or *Videodisc,* Grade 2, Module A, allows children to watch a group of their peers observing and interacting with a wide assortment of animals. Use the video to challenge children's understanding of the differences and similarities among different types of animals, including humans.

Bar Codes

Chapter 4: Video, English

Chapter 4: Video, Spanish

Play

Interactive Software

Lesson 2

Lesson Objective
Children learn how the body parts of a butterfly help it survive.

Introduce

Invite Learning
Draw a large butterfly outline on chart paper. Include the major body parts: antennas, eyes, body, wings, and six legs. Invite each child to color a part of the butterfly's wings to make a colorful poster.

Make Connections
To **assess prior knowledge,** have children point to the parts of the butterfly on the poster and ask them to explain how they think each body part helps the animal.

Teach

Encourage Student Definitions
Have children say sentences that tell how the butterfly uses its body parts. Record the sentences to use as a **baseline assessment.**

Act as a Consultant
• Have groups of children use the literature selection *The Lady and the Spider* by Faith McNulty (Harper Trophy, 1986) to discuss how a spider's legs, eyes, and mouth help it survive.

How do body parts help animals live?

You just found out that animals have many kinds of body parts. These body parts can help animals stay alive. Here is how body parts help a butterfly stay alive.

Look at the big wings of this butterfly. Wings help it fly to flowers. Flowers hold a sweet food called nectar. Some butterflies eat nectar.

A 6

Science Idea Exchange

Science Background
Butterflies and moths are insects that undergo metamorphosis. An egg laid by an adult hatches into a larva, or caterpillar. The caterpillar grows and becomes a pupa, or chrysalis. A hard shell quickly forms over the pupa, from which an adult later emerges.

Science and Language Arts
Invite children to create a group story about a butterfly that injures one of its wings. The story should include how the animal is affected by the damaged wing, and how the butterfly is nursed back to health.

Science and Art
Butterflies come in vivid colors and patterns. Show children pictures of several types of butterflies. Invite them to decorate paper cutouts of butterfly shapes. Paste on long paper strips to represent antennas and mouths. Use string to hang the butterflies as part of a classroom mobile.

The butterfly has two large eyes and two long antennas. The eyes help the butterfly see flowers. The antennas help the butterfly touch and smell the flowers.

The butterfly has six legs. It uses its legs to hold onto the flower. The butterfly has a mouth like a long tube. It uses its mouth to sip nectar from a flower.

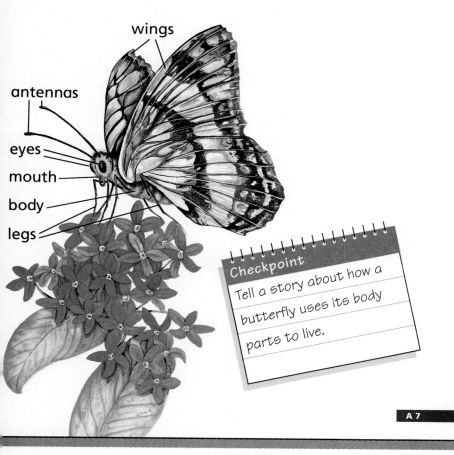

wings

antennas

eyes

mouth

body

legs

Checkpoint

Tell a story about how a butterfly uses its body parts to live.

Act as a Consultant (cont'd.)
- Help children understand that there is a relationship between an animal's body parts and its behavior. Use the spider and the butterfly as examples.

Close

Check for Understanding
- As a follow-up to the **baseline assessment,** invite children to draw a series of pictures showing what butterflies do to stay alive. Ask them to either explain each picture or write a caption for each. Look for an increased knowledge of how the body parts of a butterfly help it survive.
- **Answers to Checkpoint** Answers will vary, but may include that its wings help the butterfly fly from flower to flower, its antennas touch the flower, and its mouth sips nectar.

Connecting Lessons
In the next lesson, children will discover how an animal's actions can help it stay alive. ▶

Explorer's Activity Guide
Use Explorer's Activity Guide page 5 with this lesson to help children answer the text question, "How do body parts help animals live?" with a hands-on activity.

Achieving English Proficiency
Encourage small groups to act out butterfly activities. Some children can be flowers, some butterflies, and one might be a bird trying to catch a butterfly to eat. For props and costumes, let children cut out and color paper flower shapes to hold and wings to tie to their arms. Tell children to **describe** their actions.

Math/Science Connection
Gather pictures of different animals such as mammals, birds, insects, and spiders. Invite children to sort the animal pictures into groups according to their number of legs. Then help children make a pictograph to record the information.

Lesson 3

Lesson Objective
Children learn about animal behaviors—including hibernating, nest building, and food storing—that help animals survive.

Introduce

Key Term
hibernate

Invite Learning
Ask children to **describe** ways the spider acted that helped it stay alive in *The Lady and the Spider* by Faith NcNulty (Harper Trophy, 1986). It found a home where it could hide, captured food, and leaped away from the bird.

Make Connections
To **assess prior knowledge,** ask children to name the most important things they think a certain animal must be able to do to stay alive. Record their comments to use as a **baseline assessment**.

Teach

Observe and Listen
- Divide the class into small groups to discuss the pictures. Encourage children to ask and answer each other's questions.
- Have children **compare** the actions of people to the actions of the other animals in the pictures. (The squirrel is storing nuts, and people store food.)

What actions help animals stay alive?

What do animals do when they hear a noise? A bird may fly away. A squirrel may run and hide.

Animals have ways of acting that help them stay alive. A noise may be a sign of danger. Running away may help an animal get away from danger. The pictures tell about other ways that animals act.

Checkpoint
Tell about a way of acting that helps an animal.

A 8

A muskrat builds its home in a pond. Other animals cannot reach it.

A squirrel buries acorns. Later it digs them up and eats them.

Science Idea Exchange

Science Background
Animals have behavioral adaptations that help them survive. For example, opossums play dead to fool predators. Instincts are behaviors that are not learned, like the spider's ability to spin a web. Many animal behaviors are learned from parents, such as how to catch food.

Science and Language Arts
Invite children to draw a picture of a favorite animal. Ask them to write two sentences beneath the picture telling where the animal lives and how it finds food. Allow children to draw and write about pets or farm animals if they choose.

Special Education
Have children work in pairs to make models of animal homes. Give each pair a plastic animal. Have children make a home for it using cardboard, crayons, paper, safety scissors, string, and modeling clay. For example, children could depict a bird sitting on cardboard eggs in a nest of shredded paper. Have pairs **describe** their structures to their classmates.

A duck hides her eggs from other animals.

A woodchuck **hibernates** in winter. It hardly moves. It needs very little food.

A 9

Ask for Evidence

Suggest that children **classify** the behavior of the animals pictured. Ask: *Which animals are behaving in a way that will keep them from being hungry?* (squirrel and woodchuck) *Which animals are behaving in a way that protects them?* (duck and muskrat)

Close

Check for Understanding

● As a follow-up to the **baseline assessment,** help children write sentences telling why an animal might hibernate (so it won't need much food), why an animal would store food (so it can eat when food is scarce), and why an animal would build a nest (to keep its eggs safe). Guide children to **draw conclusions** about how these behaviors help animals survive.

● **Answers to Checkpoint** Answers may include that hibernating and storing food keep animals from being hungry; building safe nests and homes keeps animals out of danger and protects them from the weather; and running very fast helps animals escape from danger or capture food.

Connecting Lessons

In the next lesson, children will explore how an animal's color can help it avoid danger. ▶

Explorer's Activity Guide

Use Explorer's Activity Guide page 6 with this lesson to help children answer the text question, "What actions help animals stay alive?" with a hands-on activity.

Visual Literacy

To enhance the **visual literacy** connection, use the interactive overhead transparency that correlates with the above two pages. The transparency will help your students understand the key concepts presented on these pages.

Your Ideas

Lesson 4

Lesson Objective
Children learn how color can make objects difficult to see.

Introduce

Invite Learning
Display different colored sheets of construction paper. Have each child cut an animal shape from one of the colors and move it along in front of the colored sheets. The class can rate how well the animal shows up against each color: good, better, best.

Make Connections
To **assess prior knowledge**, ask children why certain colors of animals were either easy or difficult to see in front of some of the colors. Record their responses as a **baseline assessment**.

Teach

Activity
Children play a game that demonstrates how the color of an animal can help it survive. **Skills:** Recording, interpreting data, applying information

Materials (per group)
Module Kit Items: 2 sheets brown construction paper; 1 sheet white construction paper
School Supplied Items: timer; brown wrapping paper (*optional*)

How can color make things hard to see?

Could a bird see a brown caterpillar crawling on a brown twig? You can find out how color can make things hard to see.

Find out about it.

You will need:

- ⚪ white paper circles
- ⚫ brown paper circles
- ▱ brown paper
- ⏲ timer

1 Get 20 white circles and 20 brown circles.

2 Have your partner place all the circles on brown paper.

3 Have your partner start the timer.

4 Use one hand. Pick up as many circles as you can in 10 seconds. Pick up one circle at a time.

5 Count the white circles you picked up. Count the brown circles you picked up.

A 10

Science Idea Exchange

Science Anecdote
Some animals can change color to help them survive. The chameleon, a tropical lizard, can match the color of many of its surroundings. The octopus can change color almost instantly. It can turn several colors at once and can even have a striped appearance!

Science and Language Arts
Encourage children to write about a time when they had difficulty finding or seeing something because of its color. Be sure they explain why the object was difficult to see.

Science Themes
By discussing the effect of color on an animal's ability to stay alive or obtain food, children are developing their understanding of the themes of **systems and interactions** and **evolution**.

Write about it.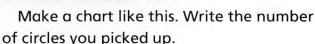

Make a chart like this. Write the number of circles you picked up.

colors	circles picked up
white	
brown	

Checkpoint

1. Which color was harder to find?

2. Take Action! Draw a picture of an animal. Use color to make the animal hard to see.

Helpful Hints
- You can use one timer if everyone begins and ends at the same time.
- *See Equipment Kit Teacher's Guide for additional hints.*

Ask for Evidence
Have children cut out a paper square, decorate it to blend in with part of the classroom environment, and place it there. Then have children search for the squares. Ask children why it was difficult to find some squares.

Close

Check for Understanding
- As a follow-up to the **baseline assessment,** ask children what color they would like to be if they were a caterpillar that lived on a brown twig. Have them tell why. Compare responses with those from Make Connections.
- **Answers to Checkpoint** 1. Brown circles are harder to find because they are harder to see against a brown background. 2. **Take Action!** Pictures should show an animal that blends in with its natural surroundings.

Connecting Lessons
In the next lesson, children will discover that both color and shape can help an animal hide from danger. ▶

Explorer's Activity Guide
Use Explorer's Activity Guide hands-on activity on page 7 to explore color and evaluate children's understanding of the lesson concept.

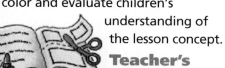

Teacher's Assessment Package
A **scoring rubric** to assess student performance is provided on page 3 of the Teacher's Assessment Package.

Activity Results
Most children will pick up more white circles than brown circles, or will pick up white circles more quickly than brown circles.

Collaborative Learning: Small Groups
Assign specific children to gather and clean up materials and to keep track of the time intervals. Each child in the Let's Explore group should have an opportunity to pick up circles, record data, and share results.

Lesson 5

Lesson Objective
Children learn how camouflage helps animals survive.

Introduce

Key Term
camouflage

Invite Learning
Draw a green branch covered with green, triangle-shaped thorns on a large piece of paper. From a separate sheet of paper, have children cut out a triangle, circle, and rectangle, color them the same shade of green, and lightly sketch in eyes. Attach these "bugs" to the poster with clear tape, and display it in the classroom. Challenge pairs of children to find the three "bugs" on the poster.

Make Connections
To **assess prior knowledge,** ask why it is hardest to find the triangle-shaped "bug." Record answers to use as a **baseline assessment.**

Teach

Observe and Listen
Listen as small groups examine the pictures in the text and discuss the animals' camouflage. If children refer only to color as camouflage, remind them to think also about shape.

deer

How do color and shape help animals?

Think about a green caterpillar on a green leaf. Its color matches the place where it lives. Its color makes the caterpillar hard to see.

A color or shape that makes an animal hard to see is **camouflage.** Camouflage can hide an animal from other animals that might eat it. Find the animals in the pictures. How does camouflage hide each animal?

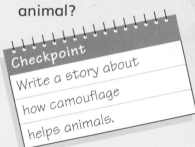

Checkpoint

Write a story about how camouflage helps animals.

A 12

Science Idea Exchange

Science Anecdote
Although many animals have color or shapes that make them hard to see, others are brightly colored and easy to see. Bright colors are sometimes a warning to predators that these animals bite, sting, or are poisonous. Some caterpillars and butterflies have warning colors.

Collaborative Learning: Small Groups
Invite groups of children to work together to make posters of "hidden" creatures. Provide crayons, paint, paper, pipe cleaners, safety scissors, and old nature magazines. Suggest that children first create the scenery and then add pictures of animals from magazines or creatures from their imaginations.

Extend the Lesson
Suggest that children think about green animals, such as green spiders, green frogs, and green insects like grasshoppers. Ask: *How do you think camouflage might help each of these animals?* (Answers might include camouflage helps predators hide so they can catch prey and helps prey hide from predators.)

walking stick

moth

hornworm

tree frogs

A 13

Ask for Evidence

Ask: *How does camouflage help animals survive?* (It lets them blend in with objects around them and not be seen by anything or anyone that might harm them.)

Close

Check for Understanding

- As a follow-up to the **baseline assessment**, ask children to imagine a green stem with two animals clinging to it. One of the animals is a black spider. The other animal is a greenish-yellow insect shaped like a leaf. There is a hungry bird looking at the stem. Ask: *Which animal would you rather be?* (the leaf-shaped insect) *Why?* (because it would be harder for the bird to see) Look for references to color and shape in children's responses.

- **Answers to Checkpoint** Stories should reflect an understanding that the shape and color of an animal help hide it from other animals.

Connecting Lessons

In the next lesson, children will examine how the parts of plants help plants stay alive. ▶

Explorer's Activity Guide
Use Explorer's Activity Guide page 8 with this lesson to help children answer the text question, "How do color and shape help animals?" with a hands-on activity.

Explore Further
Camouflage not only helps animals hide from predators but also helps some animals find food. The polar bear's white fur hides it as it stalks its prey on snow and ice. The tiger's stripes help it blend in with long stalks of grass as it hunts. Have pictures available to show to children.

Visual Literacy
To enhance the **visual literacy** connection, use the interactive overhead transparency that correlates with the above two pages. The transparency will help your students understand the key concepts presented on these pages.

Lesson 6

Introduce

Invite Learning
Have children construct a large puzzle of a tree in which each piece is from only one part of the tree, such as the roots, trunk (stem), and leaves. Have children take turns assembling the puzzle and naming the parts.

Make Connections
To **assess prior knowledge,** bring a small potted plant to class. Ask children to name its parts as you point to roots, leaves, and stems. Ask children to tell what they think each part does for the plant. Record children's comments as a **baseline assessment**.

Teach

Raise Questions
- Encourage children to run their fingers along the trunk and branches in the picture on page A15. Ask: *Have you seen a tree like this growing near where you live? How do you think this trunk and these branches would feel?*
- Ask children to **predict** what would happen if a plant had all its leaves cut off. (It would not get the food that the leaves make; it might die.)

What parts help plants live?

Pretend you are walking on this city sidewalk. You notice trees and other plants. Plants have roots that grow under the ground. The roots help hold plants in the soil.

Roots take in water from the soil. Plants need water to live. Roots help keep trees and other plants alive.

A 14

 ## Science Idea Exchange

Science Background
Leaves are green because they contain chlorophyll, a green pigment used in making food. Leaves also may contain red, yellow, or orange pigments, but these are masked by the chlorophyll. In autumn, leaves lose their chlorophyll, and other pigments become visible.

Science and Social Studies
Leaves make food that is used by plants and other organisms. Farmers grow and harvest leafy plants for people to eat. Make a class display of some of the leaves people eat (lettuce, kale, cabbage, spinach, collards, parsley, mustard).

Multicultural Connections
Some vegetables are plant roots. In South America, the roots of cassava plants may be eaten like potatoes or used to make tapioca. Sweet potatoes, the roots of the sweet potato plant, originated in regions of Mexico, Central America, and South America. In Mexico, sweet potatoes are used as a filling in dumplings called *empañadas*.

Find the trunk of this tree. It holds up the heavy branches. The trunk is a thick stem. Stems carry water from the roots to other parts of plants.

Now find the leaves on the tree. Leaves use sunlight to help make food for plants.

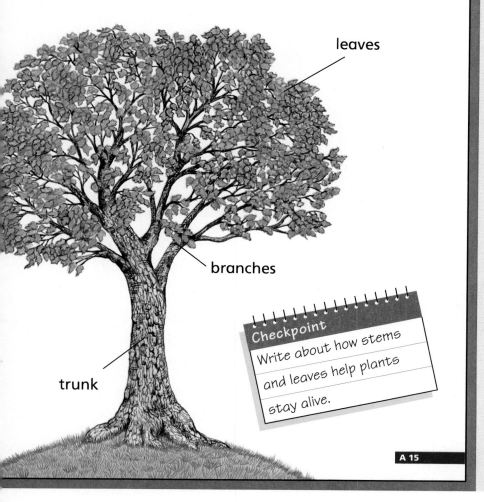

leaves

branches

trunk

Checkpoint
Write about how stems and leaves help plants stay alive.

Act as a Consultant

If possible, take children for a walk. Pair children off and ask them to **identify** the leaves and stems of plants they see. Ask them to explain to each other what each part does for the plant. Suggest that they try to find at least one plant with a hard stem (tree) and one with a soft stem. Encourage them to find as many different leaf shapes as they can.

Close

Check for Understanding

- As a follow-up to the **baseline assessment**, invite children to draw a picture of a plant. Ask them to label the plant's roots, stem, and leaves, and then write a sentence that describes what each part does for the plant.
- **Answers to Checkpoint** Roots take in water from the soil. Stems hold up the branches or leaves of a plant. Stems also carry water from the roots to other parts of the plant. Leaves make the food plants need to grow.

Connecting Lessons

In the next lesson, children will learn how plants store the water they need to survive. ▶

Explorer's Activity Guide

Use Explorer's Activity Guide page 9 with this lesson to help children answer the text question, "What parts help plants live?" with a hands-on activity.

Collaborative Learning: Role-Playing

Show children a common plant such as a coleus. Invite them to pretend they are very small and are standing at the bottom of the plant. Have small groups act out how they would climb the plant and describe what they would see as they go up.

Save the Earth

As leaves make food, they use up carbon dioxide and give off oxygen. So plants not only provide food for animals to eat, they also provide oxygen for animals to breathe. Discuss with children that green plants are a source of fresh air.

Lesson Objective
Children learn how plants store the water they need to survive.

Introduce

Invite Learning
Remove some leaves from a jade plant and let children examine them. They can observe the thickness of the leaves and squeeze them, but they should not break them.

Make Connections
To **assess prior knowledge,** ask children to describe what they think is inside the jade plant leaves. Record their descriptions to use as a **baseline assessment.** Allow children to bend and break the leaves if they wish.

Teach

Activity
Children compare how a lack of water over a period of time will affect the leaves of a jade plant and the leaves of a fern plant. **Skills:** Recognizing cause and effect, drawing conclusions

Materials (per group)
Module Kit Items: none
School Supplied Items: jade plant; fern plant; water in watering can

How do some plants store water?

Suppose you live in a place that gets very little rain. You might see a cactus growing in such a dry place.

Look at the thick stems of a cactus. The stems hold water for a long time. The stored water helps the cactus grow in the desert.

Other plants store water in their leaves. Now let's see how thick leaves hold water.

A 16

Science Idea Exchange

Science Background
Cactus and jade plants both belong to a group of plants called succulents. They store water in fleshy stems or leaves. The cactus stem not only stores water but also contains chlorophyll and carries on photosynthesis. The needles are the leaves of the cactus. The jade plant stores water in its leaves.

Science and Art
Invite children to draw a moist forest scene and a dry desert scene. Provide paper, crayons, and books or magazines with pictures of plants and animals from these ecosystems. Display forest pictures on one side of the classroom and desert pictures on the other. Discuss why different kinds of plants are able to grow in the forest and the desert.

Explorer's Activity Guide
Use Explorer's Activity Guide hands-on activity on page 10 to help children answer the question, "How

do some plants store water?"

Teacher's Assessment Package
A **scoring rubric** to assess student performance is provided on page 3 of the Teacher's Assessment Package

Observe how plants store water.

You will need: potted jade plant

 potted fern plant  water

1. Place the plants next to each other.
2. Water each plant. Make sure each plant gets the same amount of water.
3. Do not water either plant again.
4. Watch the plants until you see a change.
5. Touch the leaves carefully. Look for changes in the leaves.

Checkpoint

Tell how you know which plant stored more water. Which plant would grow better in a dry place?

A 17

A 17

Helpful Hints
- For faster results, place the plants in direct sunlight.
- *See Equipment Kit Teacher's Guide for additional hints.*

Ask for Evidence
Ask: *If you were planting a desert garden, what would the plants look like?* (plants with waxy-coated, thick stems and leaves for storing water and keeping the water from evaporating, such as the cactus or jade plant; or with very small leaves so there is less surface area for water loss, like sagebrush or the needles of cactus)

Close

Check for Understanding
- As a follow-up to the **baseline assessment,** invite children to examine several potted plants, including some succulents. Children should **classify** them as plants that can or cannot live in dry places.
- **Answers to Checkpoint** The fern leaves wilt while the leaves of the jade plant do not. Because it can store water, the jade plant doesn't wilt as quickly and so would grow better in a dry place.

Connecting Lessons
In the next lesson, children will explore how seeds are scattered so that plants grow in new places. ▶

Activity Results

Alternate Activity

Ask children to **compare** the amounts of water needed to keep the two plants healthy. Provide two measuring cups that each hold a cup of water. When a plant needs water, have children pour the contents of one cup onto it and mark that they have done so on a chart. After a few days or weeks, compare the amount of water given to each plant.

Collaborative Learning: Small Groups

Assign specific children to gather materials and water each plant. Each child in the Activity group should be involved in making observations and comparisons of the leaves of both plants.

Lesson 8

Lesson Objective
Children learn that plant seeds can be scattered through air to places where they can grow.

Introduce

Invite Learning
Invite children to drop a small feather (from a pillow) and **observe** how it falls and moves through the air.

Make Connections
To **assess prior knowledge,** have children pretend the feather is a seed that has formed in a plant, like the seeds of dandelion flowers. Have them use the feather to demonstrate and explain how seeds can be scattered to locations far from a parent plant. Record their explanations to use as a **baseline assessment.**

Teach

Activity
Children drop pieces of cotton to demonstrate how seeds can be scattered through the air. **Skills:** Observing, making analogies, drawing conclusions

Materials (per group)
Module Kit Items: cotton balls; sheets of construction paper, assorted colors
School Supplied Items: none

What helps plants grow in new places?

Do you ever blow on a dandelion? You may like watching the dandelion fruits float through the air. When fruits float through the air, the seeds inside are scattered. Scattering helps carry the seeds to new places where they can grow. You can show how seeds are scattered through the air.

A 18

Science Idea Exchange

Science Anecdote
The seed head of a dandelion is made up of many seeds. Each seed is covered by a fruit, which is attached to cottony white hairs. In wet weather, these hairs close up; the wind cannot carry them if they are wet. In dry weather the seed hairs open, and a strong wind can carry seeds many miles.

Science and Language Arts
Invite children to make a book about the life of a dandelion. The first picture might show a tiny seed in the soil. The following pictures might show the seed growing into a plant, the flower at the top of the stem, and the cottony seeds scattering in the wind. Children can write a sentence to **describe** each stage.

Collaborative Learning: Small Groups
Assign specific children to gather and clean up materials. All children in the Activity group should have an opportunity to drop cotton pieces, make observations, and share results.

Show how seeds are scattered.

You will need: cotton balls construction paper

1. Place the paper on the floor.
2. Pull a small piece from a cotton ball.
3. Stand over the paper. Hold your arm out straight from your shoulder. Drop the cotton piece.
4. Do this ten times.
5. Watch where the pieces of cotton fall.

Checkpoint
Tell where the pieces of cotton fell. How are the pieces of cotton like dandelion seeds?

A 19

Helpful Hints
- The construction paper is used as a point of reference so that children drop pieces of cotton toward the same spot. The color of the paper should contrast with the floor so it can easily be seen.
- Make sure that the pieces of cotton are about the same size and are dropped from approximately the same height.
- *See Equipment Kit Teacher's Guide for additional hints.*

Ask Open-ended Questions
Ask: *In what other ways can seeds or fruits move from one place to another?* (people and other animals carry them, float in water, animals bury them)

Close

Check for Understanding
- As a follow-up to the **baseline assessment,** ask children to write two sentences, one telling where the cotton pieces landed and another telling how dandelion seeds spread.
- **Answers to Checkpoint** Most of the cotton pieces do not land on the paper. They scatter in much the same way that the wind scatters dandelion seeds.

Connecting Lessons
In the next lesson, children will observe the structure of seeds to predict how they might be scattered. ▶

Explorer's Activity Guide
Use Explorer's Activity Guide hands-on activity on page 11 to help children answer the question, "What helps plants grow in new places?"

Teacher's Assessment Package
A **scoring rubric** to assess student performance is provided on page 3 of the Teacher's Assessment Package.

Activity Results
The cotton lands not only on the construction paper but also on the floor around it. The cotton is light enough to float on the smallest movement of air in the room.

Gifted and Talented
Challenge children to examine carefully one fruit from a dandelion seed head and a cotton ball to determine the characteristics that enable each one to be picked up and carried by the wind. Ask children to design seeds that could be carried by the wind, either on paper or by **making physical models.**

Lesson Objective
Children study the shapes of various fruits and seeds and predict whether they would be scattered by the wind or by animals. **Skills:** Organizing information, solving problems

Introduce

Invite Learning
Ask children to **predict** which of several items—a cotton ball, a pencil, a piece of paper, and a sock—will stick to hook-and-loop fastener fabric. Allow children to test their predictions.

Make Connections
To **assess prior knowledge**, ask: *How did using the hook-and-loop fastener fabric show one way some fruits containing seeds can move far from the plant they come from?* Record children's responses as a **baseline assessment**.

Teach

Observe and Listen
- Divide the class into small groups to **compare** the fruits in the pictures on pages A20–A21.
- Have pairs determine which fruits have parts like wings and which fruits have parts like hooks.

Let's Solve It!

How are seeds scattered?

Many seeds are inside fruits. Some fruits have parts like wings or hooks. Wings help seeds be scattered by wind. Hooks help seeds be scattered by animals. The hooks can stick to animal fur. When the animal moves the fruits and seeds are carried to new places.

1. Fruit A has a part like a wing. It might be scattered by wind. Fruit B has hooks. It might be scattered by animals. Look at the other fruits. How might the parts help the seeds be scattered?

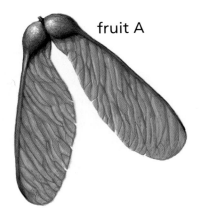
fruit A

fruit B

A 20

💡 Science Idea Exchange

Science Background
Common trees that produce winged fruits include elm, ash, maple, and pine. Closed pine cones collected in the fall will release their seeds if allowed to dry indoors. Common plants that produce hooked fruits include Queen Anne's Lace, Great Burdock, and Sticktight.

Science and Language Arts
Discuss with children other ways in which fruits scatter. The book *Seeds: Pop, Stick, Glide* by Patricia Lauber (Crown, 1981) describes seeds that travel in water or pop open to scatter themselves. It also gives several examples of plants that produce hooked or winged fruits.

Math/Science Connection
Help children add other fruits to their chart. Use fruits or seeds found outdoors or provide additional pictures of fruits or seeds for this purpose. Then have children count the number of fruits with wings and the number of fruits with hooks. Ask children to determine which kind of fruit they have in the greatest number.

2. Make a chart like this one.

fruit	how it looks	wings or hooks	how scattered
fruit A	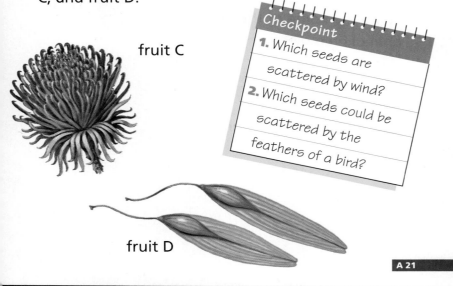	wings	wind
fruit B			
fruit C			
fruit D			

3. The chart shows fruit A. It shows its parts. It shows how the fruits and seeds are scattered. Fill in the chart for fruit B, fruit C, and fruit D.

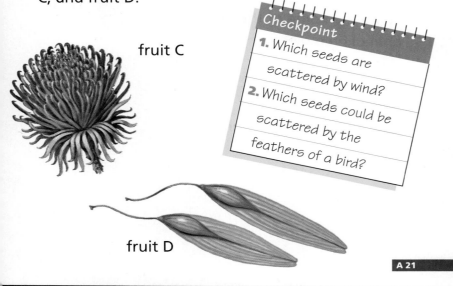

fruit C

fruit D

Checkpoint
1. Which seeds are scattered by wind?
2. Which seeds could be scattered by the feathers of a bird?

A 21

Observe and Listen (cont'd.)
- Allow pairs to work together to complete the chart and answer the questions on page A21.

Act as a Consultant
Guide pairs of children to think about and discuss what might happen if a fruit or a seed landed on a sidewalk instead of on soil. (It might not be able to grow; it might grow in a crack in sidewalk; wind might blow it onto soil.)

Close

Check for Understanding
- As a follow-up to the **baseline assessment,** ask children to explain how they decided whether a fruit or a seed would be scattered by the wind or by an animal. (Fruits with parts like wings are scattered by the wind; fruits with parts like hooks might stick to animals.) Have children compare their responses to those from Make Connections.
- **Answers to Checkpoint** 1. Fruits A and D have wings and are scattered by the wind. 2. Fruits with hooks, such as fruits B and C, could stick to and be scattered by the feathers of birds.

Connecting Lessons
In the next lesson, children will demonstrate what they have learned about animal and plant adaptations. ▶

Explorer's Activity Guide
Use Explorer's Activity Guide page 12 to help children solve the question of how fruits and seeds are scattered. You can also use this hands-on activity page to evaluate how well children understand the concept of this lesson.

Explore Further
Encourage children to **make models** of winged fruits by pasting paper wings on table tennis balls. Invite them to take their winged models outdoors to test how well they fly. They may make models of hooked fruits by covering table tennis balls with hook-and-loop fastener fabric. Affix the "fruits" to children's shoelaces and see how long they remain attached.

Extend the Lesson
Wear an old sock over a shoe and walk where you might "catch" fruits or seeds. Bring the sock to class and have children use a hand lens to examine the items picked up by the sock. Then moisten the sock and "plant" it. Keep it moist and ask children to observe what kinds of plants grow.

Lesson 10

Lesson Objective
Children play a guessing game to show the concepts they learned in this chapter.

Introduce

Invite Learning
Review the **baseline assessment** activities you used in this chapter. Choose one or more to do again that you think will help children understand the chapter concepts.

Teach

Performance Assessment Activity
Children tell of or act out adaptations of the plants and animals they have learned about. **Skills:** Communicating, naming, judging and evaluating

Materials (per group)
Module Kit Items: none
School Supplied Items: sheets of paper; pencils

Helpful Hints
- If presenters need help, allow them to refer to their written lists of plant and animal parts and behaviors.
- Allow children to ask questions of presenters if they need more information before guessing.

What did you learn?

Now you know that body parts and ways of acting help animals stay alive. You also know that special parts help plants grow. You can pretend you are a plant or an animal. Then you can play a game.

You will need: paper pencil

Play a guessing game.
1. Work with a group. Make a list of plants and animals.
2. Decide who will take the part of each plant and each animal.
3. Write the name of the plant or animal on a piece of paper.
4. Write down what parts or ways of acting help your plant or animal stay alive.
5. Act out the part of your plant or animal.
6. Ask the class to guess your plant or animal.

 ## Science Idea Exchange

Teacher's Assessment Package
Use the pages from the Teacher's Assessment Package at this time to promote **performance assessment** opportunities for your children.

Science Anecdote
Birds have many specialized body parts and ways of acting that help them survive. Most fly, but some don't. An adult ostrich, the largest bird in the world, can grow up to 2.4 m (8 ft) tall. Its wings are too tiny for flight, but it has strong legs and is able to outrun predators. Penguins don't fly; they use their wings as paddles to swim underwater and catch fish.

Collaborative Learning: Small Groups
Assign specific children to gather materials. All children in the Chapter Review group should be involved in making and playing the guessing game about plants and animals.

Raise Questions

Be sure children's questions you recorded in Lesson 1 have been answered. Then use the **constructivist** approach to ask: *What questions do you still have about the special parts that help plants grow? What else would you like to know about the parts and ways of acting of plants and animals? How can we find the answers to your questions?*

Close

Check for Understanding

● Invite each child to act out the parts or behaviors for at least one plant and one animal. Have children **compare** the parts and behaviors of plants and animals, noting similarities and differences.

● **Answers to Share what you learned**
1. Answers will vary. Children should refer to the behaviors or body parts they observed during the activity.
2. Favorite animals will vary.

Connecting Chapters

In the next chapter, children will learn that plants and animals live in habitats that provide everything needed to stay alive. ▶

Share what you learned.

1. How did you guess what your classmates were pretending to be?

2. What was your favorite animal in the game?

Explorer's Activity Guide

Use Explorer's Activity Guide page 13 as a hands-on activity to evaluate how well children understand the concepts covered in this chapter.

Alternate Activity

Encourage children to create riddles for the class to solve. Answers could be a plant or an animal studied in the chapter. Examples include "What is thick and green and doesn't need much water?" (jade plant) "If you can't swim, you can't come to my front door. Who am I?" (muskrat)

Your Ideas

_____

_____

_____

_____

_____

Chapter 2 Planning Guide
Where Things Live

Lessons / *Skills*	Materials (per group)

Lessons / *Skills*

Lesson 1
Discover Activity: **Where do you see plants and animals?**
pp. A24–A25
(organizing information)

Lesson 2
Where do plants and animals live? pp. A26–A27
(making physical models, visualizing)

Lesson 3
What lives in a water habitat? pp. A28–A29
(observing, classifying)

Lesson 4
How does a habitat help living things? pp. A30–A31
(observing, describing)

Lesson 5
Let's Explore: **How can you make a habitat?** pp. A32–A33
(making physical models)

Lesson 6
What habitats are in a zoo? pp. A34–A35
(observing, comparing)

Lesson 7
What habitat can you plan for a zoo? pp. A36–A37
(making physical models)

Lesson 8
Let's Solve It!: **How many red wolves live in wildlife parks?**
pp. A38–A39
(organizing information, solving problems)

Lesson 9
Chapter Review: **What did you learn?** pp. A40–A41
(describing, restating or explaining ideas, visualizing)

Materials (per group)

Lesson 1 Activity: *Where do you see plants and animals?*
Module Kit Items: none
School Supplied Items: scissors; old magazines; glue; pencils; sheets of paper

Lesson 2 Activity: *Make a habitat for a plant.*
Module Kit Items: potting soil *(about 1 cup)*; plastic cup; few pebbles *(or use gravel to cover bottom of cup)*
School Supplied Items: small plant; water *(about 1/2 cup)*
Advance Prep: Obtain small potted plants or grow plants from fast-germinating seeds such as radish or bean seeds. Plant the seeds several weeks before the activity.

Lesson 5 Activity: *How can you make a habitat?*
Module Kit Items: 2 crickets *(Live Material coupon)*; cricket food; soil *(about 1 cup)*; dropper
School Supplied Items: shoe box *(or large box)*; leaves; twigs; jar lid; water; netting *(optional)*
Advance Prep: Use the Live Material coupon to obtain the crickets for this activity.

Lesson 7 Activity: *Make a model of a zoo habitat.*
Module Kit Items: white pipe cleaners *(about 12)*; green pipe cleaners *(about 12)*; construction paper, assorted colors
School Supplied Items: shoe box; glue; crayons; scissors
Safety Kit Items: cover goggles *(1/child)*

Lesson 9 Activity: *Make a book about a habitat.*
Module Kit Items: none
School Supplied Items: crayons; drawing paper *(1 sheet/child)*; lined paper *(1 sheet/child)*; pencils *(1/child)*

Assessment Options	Content	Performance	Portfolio
Teacher's Assessment Package			
Chapter Test, pp. 11–12	✓		✓
Group Interview Assessment, p. 13	✓	✓	
Performance Strategies, p. 14	✓	✓	✓
Explorer's Activity Guide			
Activity worksheets, pp. 14–23		✓	✓
Chapter Review, pp. 25–26	✓		✓
Interactive Transparency Package			
Transparency 3 and 4 and BLMs	✓	✓	✓
Teacher's Guide, pp. 10–13	✓	✓	
Hands-on activities for second-language learners	✓	✓	✓
Science Literature Library			
Little Frog's Song		✓	✓
Interactive Videodisc Software			
Teacher's Guide, pp. 44–52			
Computer-based Activity	✓	✓	
Journal Presentations	✓	✓	✓
Videodisc Classroom Guide, pp. 9–16, or			
Video Reader			
Hands-on activity	✓	✓	✓
ExploraCenter Teacher's Guide, pp. 13, 17, 28			
ExploraCenter			
Science activity cards 8, 12, 23	✓	✓	✓
ScottForesman Online Service	✓	✓	✓
Online field trips	✓	✓	✓

Chapter Overview

Children begin the chapter with an investigation of where plants and animals live. By examining a water, a zoo, and a garden habitat, children discover that plants and animals get everything they need to live from their habitat. As a final activity, children make a habitat book to show what they have learned.

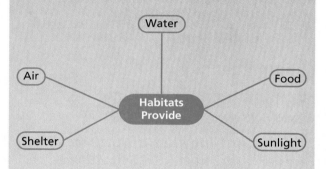

Lesson 1

Lesson Objective
Children describe places where plants and animals live.

Introduce

Invite Learning
Show the videodisc segment for this chapter. Bar codes and a description of this segment are given below on page A25.

Make Connections
To **assess prior knowledge,** invite children to draw and color a picture of a plant or an animal in the place where it lives. Save their drawings as a **baseline assessment** to use in Check for Understanding.

Teach

Discover Activity

Children select and assemble pictures of places in which plants and animals live and then name the plants and animals that live there. **Skill:** Organizing information

Materials (per group)
Module Kit Items: none
School Supplied Items: scissors; old magazines; glue; pencils; sheets of paper

---

Chapter 2

Where Things Live

Pretend you have a pen pal. You want to tell your pen pal about your home. What can you tell about the place where you live?

You might want to write about your neighborhood too. What can you tell about it? You can tell how it looks. You can tell about the plants and animals that live there. What kinds of places do plants and animals live in? Let's take a look!

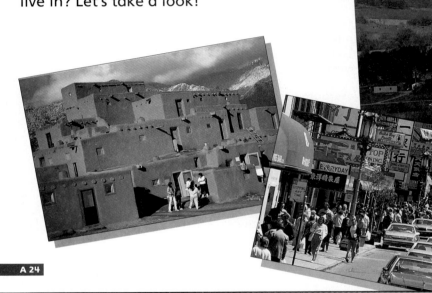

 ## Science Idea Exchange

Collaborative Learning: Small Groups
Assign specific children to gather and clean up materials. All children in the Discover Activity group should be involved in choosing pictures and writing about places where plants and animals live.

Science and Literature
After reading the literature selection *Little Frog's Song* by Alice Schertle (Harper Collins, 1992), ask children to draw a picture of a habitat that would most likely make Little Frog sing. Allow them to share their drawings and explain why Little Frog likes to live in this habitat.

Family/School Partnership: Family Support
Encourage families to be active partners in learning by suggesting that they and their children:
- name some places animals live,
- observe places where plants grow, and
- talk about what else they might find in places where plants and animals live.

Where do you see plants and animals?

1 Cut out pictures of places where plants and animals live.

2 Glue each picture on a paper.

3 Write the names of plants and animals that live in each place.

4 **Tell about it.** Write a story about one kind of place where plants and animals live.

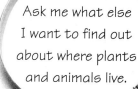

Ask me what else I want to find out about where plants and animals live.

A 25

Helpful Hints

● As you begin the activity, invite the class to brainstorm a list of places where plants and animals live.

● See *Equipment Kit Teacher's Guide* for additional hints.

What to Expect

Children might cut out nature scenes such as forests, parks, beaches, deserts, and gardens, and name plants and animals such as birds, cactuses, butterflies, spiders, and flowers.

Close

Check for Understanding

● As a follow-up to the **baseline assessment,** have children redraw the picture they made in Make Connections. Invite children to point out and explain their changes.

● **Answers to Tell about it** Answers will vary, but children's stories may have some objects or places in common, such as forests, parks, trees, and nests.

What Else Do You Want to Find Out?

Record children's questions on chart paper. Add answers and new questions as they arise in later lessons.

Connecting Lessons

In the next lesson, children will discover that different habitats have different characteristics. ▶

Explorer's Activity Guide

The **Discover Activity recording sheet** on page 14 of the Explorer's Activity Guide can be used by children to record their activity results.

Visual Literacy

Discover the Wonder Videodisc, Grade 2, Module A, provides video clips and stills that illustrate adaptations of plants and animals in vastly different habitats. Use these images to help children identify the characteristics and behaviors that enable living things to survive in their environment.

Bar Codes

Chapter 5: Video and Stills

Play

Step

Interactive Software

DISCOVER THE WONDER

Lesson 2

Lesson Objective
Children learn that a habitat is a place in which plants and animals live and that different habitats have different physical features.

Introduce

Key Term
habitat

Invite Learning
Bring in small plants for children to examine. Encourage children to list places where each plant might live.

Make Connections
To **assess prior knowledge,** have children list items they think they might see near a plant that is growing outside.

Teach

Encourage Student Definitions
Ask children what they think a habitat is. Record children's responses and keep as a **baseline assessment.**

Activity
Children make a plant habitat. **Skills:** Making physical models, visualizing

Materials (per group)
Module Kit Items: potting soil *(about 1 cup);* plastic cup; pebbles *(or use gravel to cover bottom of cup)*
School Supplied Items: small plant; water *(about 1/2 cup)*

Where do plants and animals live?

The place where a plant or animal lives is a **habitat.** Different plants and animals live in different kinds of habitats.

What can you tell about a habitat? You can tell how a habitat looks. You can tell how warm or cold it is. Think about other things to tell about a habitat. Then tell about the habitat in the picture.

A 26

 ## Science Idea Exchange

Science Background
Land habitats include temperate forests, tropical forests, grasslands, and deserts. Freshwater habitats include standing water (lakes and ponds) and running water (streams and rivers). Saltwater habitats include the open ocean, coastal waters, bays, and estuaries.

Science Themes
By describing different plant or animal habitats and making a plant habitat, children develop their understanding of the themes of **systems and interactions** and **modeling.**

Extend the Lesson
Bring to class plants with habitats that differ from the plants used in the activity. For example, a cactus needs sandy soil, strong sun, and less water. Ferns need a lighter soil, indirect sun, and moisture on their fronds as well as their roots. Invite children to **compare** the habitats of these plants.

Make a habitat for a plant.

You will need: paper cup · stones · plant · water · soil

1. Put stones in the bottom of your cup. Add soil to your cup.
2. Put your plant in the cup. Cover the roots with soil.
3. Add water to the cup.
4. Put your plant in a sunny place.

Checkpoint

Draw a picture of your plant in its habitat. What makes up the habitat?

A 27

Helpful Hints

- Save plant habitats for use in Lesson 4 and Lesson 5.
- *See Equipment Kit Teacher's Guide for additional hints.*

Raise Questions

Stimulate interest in habitats by using a **constructivist** approach. Ask: *What are some places where palm trees live? Can a palm tree live on a mountaintop? in Arctic regions? in a dry desert? What questions do you have about habitats? How can we find the answers to your questions?*

Close

Check for Understanding

- As a follow-up to the **baseline assessment,** have children revise their definition of "habitat" from Encourage Student Definitions. Children may also wish to elaborate their list of things they would see near a growing plant.
- **Answers to Checkpoint** Children should use words such as "soil," "water," "air," and "sun" to **describe** the plant's habitat.

Connecting Lessons

In the next lesson, children will learn about plants and animals that live in water habitats. ▶

Explorer's Activity Guide

Use Explorer's Activity Guide hands-on activity on page 15 to help children answer the question, "Where do plants and animals live?"

Teacher's Assessment Package

A **scoring rubric** to assess student performance is provided on page 9 of the Teacher's Assessment Package.

Collaborative Learning: Cooperative Learning

Each child in the Activity group should draw pictures and share answers. Also, each child can be assigned a specific role:

- one who puts the gravel in the cup;
- one who puts the soil in the cup;
- one who puts the plant in the soil and adds water to the cup;
- one who puts the plant in a sunny place.

Activity Results

Plants should be firmly planted in the cups. The stones should provide drainage.

Lesson 3

Lesson Objective
Children learn about some plants and animals that live in a water habitat.

Introduce

Invite Learning
Bring a clear, plastic jar containing pond water to class. Invite children to observe the water and **describe** what they see.

Make Connections
To **assess prior knowledge,** have children tell what colors they expect to see when they look at a pond. You may wish to use colored markers to list the colors on chart paper. Then ask children what plants and animals might live in a pond that would have those colors. List children's suggestions next to the appropriate color on the chart paper. Save as a **baseline assessment** to use in Check for Understanding.

Teach

Observe and Listen
- Divide the class into small groups.
- Have children take turns telling each other about the plants and animals in the picture of the habitat. Invite them to discuss whether these plants and animals could live in other habitats.
- Have children imagine and discuss what other plants and animals might live in the habitat pictured on these pages.

What lives in a water habitat?

It is time for a habitat adventure. You can find out about a water habitat. Get ready to explore the pond in the picture!

You row your boat across the water. You look around. What plants do you see? What animals do you see? What can you tell about the habitat of each plant and animal?

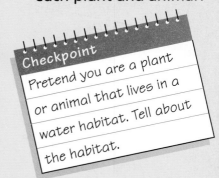
Checkpoint
Pretend you are a plant or animal that lives in a water habitat. Tell about the habitat.

A 28

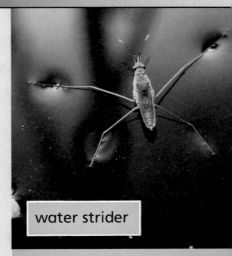
water strider

duck

dragonfly

Science Idea Exchange

Science Background
Water striders, also called pond skaters, do not actually swim; their long back legs enable them to move quickly across the water's surface. Their feet are covered with fine hairs, enabling the insect to remain on the surface of the water.

Science and Language Arts
Invite children to write an adventure story about a trip to a water habitat. Encourage them to use the pictures in the lesson for ideas.

Special Education
Play a matching game. Display on a bulletin board pictures of plants and animals that live in water habitats. Write the names of the plants and animals on cards. Encourage children to say the name on the card as they place it next to the correct picture.

pond habitat

turtle

A 29

Raise Questions

As children examine the picture, ask: *What animals live here?* (water strider, dragonfly, turtle, duck) *Where does each one spend most of its time?* (water strider on top of water, duck in water and at edge of pond, dragonfly flying above pond, turtle in water or resting on log) *What else do you see?* (trees, sunlight, sky)

Close

Check for Understanding

- As a follow-up to the **baseline assessment**, refer children to their list of pond colors, plants, and animals from Make Connections. Allow them to adjust the list if they wish. Look for an increased knowledge of the kinds of plants and animals that live in a pond.
- **Answers to Checkpoint** Answers will vary, but children will probably use words such as "stream," "pond," "fish," "trees," "bushes," "flowers," "birds," and "insects" to describe a water habitat.

Connecting Lessons

In the next lesson, children learn that a plant or animal gets everything it needs from its habitat. ▶

Explorer's Activity Guide

Use Explorer's Activity Guide page 16 with this lesson to help children answer the text question, "What lives in a water habitat?" with a hands-on activity.

Science Themes

By exploring the water habitat, children develop their understanding of the theme of **modeling.**

Visual Literacy

To enhance the **visual literacy** connection, use the interactive overhead transparency that correlates with the above two pages. The transparency will help your students understand the key concepts presented on these pages.

Lesson 4

Lesson Objective

Children learn that a habitat provides all the things necessary for a living thing to survive.

Introduce

Invite Learning

Invite children to **compare** the habitat of a tree outside with the plant habitats they made in Lesson 2. Ask how each plant gets its needs met.

Make Connections

To **assess prior knowledge,** ask children to list things an animal gets from its habitat. Record the responses on chart paper, and save as a **baseline assessment** that you can follow up in Check for Understanding.

Teach

Ask for Evidence

Encourage children to examine the picture carefully. Ask them to **name** and point to the animals in the picture. Do the same for plants. Make two lists, one for animals and one for plants, on the chalkboard.

How does a habitat help living things?

What do plants and animals get from their habitats? They get everything they need to live. Animals get food and water from their habitats. This spider catches insects in a web. The spider gets food and water from eating the insects.

Animals get the air they need from their habitats. They get a place to live. Animals may also get shelter to protect them from weather or danger.

A 30

Science Idea Exchange

Science Anecdote

Many spiders build webs to trap insects, but hunting spiders do not build webs. They pounce on insects, using their strong jaws to hold onto them. Both hunting spiders and spiders that build webs may inject their prey with a poison that paralyzes or kills them.

Math/Science Connection

On the chalkboard, list various animal habitats such as the ocean, the desert, a tree, soil, and so on. Invite children to name an animal that lives in each habitat. Add the animal names to the list on the chalkboard. Then challenge children to make up number sentences about the animals. For example, 2 whales in the ocean + 1 bird in a tree = 3 animals.

Science and Language Arts

Invite children to draw an outline of a spider on a piece of drawing paper. Then have them write things they know about spiders and their habitats around the spider outline. Invite pairs of children to explain their drawings to each other.

What else do you see in this garden? You can see that plants live in the garden too.

The plants get sunlight. Plants get water from the soil. They get air. Plants use water, sunlight, and air to make the food they need. The garden habitat has everything the plants need to live.

Checkpoint

Tell a story about a plant or animal that lives in a garden. Tell what the plant or animal gets from its habitat.

A 31

- Ask: *What does the spider get from its habitat?* (food, air, water) *What does the spider make as part of its habitat?* (a web, which is its shelter and a place to live) *How do you know that the spider gets food from its habitat?* (The web it makes catches insects.) *Why do you think the spider's web is its shelter?* (It lives on or near its web.)
- Ask: *What do plants get from their habitat?* (air, water, sunlight) *How do you know these plants are getting food from their habitat?* (Plants can make food from water, air, and sunlight.)

Close

Check for Understanding

- As a follow-up to the **baseline assessment,** give children the opportunity to revise the list they made of things that an animal gets from its habitat.
- **Answers to Checkpoint** Children may choose plants or animals from the picture in their book. They should tell how their plant gets water, air, and sunlight or how their animal gets food, water, air, shelter, and a place to live from its habitat.

Connecting Lessons

In the next lesson, children will find out how to create a habitat for crickets. ▶

Explorer's Activity Guide

Use Explorer's Activity Guide page 17 with this lesson to help children answer the text question,

"How does a habitat help living things?" with a hands-on activity.

Explore Further

If possible, take children outdoors to **observe** habitats near school. Pair children off and provide each pair with a word-and-picture checklist of plants and animals they are likely to see, such as birds, flies, ants, spiders, weeds, grass, flowers, or trees. Back in class, ask pairs to **describe** a plant or animal they saw and tell what it gets from its habitat.

Science Themes

By learning how a habitat provides all the things necessary for a living thing to live and grow, children develop their understanding of the themes of **energy** and **systems and interactions.**

Lesson 5

Lesson Objective
Children learn how to make a habitat for crickets.

Introduce

Invite Learning
Invite children to **observe** the plant habitat they made in Lesson 2 and to tell how a cricket habitat is similar to and different from it.

Make Connections
To **assess prior knowledge**, ask: *Where do you think crickets live? What might you find in places where crickets live?* Record and save children's responses as a **baseline assessment**.

Teach

Activity
Children make a classroom habitat for crickets. It includes everything the crickets need to live. **Skill:** Making a physical model

Materials (per group)
Module Kit Items: 2 crickets (*Live Material coupon*); cricket food; soil (*about 1 cup*); dropper
School Supplied Items: shoe box (*or large box*); leaves; twigs; jar lid; water; netting (*optional*)

Helpful Hints
● Crickets are available from some pet stores.

How can you make a habitat?

Crickets and other animals need food and water. What else do crickets need to live? How can you make a habitat for crickets?

Find out about it.

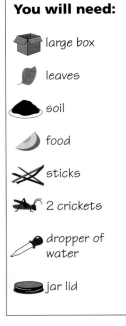

You will need:

large box

leaves

soil

food

sticks

2 crickets

dropper of water

jar lid

1. Put soil in the bottom of the box.

2. Add the sticks and leaves to the box. The crickets use sticks and leaves for shelter.

3. Put the food in the box. Put water in the jar lid. Put the lid in the box.

4. Put the crickets in the box.

5. Observe the crickets.

A 32

Science Idea Exchange

Science Background
Crickets are closely related to grasshoppers. Crickets make chirping sounds by rubbing their front wings together. The sounds are made primarily by males to help females find them. Crickets feed on plant material and may be found hiding under leaves and rocks.

Collaborative Learning: Cooperative Learning
Assign specific children to gather and clean up materials. All children in the Let's Explore group should make observations, record data, and share results. Also, each member of the group can be assigned a specific role:

● one who puts the soil, leaves, and twigs in the box;
● one who puts food in the box;
● one who fills the jar lid with water and puts the lid in the box;
● one who puts the crickets in the box.

Write about it.

Make a chart like this. Write or draw what you found out about a habitat for crickets.

what crickets need	what habitat has
food	
water	
shelter	

Checkpoint

1. What did the crickets get from the habitat you made?

2. Take Action! Draw a picture of the crickets in the habitat you made.

A 33

Helpful Hints (cont'd.)

- Put netting or a screen over the box so the crickets cannot jump out.
- Save the habitats for use in Lesson 7.
- *See Equipment Kit Teacher's Guide for additional hints.*

Observe and Listen

Encourage children to discuss among themselves the reasons for using each item they are putting into the habitat.

Close

Check for Understanding

- As a follow-up to the **baseline assessment,** let children revise their answers from Make Connections about what the habitats of crickets contain.
- **Answers to Checkpoint** 1. food (vegetables, fruit, bread), water (in food), air, shelter (sticks and leaves), and place to live (box) 2. **Take Action!** Children's pictures should show the crickets' habitat (box) containing slices of food, soil, sticks, and leaves.

Extend the Activity

If crickets are living in an area near the school, help children **compare** the habitats they constructed with outdoor habitats.

Connecting Lessons

In the next lesson, children will learn that zoos provide habitats with everything animals need to live. ▶

Explorer's Activity Guide

Use Explorer's Activity Guide hands-on activity on page 19 to explore habitats and evaluate children's understanding of the lesson concept.

Teacher's Assessment Package

A **scoring rubric** to assess student performance is provided on page 9 of the Teacher's Assessment Package.

Activity Results

The cricket habitat should contain plants, including fruits and vegetables, as the crickets' source of food and water, the box as their place to live, and the sticks and leaves as their shelter. The chart should act as children's checklist and show that the habitat has included everything the crickets need.

Science and Language Arts

Have children suggest simple sentences about crickets. (For example: Crickets jump. Crickets make sounds.) Write the sentences on the chalkboard. Have children refer to the sentences and write their own paragraph about crickets.

Lesson 6

Lesson Objective
Children learn that some animals get everything they need to live in zoo habitats.

Introduce

Invite Learning
Invite children to name animals that live in a zoo. Record their responses on chart paper.

Make Connections
To **assess prior knowledge,** challenge children to draw pictures of zoo habitats for some of the animals they named in Invite Learning. Save their pictures as a **baseline assessment.**

Teach

Observe and Listen
- Ask pairs of children to carefully **observe** and discuss what they see in the pictures.
- Listen as children explain to each other what each of the animals shown on pages A34–A35 gets from its habitat.

Act as a Consultant
Ask children to **compare** the habitats pictured in the text. Guide them to understand that although habitats are different, they all meet the same basic animal needs of food, water, air, shelter, and a place to live.

What habitats are in a zoo?

You see monkeys swinging from trees. You watch seals splashing in water. Where are you? You are visiting the zoo.

Many animals live at the zoo. People who work at the zoo give food and water to the animals. Look at the zoo habitats of these animals. Each animal gets everything it needs from its zoo habitat.

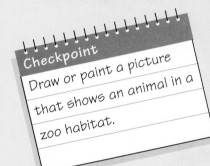

Checkpoint
Draw or paint a picture that shows an animal in a zoo habitat.

A 34

monkey

tiger

 ## Science Idea Exchange

Science Anecdote
Zoo kitchens must provide not only nutritious meals, but also the correct amount of food and water to meet animals' needs. Different animals require different amounts of food. Some reptiles are fed only once a week, while the Asian elephant eats about 68 kg (150 lbs) of grass, leaves, and bark a day!

Science and Language Arts

Invite groups to play "Guess My Animal." Have children take turns thinking of an animal while the rest of the group asks questions about the animal's habitat. Examples include: "Does it live in a pond?" and "Does it eat insects?" Then have children try to guess the animal being described.

Science and Social Studies
Invite children to explore how zookeepers help their community. Then have them write a sentence describing one job of a zookeeper. Encourage children to illustrate their sentence. Compile the pages in a book.

panda

giraffe

A 35

Encourage Student Definitions

Enlarge children's concept of shelter by suggesting they look again at the animal habitats shown in the pictures and define the word "shelter."

Ask Open-ended Questions

Ask: *How do you think zoo habitats are different from each other?* (Some are larger; some have trees and others have small plants.) *Do you think two different animals could live in each other's habitat? Why or why not?* (One animal might not find what it needs to survive in another animal's habitat.)

Close

Check for Understanding

- As a follow-up to the **baseline assessment,** ask children to draw another picture of a zoo habitat. **Compare** these pictures with their pictures from Make Connections.
- **Answers to Checkpoint** Children's drawings or paintings should show the animal and those things in its habitat that provide food, water, air, shelter, and a place to live.

Connecting Lessons

In the next lesson, children will learn about the habitat of the koala. ▶

Explorer's Activity Guide

Use Explorer's Activity Guide page 20 with this lesson to help children answer the text question, "What habitats are in a zoo?" with a hands-on activity.

Science and Music

Play the song "Little White Duck" found on the Raffi album *Everything Grows* (MCA Records, Inc., 1987). Invite children to **name** the animals in the song and to tell how they interact with their habitats. Help children write new words to the song, using different animals and habitats.

Visual Literacy

To enhance the **visual literacy** connection, use the interactive overhead transparency that correlates with the above two pages. The transparency will help your students understand the key concepts presented on these pages.

Lesson 7

Lesson Objective
Children learn how the koala meets its needs in its tree habitat.

Introduce

Invite Learning
Invite children to examine their cricket habitats from Lesson 5 and tell how a koala's habitat might be different from and similar to a cricket's.

Make Connections
To **assess prior knowledge,** ask children to describe some habitats they have observed at the zoo or in the pictures in the previous lesson. List items in their descriptions, such as rocks, trees, and grass. Ask: *Which of these things might be in the habitat of a koala?* Save the list as a **baseline assessment.**

Teach

Activity
Children design and construct a model of a habitat for a koala. **Skill:** Making physical models

Materials (per group)
Module Kit Items: white pipe cleaners *(about 12);* green pipe cleaners *(about 12);* 3 sheets construction paper, assorted colors
School Supplied Items: shoe box; glue; crayons; scissors
Safety Kit Items: cover goggles *(1/child)*

What habitat can you plan for a zoo?

Look in this tree. Tell about the animal you see. It is a koala. The tree is its habitat. How does this koala get everything it needs?

The koala gets food and water from eating leaves. It gets shelter from the tree.

Pretend you work in a zoo. Your job is to make a habitat for a koala.

A 36

Science Idea Exchange

Science Anecdote
Koalas are Australian mammals that spend most of their time in trees. They eat the leaves that grow at the tips of eucalyptus branches, getting liquids they need from these leaves. Koalas raise their young in a pouch, like kangaroos. Koalas are not related to bears.

Science and Art
Invite children to paint a picture of a koala on heavy paper and cut it into puzzle pieces. Have children exchange their puzzles with a partner to put together again. Store puzzle pieces in envelopes.

Multicultural Connection
Many cultures throughout history have established zoos. Perhaps the first known zoo was constructed in 1500 B.C. by Queen Hatshepsut of Egypt. Rulers in areas of China, India, and northern Africa also built zoos at later dates. The ancient Greeks and the Aztecs of what is now Mexico were also known to have established zoos.

Make a model of a zoo habitat.

You will need: cover goggles shoe box

 construction paper crayons  glue

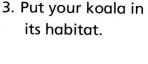 scissors ⁓⁓⁓ pipe cleaners

1. Draw a picture of a koala. Cut out your picture.
2. Make a habitat for the koala in your shoe box.
3. Put your koala in its habitat.

Checkpoint

Do a radio show. Tell about the new zoo habitat for the koala. Invite people to come to the zoo.

Helpful Hints

- For the radio show in Checkpoint, have children work in groups. Assign a role to each group member (announcer, interviewer, zookeeper, director).
- *See Equipment Kit Teacher's Guide for additional hints.*

Observe and Listen

Suggest that each child color and cut out a koala and a tree to put in the group's shoe box. Guide children to talk about the habitat with other members of their group.

Close

Check for Understanding

- As a follow-up to the **baseline assessment,** have children revise their list from Make Connections. Look for increased knowledge of how items in the koala's habitat meet its needs.
- **Answers to Checkpoint** Group approaches may vary. All groups should explain ways the zoo habitat gives the koala what it needs to survive.

Connecting Lessons

In the next lesson, children will learn that when animals cannot survive in their natural habitat, they are sometimes taken to zoos and wildlife parks to live. ▶

Explorer's Activity Guide

Use Explorer's Activity Guide hands-on activity on page 21 to help children answer the question, "What habitat can you plan for a zoo?"

Teacher's Assessment Package

A **scoring rubric** to assess student performance is provided on page 9 of the Teacher's Assessment Package.

Activity Results

The habitat model should show the koalas in the leafy treetops. Children should be able to identify the trees as the koalas' shelter and source of food and water.

Collaborative Learning: Small Groups

Assign specific children to gather and clean up materials. Each child in the Activity group should draw and cut out a koala and make a tree for the group's shoe box.

Lesson 8

Lesson Objective

Children learn that some red wolves are taken to live in zoos and wildlife parks where their needs can be met.

Skills: Organizing information, solving problems

Introduce

Invite Learning

Invite children to name and act as their favorite zoo animal. Ask: *How would you feel if that kind of animal no longer lived on the earth? Why?*

Make Connections

To **assess prior knowledge,** ask children how they think animals might be helped when they cannot get what they need from their natural habitats. List their responses on chart paper and save them as a **baseline assessment** to refer to in Check for Understanding.

Teach

Observe and Listen

- Encourage children to study the pictures carefully and count the wolves in each one.
- Have children fill out their charts. Allow time for them to discuss questions they have related to the chart.

How many red wolves live in wildlife parks?

Sometimes red wolves cannot live in their habitat. Some of these red wolves are sent to live in wildlife parks. These habitats have everything the red wolves need to live.

1. Look at the pictures. You can see that 20 red wolves were sent to habitat A. How many wolves went to each of the other habitats?

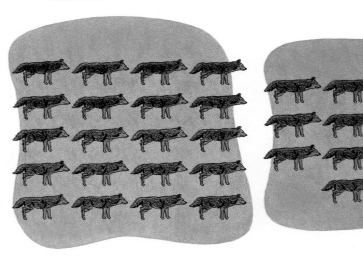

habitat A   habitat B

A 38

 ## Science Idea Exchange

Science Anecdote

Two kinds of wolves found in North America are the gray (timber or tundra) wolf and the red wolf. The young are born in sheltered areas called dens. Red wolves, for years virtually extinct in the wild, have recently been reintroduced to the swamplands of eastern North Carolina.

Science and Language Arts

Challenge children to work in groups to write and draw a picture story about a red wolf or another animal that was unable to survive in its natural habitat and was moved to a wildlife park. Then invite a member of each group to read the story to the class.

Math/Science Connection

Let children work in small groups to make a poster about animals. Help children list the numbers 1 to 12 down the left side of the poster-board. Have children draw or cut out pictures of animals that might live in a park. Then have them glue the correct number of a kind of animal beside each number.

2. Draw a chart like this one.

habitat	number of wolves
habitat A	20
habitat B	
habitat C	

3. The chart shows how many red wolves live in habitat A. Fill in the chart for habitats B and C.

habitat C

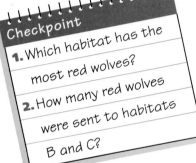

Checkpoint
1. Which habitat has the most red wolves?
2. How many red wolves were sent to habitats B and C?

Encourage children to **describe** a wildlife park, using phrases such as "out in the open," "not in cages," "there is food and water," or "there is shelter." Then help children use the words and phrases to write a few sentences that tell what a wildlife park is.

Close

Check for Understanding
• As a follow-up to the **baseline assessment,** have children revise their list of ideas from Make Connections. Look for the inclusion of information about wildlife parks as a way that animals might be helped when their natural habitats cannot provide what they need.
• **Answers to Checkpoint** 1. Habitat A has the most wolves. 2. A total of 17 wolves were sent to habitats B and C.

Connecting Lessons
In the next lesson, children will make a book about plant and animal habitats. ▶

Explorer's Activity Guide
Use Explorer's Activity Guide page 23 to help children solve the question of how many red wolves live in wildlife parks. You can also use this hands-on activity page to evaluate how well children understand the concept of this lesson.

Save the Earth
Explain to children that there are very few red wolves left. They were killed by people or lost their shelter and food supply as land was cleared. Ask children how wildlife parks are keeping red wolves and other animals from disappearing. Explain that some animals born in wildlife parks are returned to the wild.

Achieving English Proficiency
Help children form small groups. Provide each group with pictures of endangered animals. Invite children to examine the pictures and talk about the habitat in which each might live. Encourage groups to share their observations with the class.

Lesson 9

Lesson Objective
Children make a book to show the concepts they learned in this chapter.

Introduce

Invite Learning
Review the **baseline assessment** activities you used in this chapter. Choose one or more to do again that you think will help children understand the chapter concepts.

Teach

Performance Assessment Activity
Children draw pictures of, and write stories about, a plant or an animal and its habitat. **Skills:** Describing, restating or explaining ideas, visualizing

Materials (per group)
Module Kit Items: none
School Supplied Items: crayons; drawing paper *(1 sheet/child)*; lined paper *(1 sheet/child)*; pencils *(1/child)*

Helpful Hints
● As children work on their books, ask: *What does a plant need from its habitat?* (water, sunlight, air) *What do animals need from their habitats?* (food, water, air, shelter, place to live)
● *See Equipment Kit Teacher's Guide for additional hints.*

What did you learn?

You learned what plants and animals get from their habitats. Now make a habitat book. Show a habitat for a plant or animal. Then tell about the habitat.

You will need: crayons paper  pencil

Make a book about a habitat.

1. Draw a picture of a plant or animal on your paper.
2. Add a habitat for the plant or animal to your picture.
3. Write a story on another paper. Tell what the plant or animal needs to live.
4. Make a cover for your book.
5. Put the pages inside the cover.

 ## Science Idea Exchange

Teacher's Assessment Package
Use the pages from the Teacher's Assessment Package at this time to promote **performance assessment** opportunities for your children.

Managing Groups
Assign specific children to gather and clean up materials. All children in the Chapter Review group should make a habitat book, then share their pictures and stories.

Science and Social Studies
Provide magazines that have pictures of animals from around the world in their habitats. Have children cut out the pictures and make a large collage. Then discuss the various habitats, including where they can be found and how some animals are unique to certain regions.

Share what you learned.

1. Can other plants and animals live in your habitat?
2. What can you tell about a habitat near your school?

A 41

Raise Questions

Make sure children's questions you recorded in What Else Do You Want to Find Out? in Lesson 1 have been answered. Then, using a **constructivist** approach, ask: *Is there anything else you want to know about habitats? How can we find the answers to your questions?*

Close

Check for Understanding

- Children's pictures and stories should show that plants need water, air, and sunlight, and animals need food, water, air, shelter, and a place to live.
- **Answers to Share what you learned**
  1. Answers will vary, but should indicate whether the children's habitats could provide water, air, and sunlight for plants, and food, water, air, shelter, and a place to live for animals. 2. Answers will vary, but should explain how the habitat near the school fulfills the needs of the plants or the animals that live there.

Connecting Chapters

In the next chapter, children will discover how living things are classified. ▶

Explorer's Activity Guide

Use Explorer's Activity Guide pages 25–26 as a hands-on activity to evaluate how well children understand the concepts covered in this chapter.

Activity Results

Children's pictures and stories in a book format should show that the plant can get water, sunlight, and air in its habitat, or that the animal can get food, water, air, shelter, and a place to live in its habitat.

Extend the Lesson

Encourage children to draw several pictures of plants, animals, and habitats. Suggest that they draw pictures and write stories about water, garden, or zoo habitats.

Chapter 3 Planning Guide
Grouping Living Things

Lessons / *Skills*

Lesson 1
Discover Activity: **How can you group things?** pp. A42–A43
(comparing, contrasting, classifying)

Lesson 2
Is it living? pp. A44–A45
(classifying, making decisions)

Lesson 3
How are living things grouped? pp. A46–A47
(describing, classifying)

Lesson 4
What are some groups of animals? pp. A48–A49
(observing, classifying, comparing)

Lesson 5
What are some kinds of body coverings? pp. A50–A51
(observing, describing)

Lesson 6
What are some other groups of animals? pp. A52–A53
(observing, contrasting)

Lesson 7
Let's Explore: **How can you make a model of an insect?**
pp. A54–A55
(recording, making physical models)

Lesson 8
Let's Solve It!: **How do you group plants?** pp. A56–A57
(organizing information, solving problems)

Lesson 9
Chapter Review: **What did you learn?** pp. A58–A59
(classifying)

Materials (per group)

Lesson 1 Activity: *How can you group things?*
Module Kit Items: none
School Supplied Items: drawing paper *(1 sheet/child)*; crayons; scissors *(1/child)*

Lesson 2 Activity: *Group living and nonliving things.*
Module Kit Items: none
School Supplied Items: old magazines; scissors *(1/child)*
Advance Prep: Begin collecting old magazines a week before the activity.

Lesson 5 Activity: *Observe body coverings.*
Module Kit Items: fish scale; feather; hand lens
School Supplied Items: drawing paper *(1 sheet/child)*; pencils *(1/child)*

Lesson 7 Activity: *How can you make a model of an insect?*
Module Kit Items: pipe cleaners *(about 8/child; green and/or white)*; modeling clay *(about 1/2 stick/child)*; white construction paper
School Supplied Items: insect picture; glue; scissors
Safety Kit Items: cover goggles *(1/child)*

Lesson 9 Activity: *Play a matching game.*
Module Kit Items: 16 index cards
School Supplied Items: pencils

Module A
Living Things

Assessment Options

	Content	Performance	Portfolio
Teacher's Assessment Package			
Chapter Test, pp. 17–18	✓		✓
Group Interview Assessment, p. 19	✓	✓	
Performance Strategies, p. 20	✓	✓	✓
Explorer's Activity Guide			
Activity worksheets, pp. 27–36		✓	✓
Chapter Review, pp. 37–38	✓		✓
Interactive Transparency Package			
Transparency 5 and BLM	✓	✓	✓
Teacher's Guide, pp. 14–15	✓	✓	
Hands-on activities for second-language learners	✓	✓	✓
Science Literature Library			
Fireflies in the Night		✓	✓
Interactive Videodisc Software Teacher's Guide, pp. 44–52			
Computer-based Activity	✓	✓	
Journal Presentations	✓	✓	✓
Videodisc Classroom Guide, pp. 9–16, **or Video Reader**			
Hands-on activity	✓	✓	✓
ExploraCenter Teacher's Guide, pp. 12, 13, 15, 17, 28, 29, 30, 32			
ExploraCenter			
Science activity cards 7, 8, 10, 12, 23, 24, 25, 27	✓	✓	✓
ScottForesman Online Service			
Online field trips	✓	✓	✓

Chapter Overview

Children begin the chapter by determining different ways of grouping. They learn that things can be grouped as living and nonliving. They further discover that living things can be grouped in a variety of ways. Children's exploration of grouping culminates in playing a matching game.

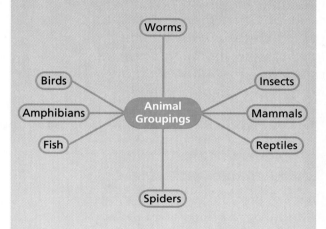

Lesson Objective
Children use prior knowledge to classify objects in various ways.

Introduce

Invite Learning
Show the videodisc segment for this chapter. Bar codes and a description of this segment are given below on page A43.

Make Connections
To **assess prior knowledge**, show children a simple collection, such as a collection of rocks, stamps, or baseball cards, or ask children to describe collections they have at home. Ask: *In what ways are the things in the collection alike? How might the things in the collection be grouped?*

Teach

Discover Activity

Children group drawings of shoes by a variety of characteristics. **Skills:** Comparing, contrasting, classifying

Materials (per group)
Module Kit Items: none
School Supplied Items: drawing paper *(1 sheet/child)*; crayons; scissors *(1/child)*

Chapter 3

Grouping Living Things

Look at all these shoes! Do any of them look like yours? Do any of them look alike? Things that are alike can be grouped together.

Now look around your classroom. Find more shoes. How could you group these shoes?

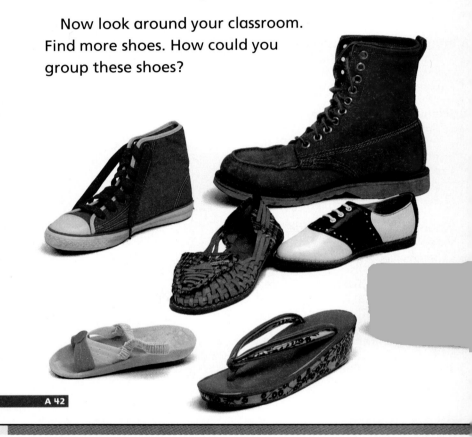

A 42

Science Idea Exchange

Collaborative Learning: Small Groups
Assign specific children to gather and clean up materials. Each child in the Discover Activity group should draw a picture of a shoe and participate in grouping the shoe pictures.

Science and Literature
Challenge children to find out why the firefly is classified as a beetle as you read the literature selection *Fireflies in the Night* by Judy Hawes (HarperCollins, 1991). (Beetles have a pair of front wings that cover and protect the body.)

Family/School Partnership: Family Support
Encourage families to be active partners in learning by suggesting that they and their children:
- group objects at home according to color, size, shape, and so on,
- sort pictures of animals into groups, and
- sort pictures of plants into groups.

How can you group things?

1 Draw your favorite shoe.

2 Color the shoe. Then cut it out.

3 Sit in a circle with your classmates. Put your shoe picture in the center of the circle.

4 Find the shoes that are the same color. Put them in a group.

5 Group the shoes in as many other ways as you can.

6 **Tell about it.** Write down how the shoes in each group are alike.

Ask me what else I want to find out about grouping things.

Helpful Hints

- Divide the class into groups after children have drawn their shoes.
- Marbles, crayons, blocks, buttons, books, or children's actual shoes can be substituted for children's drawings.
- *See Equipment Kit Teacher's Guide for additional hints.*

What to Expect

Children may sort shoe drawings by type of shoe, by whether or not shoes have shoelaces, or by whether or not shoes have heels.

Close

Check for Understanding

- Ask children to demonstrate one of the ways they sorted their drawings of shoes.
- **Answers to Tell about it** In one group, shoes may be the same color; in another, they may be the same size or shape. Accept any grouping children can explain.

What Else Do You Want to Find Out?

Record children's questions on chart paper and use them to invite exploration of chapter topics.

Connecting Lessons

In the next lesson, children will learn how things are classified as living or nonliving. ▶

Explorer's Activity Guide

The **Discover Activity recording sheet** on page 27 of the Explorer's Activity Guide can be used by children to record their activity results.

Visual Literacy

Discover the Wonder Videodisc, Grade 2, Module A, focuses on the nature of living and nonliving things and challenges children to use their creativity and imagination in expressing their ideas about objects in the world around them.

Bar Codes

Chapter 6: Stills

Step

Interactive Software

DISCOVER THE WONDER

Lesson Objective
Children learn how things are classified as either living or nonliving.

Introduce

Key Terms
living
nonliving

Invite Learning
Show pictures of a rock, grass, a tree, a book, a dog, a door, a bush, a fox, and a desk, or any other living and nonliving things. Invite children to group the objects in as many ways as they can.

Make Connections
To **assess prior knowledge,** write the headings "Living" and "Nonliving" on chart paper. Ask children to tape the pictures from Invite Learning under the correct headings. Save the chart to use as a **baseline assessment.**

Teach

Activity
Children cut out pictures and classify things as living or nonliving. **Skills:** Classifying, making decisions

Is it living?

Pretend you are taking a walk. You might see a bird. You might see grass. How are the bird and the grass alike? They are **living things.** Living things can grow.

What other things do you see? You might see a building. You might see a rock. Buildings and rocks are **nonliving things.** They do not grow. What other nonliving things might you see?

A 44

Science Idea Exchange

Science Background
Both living and nonliving things are made of matter. Living things grow and reproduce; nonliving things do not. Life requires energy, so all living things eat or make their own food. Living things can also respond to their surroundings: plants grow toward light, birds fly from danger.

Collaborative Learning: Small Groups
Assign specific children to gather and clean up materials. Each child in the Activity group should be involved in choosing pictures, grouping living and nonliving things, and sharing stories about their pictures.

Your Ideas
_____
_____
_____
_____
_____

Group living and nonliving things.

You will need: magazines ✂ scissors

1. Look at the pictures in the magazines.
2. Cut out pictures of living things. Cut out pictures of nonliving things.
3. Put pictures of living things in a group. Put pictures of nonliving things in a group.

Checkpoint
Tell a story about one of your pictures.

A 45

Materials (per group)
Module Kit Items: none
School Supplied Items: old magazines; scissors

Helpful Hints
- Children could paste the pictures on paper and make a book. One chapter could be titled "Living Things" and the other titled "Nonliving Things."
- *See Equipment Kit Teacher's Guide for additional hints.*

Encourage Student Definitions
Work with children to come up with class definitions for "living things" and "nonliving things."

Close

Check for Understanding
- As a follow-up to the **baseline assessment,** refer to the chart children made in Make Connections. Ask them to make any needed changes, and to explain why the objects belong in the groups into which they put them.
- **Answers to Checkpoint** Stories should reflect children's understanding of the differences between living and nonliving things.

Connecting Lessons
In the next lesson, children will learn how living things can be classified as animals or plants. ▶

Explorer's Activity Guide
Use Explorer's Activity Guide hands-on activity on page 28 to help children answer the question, "Is it living?"

 **Teacher's Assessment Package**
A **scoring rubric** to assess student performance is provided on page 15 of the Teacher's Assessment Package.

Activity Results
Children will have classified things in the pictures as either living or nonliving.

Your Ideas

_____

_____

_____

_____

_____

Lesson 3

Introduce

Invite Learning
Invite individual children to act out what their favorite animal does. Then ask them to act out what a plant does.

Make Connections
To **assess prior knowledge**, ask children to tell how the animals and plants they acted out in Invite Learning behave differently.

Teach

Encourage Student Definitions
Make two lists on the chalkboard, one for plants and one for animals. Write words and phrases children suggest to describe things that are true about plants and things that are true about animals. Keep the lists as a **baseline assessment.** You can use the lists to follow up on this assessment in Check for Understanding.

How are living things grouped?

Pretend you are visiting a park. You see living things in the park. How can you group these living things?

You can put the chipmunk, bird, and the ladybug into one group. How are they alike? They are animals. Most animals can move from place to place. Animals eat the food they find in their habitats.

A 46

Science Idea Exchange

Science Background
The living world is divided into five kingdoms: monerans (bacteria); protists (single-celled protozoans like *Amoeba*); fungi (mushrooms, molds); plants (organisms that make food by photosynthesis and whose cells have walls made of cellulose); and animals (multi-cellular organisms that eat food).

Science and Language Arts
As children present their commercials for Checkpoint, you can encourage both speaking and listening skills. After each commercial is over, ask volunteers to tell in their own words what the commercial announcer said.

Achieving English Proficiency
Invite children to make picture dictionaries for plants and animals. Vocabulary words for plants could include "flower," "bush," "grass," and "oak tree." Animal words could include "bird," "butterfly," "snake," and "giraffe." Ask children to write each word and draw a picture beside the word to illustrate it.

You can put the grass and the trees into another group. How are grass and trees alike? They are plants. Plants cannot move from one place to another. Plants use sunlight to make the food they need.

Checkpoint
Write a commercial for a new park. Tell what groups of living things people can see in the park.

A 47

Encourage groups of children to look through the literature selection *The Lady and the Spider* by Faith McNulty (Harper & Row, 1986). Challenge them to **list** all the plants and then all the animals that appear in the book.

Helpful Hint
For children who want to use visuals in their commercials for Checkpoint, you can provide drawing materials and magazines that feature photographs of animals and plants.

Close

Check for Understanding
- As a follow-up to the **baseline assessment,** have children **compare** and **contrast** plants and animals. Then ask them to compare their ideas with the descriptive lists they made in Encourage Student Definitions.
- **Answers to Checkpoint** In their commercials, children should say that the groups of living things in the park are plants and animals. They should also be able to name some living things and tell the group to which they belong.

Connecting Lessons
In the next lesson, children will learn that animals are classified into several different groups. ▶

Explorer's Activity Guide
Use Explorer's Activity Guide page 29 with this lesson to help children answer the text question, "How are living things grouped?" with a hands-on activity.

Special Education
Provide photographs of different kinds of plants and animals to pairs of children. Invite children to choose a photograph, show it to their partner, say what it is, and tell whether it is a plant or an animal.

Your Ideas

_____

_____

_____

_____

Lesson 4

Lesson Objective

Children learn that some animals are classified as mammals, birds, amphibians, fish, or reptiles.

Introduce

Invite Learning

Invite children to show how they would act and sound if they were a dog, an eagle, a frog, a shark, and a snake.

Make Connections

To **assess prior knowledge**, write the names of different mammals, birds, amphibians, fish, and reptiles on cards. Ask children to group the cards, and to explain how the animals in a group are alike. Record children's explanations of the groupings to use as a **baseline assessment**.

Teach

Act as a Consultant

Provide pictures of animals from each group and let children **compare** them to the illustration in the book. Allow children to work together to **classify** all the animals.

What are some groups of animals?

Imagine walking into this pet store. There are so many animals to see!

First find the animals that live in water. Did you find the fish? Now look for the birds. How are they alike? Notice that animals that are alike are grouped together. Find other groups of animals in the picture.

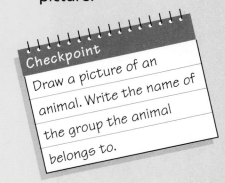

Checkpoint
Draw a picture of an animal. Write the name of the group the animal belongs to.

Canaries belong to a group called **birds**.

Turtles belong to a group called **reptiles**.

 Science Idea Exchange

Science Background

Mammals have fur or hair and usually bear live young. Birds have feathers and lay eggs. Most amphibians have smooth skin, live in or near water, and lay eggs in water. Most fish have scales, live in water, and lay eggs or bear live young. Most reptiles have scales and lay leathery eggs on land.

Math/Science Connection

Invite children to count the number of animals shown in the picture for each animal group. Write children's responses on the chalkboard. Challenge children to make up and solve simple word problems about the animals. For example, *How many more legs does a kitten have than a bird? How many wings altogether do the birds in one cage have?*

Science and Social Studies

Make children aware that there are different kinds of animals in different parts of the country, and that people who live in rural areas often see more kinds of animals than people who live in the city. Discuss the kinds of animals that live in your community, and help children **classify** them.

Goldfish belong to a group called **fish.**

Frogs belong to a group called **amphibians.**

Cats belong to a group called **mammals.**

A 49

Encourage Student Definitions

Have children ask and answer questions such as: *What does a dog have that a canary doesn't?* (fur, four legs) *What does a fish have that a reptile doesn't?* (fins) Then help children list the characteristics of mammals, birds, amphibians, fish, and reptiles.

Ask Open-ended Questions

Using a **constructivist** approach, ask: *What kind of animal would you like to learn more about? What questions do you have about this animal? How can we find the answers to your questions?*

Close

Check for Understanding

- As a follow-up to the **baseline assessment**, list the five animal classifications on the chalkboard. Then have children place the cards from Make Connections under the appropriate classification. Ask children to tell how the animals in each group are alike.
- **Answers to Checkpoint** Children's drawings should have appropriate labels indicating the animal's group name.

Connecting Lessons

In the next lesson, children will learn to classify animals based on their body coverings. ▶

Explorer's Activity Guide

Use Explorer's Activity Guide page 30 with this lesson to help children answer the text question, "What are some groups of animals?" with a hands-on activity.

Explore Further

Take children on a visit to a local pet store. If there are shops in your area that specialize in fish, birds, or reptiles, you might want to visit more than one. You could invite children with small pets to bring them to class. Have children keep a list of the different animals they see and classify them into groups.

Visual Literacy

To enhance the **visual literacy** connection, use the interactive overhead transparency that correlates with the above two pages. The transparency will help your students understand the key concepts presented on these pages.

Lesson 5

Lesson Objective
Children learn that animals in different groups have different kinds of body coverings.

Introduce

Invite Learning
Have children tell about all the animals they have touched. Ask them to tell what the animals felt like and to note any similarities among the way the animals felt.

Make Connections
To **assess prior knowledge**, write the headings "Mammal," "Bird," "Reptile," "Amphibian," and "Fish" on the chalkboard. Ask children to tell what these groups of animals feel like. Record and save their responses to use as a **baseline assessment**.

Teach

Activity
Children use a hand lens to observe a feather and fish scales. Then children draw and write about their observations.
Skills: Observing, describing

Materials (per group)
Module Kit Items: fish scale; feather; hand lens
School Supplied Items: sheets of drawing paper; pencils

What are some kinds of body coverings?

Imagine petting this soft, furry puppy. A puppy is a mammal. Mammals have hair or fur covering their bodies. Do other kinds of animals feel furry? Reptiles have rough, dry skin. Amphibians have smooth, wet skin.

Birds have feathers covering their bodies. Most fish have scales covering their bodies. What are feathers and scales like?

A 50

 ## Science Idea Exchange

Science Background
Some animals have coverings that help them stay warm in very cold climates. The polar bear's thick, oily fur traps a layer of air that keeps the bear's body heat inside. Penguins have short, closely packed feathers that trap body heat and keep warm air next to their skin.

Collaborative Learning: Small Groups
Assign specific children to gather and clean up materials. Each child in the Activity group should make and record observations and be involved in sharing observations and stories about body coverings.

Multicultural Connection
Most Native Americans view birds as symbols of freedom and wisdom. Traditionally, they used feathers as decorations for clothes and tools, as sacred symbols, and on arrows. Display and discuss pictures that show Native Americans' traditional uses for feathers. If possible, invite a Native American to talk about feathers.

Observe body coverings.

You will need:  bird feather ○ hand lens

🐟 fish scales ☐ paper ✏️ pencil

1. Look at the feather with the hand lens. Draw what you see.
2. Touch the feather. Feel the different parts. Write down how the feather feels.
3. Look at the fish scales with the hand lens. Draw what you see.
4. Touch the fish scales. Write down how the scales feel.

Checkpoint
Write a story about an animal. Tell about its body covering.

A 51

Safety Tips
- Be sure to wash fish scales.
- Caution children not to put their fingers in their mouth after touching feathers and scales. Have them wash their hands after the activity.

Helpful Hints
- Feathers can be obtained from pet stores, novelty shops, or farms.
- Fish scales can be obtained from stores where fish are cleaned.
- *See Equipment Kit Teacher's Guide for additional hints.*

Observe and Listen
As the groups **observe** and touch the feather and the fish scales, encourage them to discuss how the feather and scales look and feel.

Close

Check for Understanding
- As a follow-up to the **baseline assessment,** reread with children the chart from Make Connections. Ask them to make any needed changes.
- **Answers to Checkpoint** Stories will vary, but all children should associate their animal with the correct body covering.

Connecting Lessons
In the next lesson, children will learn about the different characteristics of worms, spiders, and insects. ▶

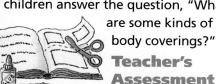

Explorer's Activity Guide
Use Explorer's Activity Guide hands-on activity on page 31 to help children answer the question, "What are some kinds of body coverings?"

Teacher's Assessment Package
A **scoring rubric** to assess student performance is provided on page 15 of the Teacher's Assessment Package.

Activity Results
Children should discover that the body coverings of fish and birds look and feel very different. Fish scales are either smooth or rough, depending on the kind of fish. Bird feathers have a stiff shaft and soft barbs.

Science Themes
By observing feathers and scales, children develop their understanding of the theme of **diversity.**

Lesson Objective
Children learn about the different characteristics of worms, spiders, and insects.

Introduce

Key Term
insect

Invite Learning
Have children observe pictures of worms, spiders, and insects. Encourage children to talk about what they see.

Make Connections
To **assess prior knowledge**, make concept maps on chart paper for "Worms," "Spiders," and "Insects." Ask children to share anything they know about each kind of animal. Write their ideas on the concept maps and keep them to use as a **baseline assessment**.

Teach

Observe and Listen
Children may have the idea that spiders are insects. Invite the groups to **contrast** the pictures of the ant and the spider and discuss how they are different.

What are some other groups of animals?

Pretend you are digging in this soil. You find a worm. You look at it. The worm has a long soft body. It does not have legs. You watch the worm crawl around the ground. The worm in this picture lives in soil. Other worms live in water.

A 52

Science Idea Exchange

Science Background
Charles Darwin recognized the importance of the earthworm: "It may be doubted whether there are any other animals which have played so important a part in the history of the world, as have these lowly organized creatures." As it burrows through the ground, the earthworm mixes and loosens the soil, allowing air and water to enter, making it easier for plant roots to penetrate soil and absorb nutrients from it. Organic wastes from the earthworm enrich the soil with minerals and nitrogen. A fertile field can contain millions of earthworms.

Science and Language Arts
Ask children to draw a series of pictures that tell a story about a worm, spider, or insect. Then invite children to show their pictures and tell their story to the rest of the class. You might use a hole punch and yarn to bind the pictures into books.

You see an ant on a nearby flower. Ants belong to a group of animals called **insects.** Ants and other insects have three main body parts. Insects have six legs. Many ants do not have wings. Insects such as bees do have wings.

You find other animals on the ground. You see a spider. It has two main body parts. You notice that the spider does not have wings. You count eight legs on the spider.

Checkpoint

Draw a picture of a spider. Show the body parts of the spider.

Using a **constructivist** approach, ask: *How do you know that a spider is not an insect?* (It has two body parts and eight legs; an insect has three body parts and six legs.) *What else do you want to know about worms, spiders, and insects? How can we find the answers to your questions?*

Ask for Evidence

Refer children to the second two-page illustration in the module literature selection, *The Lady and the Spider* by Faith McNulty (Harper & Row, 1986). Ask children to identify the ant and the spider in the picture and to tell how they know which is which.

Close

Check for Understanding

- As a follow-up to the **baseline assessment,** have children look at the concept maps from Make Connections. Ask if there are any ideas or words they would like to add.
- **Answers to Checkpoint** Drawings should show eight legs and two main body parts.

Connecting Lessons

In the next lesson, children will make a model of an insect. ▶

Explorer's Activity Guide

Use Explorer's Activity Guide pages 33–34 with this lesson to help children answer the text

question, "What are some other groups of animals?" with a hands-on activity.

Save the Earth

Many farmers and gardeners use helpful insects to control the number of harmful insects that attack their crops. For example, ladybugs eat aphids, stalk borers, weevils, whiteflies, and Colorado potato beetles. Have children make posters encouraging the use of natural pest control.

Your Ideas

_____

_____

_____

_____

_____

Lesson 7

Lesson Objective
Children learn they can illustrate characteristics of an insect by making a model.

Introduce

Invite Learning
Have children list everything they know about insects. Record their list on the chalkboard.

Make Connections
To **assess prior knowledge**, ask children to make drawings of insects. Encourage them to use the list developed in Invite Learning to guide them.

Teach

Activity
Children make a model of an insect.
Skills: Recording, making physical models

Materials (per group)
Module Kit Items: pipe cleaners *(about 8/child; green and/or white)*; modeling clay *(about 1/2 stick/child)*; white construction paper
School Supplied Items: insect picture; glue; scissors
Safety Kit Items: cover goggles *(1/child)*

Helpful Hints
- If appropriate, children can use the drawings from Make Connections as a plan for their models.

How can you make a model of an insect?

Suppose you see an insect on your way to school. You want to tell a classmate about the insect. One way to tell about the insect is to make a model.

Find out about it.

You will need:

 cover goggles

 picture of an insect

 clay

 paper

 pipe cleaners

 scissors

 glue

1 Get a picture of an insect from your teacher. Look closely at the picture.

2 Make the main body parts of the insect out of pieces of clay. Use pipe cleaners to put the parts together.

3 Make legs from pipe cleaners.

4 Put the legs on the body of the insect.

5 Add other parts your insect might have.

A 54

Science Idea Exchange

Science Background
The three main body parts of insects are the head, thorax, and abdomen. Mouth parts, antennas, and eyes are located on the head. Wings and legs are located on the thorax, which is made up of three segments. The abdomen may have as many as eleven segments.

Science and Language Arts
Write several sentences on the chalkboard for children to copy, leaving blanks for them to fill in. For example, "All insects have [six] legs." "All insects have [three] main body parts." "Bees and butterflies have [wings]."

Gifted and Talented
Invite children to make models showing all the life stages of a dragonfly or other insect that undergoes metamorphosis. Help children locate books or magazines containing pictures they can refer to for their models.

Write about it. ✏

Make a chart like this one. Write down how many parts your model has.

kind of part	how many parts
main body parts	
legs	
wings	
antennas	
eyes	

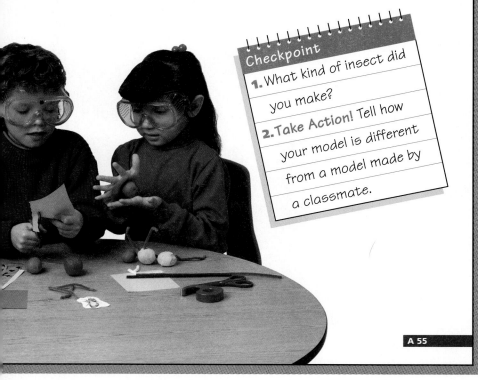

Checkpoint

1. What kind of insect did you make?

2. **Take Action!** Tell how your model is different from a model made by a classmate.

A 55

Helpful Hints (cont'd.)

- Children can make models of the ant shown on page A53 or you can use your own pictures or diagrams, as long as all body parts are clearly visible.
- Point out that some winged insects have one pair of wings and others have two pairs. Most insects have two eyes. Many insects have antennas (long, slender, segmented feelers on the head that function primarily as organs of touch).
- *See Equipment Kit Teacher's Guide for additional hints.*

Observe and Listen

Observe children as they make their models, and listen to their discussions as they chart their information. Allow children to share their completed models and charts with each other.

Close

Check for Understanding

Answers to Checkpoint 1. The type of insect will vary from child to child, but all should at least show three main body parts and six legs. 2. **Take Action!** Other children's models may or may not include wings, antennas, and eyes.

Connecting Lessons

In the next lesson, children will learn how plants can be classified. ▶

Explorer's Activity Guide

Use Explorer's Activity Guide hands-on activity on page 35 to explore insects and evaluate children's understanding of the lesson concept.

Teacher's Assessment Package

A **scoring rubric** to assess student performance is provided on page 15 of the Teacher's Assessment Package.

Activity Results

Children's models and charts should show that insects have three main body parts; six legs; zero, two, or four wings; and most will have two eyes and two antennas.

Collaborative Learning: Small Groups

Assign specific children to gather and clean up materials. All children in the Let's Explore group should be involved in making the model insect, recording data, and sharing their models and charts.

Lesson 8

Lesson Objective
Children learn that plants can be classified according to the vein patterns in their leaves. **Skills:** Organizing information, solving problems

Introduce

Invite Learning
Have children make leaf rubbings of several leaves that have straight line and weblike vein patterns.

Make Connections
To **assess prior knowledge**, have children group their leaf rubbings. Keep the groupings to use as a **baseline assessment.** You can follow up on this assessment in Check for Understanding.

Teach

Observe and Listen
- As pairs of children carefully look at the pictures, encourage them to **describe** the leaves to each other.
- Let each pair decide which leaf each child will record on the chart.

Let's Solve It!

How do you group plants?

Pretend you are looking at plants with flowers. You see veins in the leaves.

The veins of some leaves are in straight lines. The veins of other leaves spread out like a web.

1. Look at the pictures. Leaf A has veins that are spread out. Leaf B has veins that are in straight lines. How do the veins in leaf C and leaf D look?

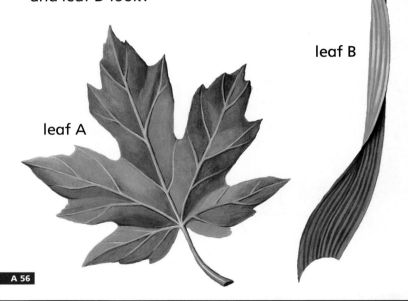

leaf B

leaf A

A 56

💡 Science Idea Exchange

Science Background
Flowering plants can be classified as either monocot or dicot. The veins in a monocot leaf run parallel to each other. The veins in a dicot leaf are spread out in many directions, like a web.

Math/Science Connection
Provide further practice with charts by suggesting children work in groups of three or four to classify additional leaves. Provide each group with one leaf for each child, or ask each child to bring a leaf to class. Tell children to make a chart similar to the one in the book.

Collaborative Learning: Cooperative Learning
Invite children to work in groups as they chart information about leaves they bring to class. Assign each group member a task:
- make a chart like the one in the book;
- assign a letter to each leaf;
- draw leaves on the chart;
- fill in Xs on the chart.

2. Make a chart like this one.

leaf	how leaf looks	veins in straight lines	veins that spread out
leaf A	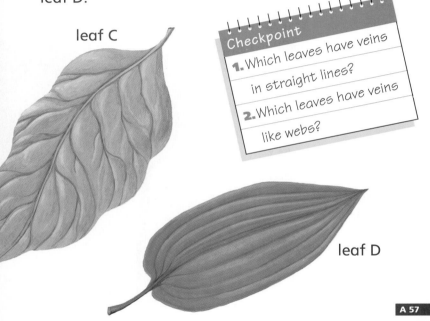		X
leaf B		X	
leaf C			
leaf D			

3. The chart tells about the veins in leaf A and leaf B. Fill in the chart for leaf C and leaf D.

leaf C

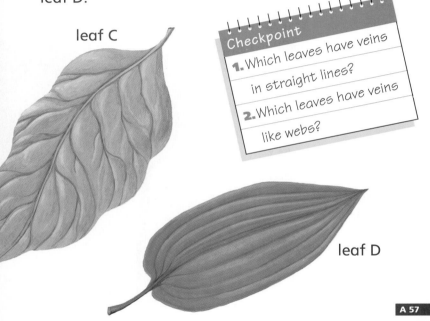

Checkpoint

1. Which leaves have veins in straight lines?

2. Which leaves have veins like webs?

leaf D

Raise Questions
Stimulate children's interest in leaf classification by using a **constructivist** approach. Ask: *How did you group your leaves? Can you think of other ways to group leaves? What questions do you have about grouping leaves? How can we find the answers to your questions?*

Encourage Student Definitions
Help children in developing a definition for the word "vein." Ask: *What do veins look like? What kinds of patterns do the veins make on different leaves?*

Close

Check for Understanding
● As a follow-up to the **baseline assessment**, have children reclassify their leaf rubbings. Look for whether or not they classify them according to the vein pattern.
● **Answers to Checkpoint** 1. Leaves B and D have veins in straight lines. 2. Two leaves, leaves A and C, have veins like webs.

Connecting Lessons
In the next lesson, children will play a game in which they classify animals and plants. ▶

Explorer's Activity Guide
Use Explorer's Activity Guide page 36 to help children solve the question of how plants are grouped. You can also use this hands-on activity page to evaluate how well children understand the concept of this lesson.

Science Themes
By recognizing different vein patterns of leaves, children develop their understanding of the theme of **scale and structure.**

Your Ideas

_____

_____

_____

_____

_____

Lesson 9

Lesson Objective
Children play a matching game to show the concepts they learned in this chapter.

Introduce

Invite Learning
Review the **baseline assessment** activities you used in this chapter. Choose one or more to do again that you think will help children understand the chapter concepts.

Teach

Performance Assessment Activity
Children make game cards and play a matching game. **Skill:** Classifying

Materials (per group)
Module Kit Items: 16 index cards
School Supplied Items: pencils

Helpful Hints
- As an alternate to note cards, you can provide paper with dotted cutting lines.
- Point out to children that the first partner writes any eight words or phrases from the two columns. The second partner writes the remaining eight words or phrases from the columns.
- See Equipment Kit Teacher's Guide for additional hints.

What did you learn?

You can match living and nonliving things with words that tell about them.

You will need: [ ] note cards pencil

Play a matching game.
1. Get 8 note cards from your teacher.
2. Write 8 things from this list on your note cards.

worm	nonliving
bird	plant
spider	long, soft body
fish	veins
insect	feathers
building	8 legs
tree	scales
leaf	6 legs

3. Tell your partner to write the 8 other things on note cards.

Science Idea Exchange

Teacher's Assessment Package
Use the pages from the Teacher's Assessment Package at this time to promote **performance assessment** opportunities for your children.

Science Background
Classifying plants or animals based on their similarities and differences helps biologists identify evolutionary relationships. For example, the jointed appendages of insects, spiders, and crustaceans (crabs, shrimp) indicate they have a shared ancestry. As a result, they are called arthropods, which means "jointed foot" in Greek.

Science and Language Arts
Encourage children to make up riddles about living things that include information about classification. Invite children to say their riddles to the class so other children may solve them. For example, "I am an animal that has two body parts and eight legs. What am I?" (spider)

4. Put all the cards face down on the table.
5. Turn one card over.
6. Pick up another card to match the first card. Turn the card face down if it is not a match.
7. Play until a match is made. Keep the matched cards face up on the table.
8. Take turns until all the cards are matched.

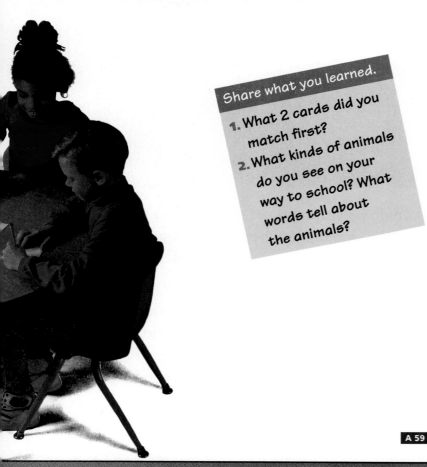

Share what you learned.

1. What 2 cards did you match first?
2. What kinds of animals do you see on your way to school? What words tell about the animals?

Observe and Listen
Walk around the room as children play their matching games. Observe the matches children have made.

Act as a Consultant
You might ask children to explain the matches they have made. Ask: *Why do these two cards match?* If children's matches are not correct, you might guide them to understand which cards make better matches.

Raise Questions
Using a **constructivist** approach, return to the chart children made at the beginning of this chapter with questions about grouping living things. Ask: *Have all of your questions been answered? What other questions do you have?* Help children find the answers to their questions.

Close

Check for Understanding
● Invite children to show their matching cards and say a sentence that tells why they match.
● **Answers to Share what you learned** 1. Children's cards should include a name of an object or living thing and a word or phrase that describes that object or living thing. 2. Children will most likely mention birds, squirrels, pets, and insects.

Explorer's Activity Guide
Use Explorer's Activity Guide pages 37–38 as a hands-on activity to evaluate how well children understand the concepts covered in this chapter.

Activity Results
Children should be able to match all the cards and review what they learned in the chapter about classifying.

Collaborative Learning: Small Groups
Assign specific children to gather materials. All children in the Chapter Review group should help prepare the game cards, then take turns playing the matching game.

People at Work

Nature of Work

Pet store workers care for the animals in their stores by feeding them, giving them water, cleaning their cages, and monitoring their overall health. Workers order items sold in the pet stores, such as cages and nest materials for birds; aquariums, pumps, and filters for fish; scratching posts and litter boxes for cats; exercise wheels for hamsters; and leashes and toys for dogs. They also serve the customers who come into the store. Some workers may tell customers about the needs of a particular animal and help the customer decide if the animal is the right pet for them.

Places of Work

Pet store workers might work in stores that sell any kind of pet that a person would want to buy. They may also work at an animal shelter or boarding kennel.

Training

Some pet store workers learned about animals by raising family pets. Some may be studying for degrees in biology or animal studies. Still others may be getting training in veterinary medicine.

Preparation

Children can take care of their pets at home or any animals at school. They can also get jobs in their neighborhood feeding, playing with, brushing, or walking other people's pets.

People at Work

A visit to a pet store

Imagine visiting a pet store. You see rabbits sleeping. You hear birds singing. You watch fish swimming in aquariums. What else might you see?

Pet store workers take care of the animals. The workers make sure the animals stay healthy. The workers clean the cages. They clean the aquariums. Pet store workers give the animals food and water every day.

A 60

 ## Science Idea Exchange

Examine the Career

Ask children to name qualifications of a pet store worker (examples: love animals, know pet health care, able to identify breeds, understand pet training techniques).

Explore Further

Children interested in learning more about working in a pet store might visit such a store with a parent or guardian. They can ask questions of the workers in the store and report to their classmates on what they learned and observed. Photographs taken at the store would be an interesting addition to the report.

How does an aquarium work?

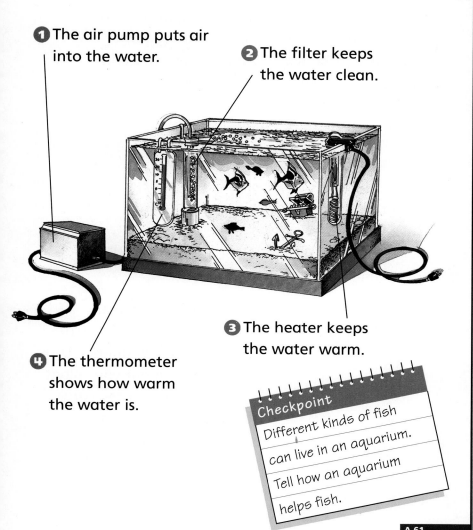

1 The air pump puts air into the water.

2 The filter keeps the water clean.

3 The heater keeps the water warm.

4 The thermometer shows how warm the water is.

Checkpoint

Different kinds of fish can live in an aquarium.

Tell how an aquarium helps fish.

A 61

Science Background
You may wish to share some of the following information about pets with children:
- In North America, there are 37 breeds of cats, 150 breeds of dogs, and 42 breeds of rabbits.
- After Admiral Richard Byrd traveled with a group of explorers to the South Pole in 1947, he gave great praise to his playful fox terrier, Igloo. Igloo consistently kept the explorers' spirits up by making them laugh, allowing them to forget the misery of the extreme cold.
- Bringing pets into hospitals and nursing homes to visit with patients and residents often results in the people feeling happier, which helps them respond better to medical treatment and recover faster.
- People who study animal behavior have found that cats who are gently petted and scratched by their owners become more affectionate toward them.
- For healthy pets, most pet store owners and veterinarians recommend a balanced diet of formulated pet food rather than "people food" or table scraps.

Discussion
Ask: *If you wanted to find out something important about working in a pet store, what one question would you ask?* (Answers will vary, yet the best answers should reflect some insight gained from the chapter concepts.)

Answers to Checkpoint
An aquarium gives fish clean, warm water and sufficient air for fish to live.

Collaborative Learning: Small Groups
Have children working in groups of three or four design their own pet store. The groups can decide whether each child should be responsible for certain animals and whether to draw a picture of the inside of the pet store or make a floor plan.

Show What You Know

- You can use the first paragraph in the text to begin assessing what children know about plants and animals. Children can develop a list of items they might include in the nature show as you record their ideas on the chalkboard.
- Some children may not fully understand the concept of a show. Help them understand that it is a presentation of people's projects that display particular knowledge. In this case, their knowledge of plants and animals is being showcased.

Plan Your Nature Show

Have children list their steps verbally or in writing before doing their projects. Ask how they will share their projects. Some children may decide to write, while others prefer oral plans.

Assessment Projects

- **Make a mobile** Children may model their drawings of plants or animals after photos in the textbook or magazines. Also, some children may wish to write about their plant or animal on note cards and hang the cards from the larger picture. Children's pictures or writing might describe an animal's or a plant's appearance, habitat, or behavior. Children may also tell what group their animal or plant belongs to.

Module Review

Show what you know.

Suppose you want to tell about one animal or plant. You can tell how it looks. You can tell about its habitat. What else can you tell? Choose an animal or plant you want to tell about. Have a nature show to tell others about your plant or animal.

Plan your nature show.

1. Pick a project you would like to do.
2. Get what you need to do your project.
3. What will you do first?
4. Think about how you will tell about your animal or plant.

A 62

Make a mobile.

Draw a big picture of your plant or animal. Draw pictures about your plant or animal on note cards. Tape yarn to each card. Tape the cards to the big picture. Hang your mobile!

Science Idea Exchange

Develop a Project

Children may choose to do one of the projects in the book, or they may be able to develop one of the ideas from the class list into a project for the nature show.

Explorer's Activity Guide

For a **Home/School Connection**, use Explorer's Activity Guide pages 39–40. This letter home describes the concepts children have learned in this module and also provides a hands-on activity that the family can do together.

Using Multiple Intelligences (See page T5.)

The projects presented on these pages provide the opportunity for children to show their understanding of concepts using their strongest individual problem-solving abilities, or intelligences. The chart at right shows which of the seven intelligences are developed within each project and which chapter concepts each project assesses.

Put on a play.

Pretend to be an animal or plant. Act out what your animal or plant does. Show other things about your animal or plant. See if your classmates can guess what you are.

Give a report.

Write a report about your animal or plant. Draw pictures that go with your report. Give your report to your class.

Share what you know.

1. Show others what you have done.
2. What did you like the most about the way your project turned out?

A 63

Assessment Projects (cont'd.)

- **Put on a play** Children's plays should focus on body posture and movement to show understanding of concepts. A few spoken words might help them communicate concepts.
- **Give a report** You might suggest that children pretend they are tour guides or teachers who want to share what they know.

Share What You Know

1. Encourage children to share their projects in a format that is comfortable for them: large group, small group, or one-on-one.
2. Discuss with children how they planned their own projects and one specific thing they liked most about them. Also, ask them what they would do differently if they were to do the project again.

Performance Assessment

The module assessment projects can be used as performance assessment activities.

Nature Show

Project	Intelligence	Chapters Covered
Mobile	visual/spatial	1, 2, 3
Play	visual/spatial body/kinesthetic interpersonal	1, 2, 3
Report	verbal/linguistic visual/spatial interpersonal	1, 2, 3

Family/School Partnership: Progress Report

Share with families their child's progress in the following areas:
- makes and records observations
- compares and contrasts objects
- classifies in more than one way
- experiments to solve problems
- asks questions and communicates information

Module A
Math/Science Connection

Graph the Growth of a Bean Seed

Remind children that plants need water, air, and sunlight to live and grow. Invite children to explain how the different parts of a plant help it live and grow. Can a plant be grown from a seed in the classroom? How tall will the plant grow? How fast will it grow?

PROBLEM
Invite children to plant a bean seed and observe the plant that grows. Their challenge is to measure the plant as it grows and record their observations.

Materials (per group)
self-sealing plastic sandwich bag, paper towel, stapler, 4 pole bean seeds, masking tape, 4 different-colored markers, spray bottle, aluminum foil

Advance Preparation: Soak pole bean seeds overnight. Cover a bulletin board with graph paper (*1-cm square*).

SOLVE THE PROBLEM
- Help each group fold a paper towel into fourths and place the paper towel in a plastic bag. Then help children make a horizontal row of four staples a few centimeters from the bottom of the bag. Have children place four pole bean seeds in the bag, one above each staple.

- Instruct each group to choose a name and then use masking tape to make a name label. Have each group tape their name label on the bag below the seeds.

- Tell children to spray water into the bag to moisten the paper towel, allowing some water to collect below the staples. Help children seal the bag and staple it to the bulletin board. Remind them to keep the paper towel moist

throughout the activity. Suggest that children cover the back of the bag with aluminum foil to keep the bulletin board and the graph paper dry.

- When the stem starts to grow, have children open the plastic bag. When the plant grows out of the bag, help children tape the stem to the bulletin board, moving the tape as needed when the stem becomes longer.

- Have children observe and measure the growth of their plant each week. Help children chart the plant's growth on the graph paper on the bulletin board. Each child in the group can use a different-colored marker to fill in the number of centimeter squares their plant grows.

Share the Solutions

Challenge children to compare the rates of growth among the bean plants. Then discuss the following questions:

- Did your plant grow to the same height as the other plants in the class?

- What might make some plants grow taller than others?

- Did your bean plant grow slower or faster than other plants in the class?

- What might make some plants grow slower or faster than others?

EXTEND THE PROBLEM

- Encourage children to measure their height and compare it with the height of their plant.

- You may want children to grow other plants such as mung bean plants. Then they can compare the rate of growth between the two kinds of plants.

- Have children sort a variety of legume seeds such as beans, peas, and lentils using attributes such as size, color, and shape.

- Challenge children to make a repeat pattern using a variety of legumes.

Your Ideas

Changes Over Time

Module B

Module B Planning Guide
Changes Over Time

Module At-a-Glance

Lessons/Concepts

Chapter 1 Discovering Dinosaurs p. B4

CONCEPT: People have learned about the sizes, shapes, and behavior of dinosaurs.

STRANDS: Life, History

1. **How did dinosaurs look?** p. B5 *(what dinosaurs looked like)*
2. **How big were dinosaurs?** p. B6 *(dinosaur sizes)*
3. **How long were some dinosaurs?** p. B8 *(dinosaur lengths)*
4. **What did dinosaurs eat?** p. B10 *(dinosaur diets)*
5. **How were dinosaurs named?** p. B12 *(naming dinosaurs)*
6. **How fast did dinosaurs move?** p. B14 *(dinosaur speed)*
7. **How are dinosaurs alike and different?** p. B16 *(similarities and differences of dinosaurs)*
8. **What did you learn?** p. B18 *(modeling dinosaurs)*

Chapter 2 Dinosaur Detectives p. B20

CONCEPT: Most of what people know about dinosaurs is inferred from studying fossils.

STRANDS: Earth, Life, History

1. **What can objects tell about a person?** p. B21 *(making inferences from evidence)*
2. **How do we learn about dinosaurs?** p. B22 *(studying fossils)*
3. **How can you make a fossil?** p. B24 *(fossils)*
4. **How do fossils form?** p. B26 *(fossil formation)*
5. **How do we get fossils?** p. B28 *(uncovering fossils)*
6. **What can dinosaur fossils show?** p. B30 *(making inferences from dinosaur fossils)*
7. **How do dinosaur bones fit together?** p. B32 *(dinosaur skeletons)*
8. **What else can fossils show?** p. B34 *(how dinosaurs cared for young)*
9. **What was life like long ago?** p. B36 *(life long ago)*
10. **How can you measure fossils?** p. B38 *(comparing plant fossils)*
11. **What did you learn?** p. B40 *(animal and plant fossils)*

Chapter 3 A Changing World p. B42

CONCEPT: Changes in the habitats of plants and animals can affect the plants and animals. Pollution can harm living things, but there are also ways people can help living things.

STRANDS: Physical, Life, Technology, History

1. **What happened to dinosaurs?** p. B43 *(explanations of dinosaur disappearance)*
2. **How did dinosaurs disappear?** p. B44 *(theories of extinction)*
3. **What else became extinct?** p. B46 *(changes in habitat)*
4. **What living things are in danger?** p. B48 *(endangered plants and animals)*
5. **What else can change living things?** p. B50 *(polluted water)*
6. **How does air become polluted?** p. B52 *(polluted air)*
7. **How can people help living things?** p. B54 *(providing habitats)*
8. **How do zoos help endangered animals?** p. B56 *(zoo habitats)*
9. **What did you learn?** p. B58 *(changes in the world)*

People at Work pp. B60–B61
Module Review pp. B62–B63
Kids Did It pp. 4–5
Study Guide pp. 14–17
Experiment Skills pp. 32–33

Themes: *Diversity, Scale and Structure, Patterns of Change*

In this module, children discover the diversity of dinosaurs by comparing the shape, size, and behavior of different dinosaurs. They also learn how life on the earth has changed over time.

YOU ARE HERE

MODULE A · MODULE B · MODULE C · MODULE D

Activity Opportunities

Pupil's Edition	Teacher's Edition/Ancillaries

Discover Activity p. B5
Let's Explore pp. B8–B9
Activity p. B11
Let's Solve It! pp. B16–B17
Chapter Review pp. B18–B19
	Explorer's Activity Guide
	    pp. 41–51
	ExploraCenter Teacher's Guide
	    pp. 9, 14, 22
	Videodisc Classroom
	    Guide pp. 17–24
	Interactive Transparency
	    Guide pp. 16–17
	Interactive Videodisc Software
	    Teacher's Guide pp. 53–61

Discover Activity p. B21
Activity p. B23
Let's Explore pp. B24–B25
Activity p. B29
Activity p. B33
Let's Solve It! pp. B38–B39
Chapter Review pp. B40–B41
	Explorer's Activity Guide
	    pp. 53–69
	ExploraCenter Teacher's Guide
	    pp. 9, 14, 22
	Videodisc Classroom
	    Guide pp. 17–24
	Interactive Transparency
	    Guide pp. 18–21
	Interactive Videodisc Software
	    Teacher's Guide pp. 53–61

Discover Activity p. B43
Let's Explore pp. B50–B51
Activity p. B53
Activity p. B55
Let's Solve It! pp. B56–B57
Chapter Review pp. B58–B59
	Explorer's Activity Guide
	    pp. 70–82
	ExploraCenter Teacher's Guide
	    pp. 9, 14, 18
	Videodisc Classroom
	    Guide pp. 17–24
	Interactive Transparency
	    Guide pp. 22–23
	Interactive Videodisc Software
	    Teacher's Guide pp. 53–61

	Explorer's Activity Guide • Family letter pp. 83–84 **Teacher's Edition** • Math/Science Connection pp. B63a–B63b

Assessment Opportunities
(CONTENT · PORTFOLIO · PERFORMANCE)

Pupil's Edition	Teacher's Edition/Ancillaries

Checkpoint pp. B7, B9, B11,
B12, B15, B17
Chapter Review
    Performance Assessment
    Activity pp. B18–B19
	Teacher's Edition
	• Check for Understanding
	    pp. B5, B7, B9, B11, B13,
	    B15, B17, B19
	Teacher's Assessment Package
	• Activity Rubrics p. 25
	• Chapter Test pp. 27–28
	Explorer's Activity Guide
	• Chapter Review pp. 50–51

Checkpoint pp. B23, B25, B27,
B29, B30, B33, B35–B36,
B39
Chapter Review
    Performance Assessment
    Activity pp. B40–B41
	Teacher's Edition
	• Check for Understanding
	    pp. B21, B23, B25, B27,
	    B29, B31, B33, B35, B37,
	    B39, B41
	Teacher's Assessment Package
	• Activity Rubrics pp. 31–32
	• Chapter Test pp. 33–34
	Explorer's Activity Guide
	• Chapter Review p. 69

Checkpoint pp. B45, B47, B48,
B51, B53, B55, B57
Chapter Review
    Performance Assessment
    Activity pp. B58–B59
	Teacher's Edition
	• Check for Understanding
	    pp. B43, B45, B47, B49,
	    B51, B53, B55, B57, B59
	Teacher's Assessment Package
	• Activity Rubrics p. 37
	• Chapter Test pp. 39–40
	Explorer's Activity Guide
	• Chapter Review pp. 81–82

Module Review
    pp. B62–B63
	**Teacher's Assessment
	Package**
	• Performance Assessment
	    Test pp. 43–44

Module B Event
Across the Ages Museum

Planning

Planning the Museum

Throughout this module, children will engage in many activities that could become exhibits in an Across the Ages Museum. Families and other children in the school may be invited to view the exhibits.

Encourage every child to participate in planning and setting up the museum. To prepare for this module event, you may choose to collect visuals and written materials produced during the activities in the module.

Getting Started

Visualizing animals and plants that no longer exist and understanding how people learn about them are important aspects of this module. Many of the activities in the module may be used or expanded upon for exhibit ideas. For instance, children may expand the dioramas made at the end of Chapter 1 and use them as the basis for an interesting and informative exhibit.

Activity Options

Social Studies Connection

Have children prepare an exhibit showing where some of the dinosaurs mentioned in the chapter have been found. Rich dinosaur deposits exist in southern Alberta, Canada; and in parts of Colorado, Utah, Montana, and Wyoming. Other parts of the world with dinosaur deposits include Germany, Mongolia, and Tanzania. Children may attach small drawings or models of various dinosaurs to a large world map. If pictures of "digs" are available, these might be included in the display.

Life Science Connection

Have children use the charts they made in chapters 1 and 2 in the museum. Charts, placed side-by-side, can be used by volunteers to show the relationship between a dinosaur's size and structure and the food it consumed.

Environmental Connection

Encourage children to adopt an endangered animal in a zoo adoption program. To raise money for the adoption, have children set up a recycling booth in the museum. At the booth display pictures or other information about the animal that children have adopted. Contributions could be used to help take care of the animal.

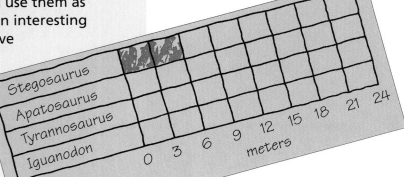

Stegosaurus
Apatosaurus
Tyrannosaurus
Iguanodon

0   3   6   9   12   15   18   21   24
meters

Using Multiple Intelligences (See page T5.)

The activities presented on these pages provide the opportunity for students to show their understanding of concepts using their strongest individual problem-solving abilities, or intelligences. The chart shows which of the seven intelligences are developed within each activity option. In addition, all students can develop interpersonal intelligence as they participate in the Module Event, Across the Ages Museum.

Across the Ages Museum

Activity	Intelligences
Social Studies Connection	verbal/linguistic
Life Science Connection	visual/spatial
Environmental Connection	interpersonal
Language Arts Connection	body/kinesthetic

Language Arts Connection

Help children write and perform a play about dinosaurs. Have children design simple costumes and scenery. If possible, video-tape the performance and show it to the museum's visitors.

Let Parents Try It

Invite parents and guardians to make their own fossils or fossil prints. Provide embedding items such as chicken bones, shells, or leaves as well as small disposable dishes of damp sand or small pieces of modeling clay. Visitors may embed or leave imprints of items to make model fossils.

The Big Event

Set up various areas in the room to display the exhibits that you and the children have selected to include in the museum. A large diorama could be made by the entire class as the focal point of the museum. Give each child responsibility for one feature of this diorama. Include other exhibits such as how fossils are formed, physical characteristics of dinosaurs, how habitat changes threaten animals, and an art exhibit from the various activities in the module. Set up one corner of the room with a television monitor and chairs to allow visitors to view the videotaped play. Children should take turns monitoring exhibits, explaining the dioramas, or answering questions.

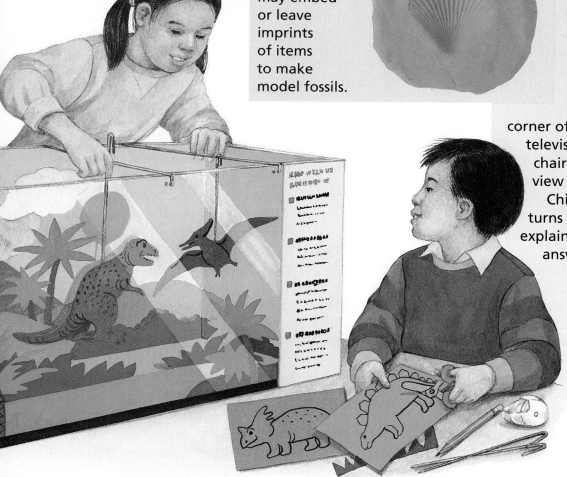

Module B
Across the Curriculum

Science Background

Dinosaur Fossils

Dinosaurs were the dominant land animals during the Mesozoic Era, from about 230 to 65 million years ago. The first recorded dinosaur remains found consisted of a few teeth and bones discovered in Essex, England in 1822. Since then, many dinosaur teeth and bones have been found all over the world. From the different types of teeth, scientists can hypothesize what a dinosaur ate; from the bones, scientists can estimate a dinosaur's size and body structure. Scientists believe that dinosaurs weighed from about 4 pounds (1.8 kg) to 160,000 pounds (72,600 kg). Fossil footprints can indicate the dinosaur's size and weight and if the dinosaur walked on two legs or four. Findings of fossils of unhatched dinosaur eggs have given scientists more information about dinosaurs, their reproduction, and how they cared for their young.

Causes of Extinction

Environmental change can cause the extinction of animals and plants. Often, that change is caused by human activity, such as draining wetlands, building dams, and cutting down forests. All of these activities can permanently damage an ecosystem so that it can no longer support life as it once did.

Pollution is a form of environmental damage. For example, some pesticides have found their way into the food chain, harming plants and animals. Industrial waste and chemical runoff have polluted waterways and imperiled aquatic life in many places.

Public awareness and action, as well as cooperation from governments around the world, are needed to help correct damage when possible and limit further damage to the environment.

Science Across Cultures

Learning About Early Cultures

In the same way that paleontologists use excavated fossils to learn about dinosaurs and other extinct animals, archaeologists use excavated artifacts to learn about past human cultures. To interpret the artifacts, archaeologists rely on information from many sciences: geology, botany, zoology, physical anthropology, chemistry, physics, and even specialties such as forensic medicine.

Over 90 percent of the information on prehistoric cultures comes from artifacts found in Africa and southern Asia. Pointed stones from as early as 40,000 to 10,000 B.C. indicate that hunting was an important activity at that time. Excavations in Nubian cemeteries dating from 10,000 B.C. uncovered bodies containing stone arrow points. These bodies and arrows suggest that intercommunity conflict may have existed at the time. Iron tools excavated in central Africa indicate that people in that region understood mining and smelting several hundred years before Egyptians acquired these skills.

Early writing, recorded on tortoise shell and bones, as well as tools and building sites show that the Chinese lived in cities before 1000 B.C. An army of life-sized terra cotta soldiers, unearthed near the tomb of Shi Huangdi, China's ruler in 200 B.C., exhibits remarkable detail. The clothing and weapons provide insights into people's lifestyles and demonstrate the significance of the imperial presence in the early Chinese empire.

Perhaps the most famous artifacts are the Pyramids in Egypt. Pictures on the walls of these burial sites show ritual ceremonies, historical events, and daily human activities, leading archaeologists to a better understanding of the culture, religious beliefs, and lifestyles of early Egyptians.

Cross-curricular Activities

The activities in this module provide many opportunities to make connections between science and other areas of the elementary curriculum.

In addition, the wide variety of cross-curricular activities helps make learning both interesting and fun!

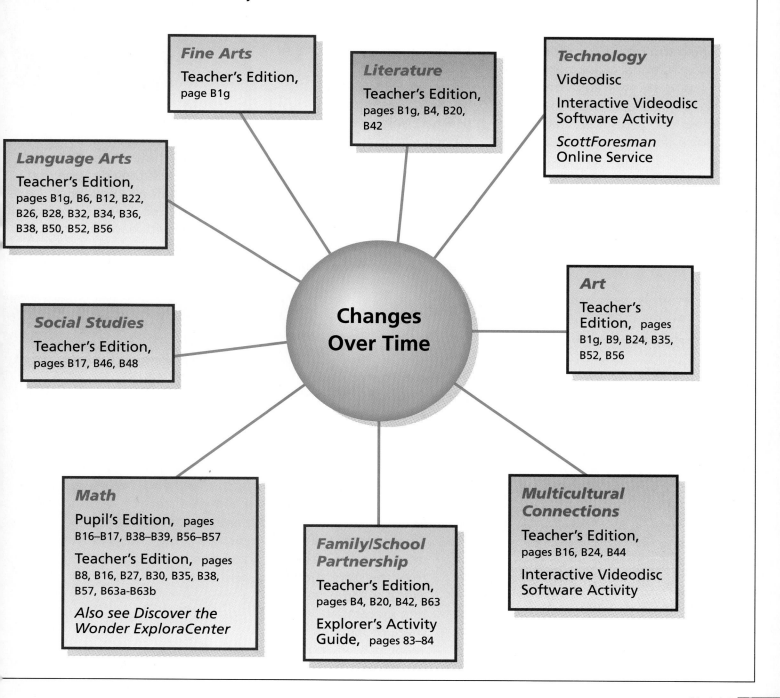

Fine Arts
Teacher's Edition, page B1g

Literature
Teacher's Edition, pages B1g, B4, B20, B42

Technology
Videodisc
Interactive Videodisc Software Activity
ScottForesman Online Service

Language Arts
Teacher's Edition, pages B1g, B6, B12, B22, B26, B28, B32, B34, B36, B38, B50, B52, B56

Changes Over Time

Art
Teacher's Edition, pages B1g, B9, B24, B35, B52, B56

Social Studies
Teacher's Edition, pages B17, B46, B48

Math
Pupil's Edition, pages B16–B17, B38–B39, B56–B57
Teacher's Edition, pages B8, B16, B27, B30, B35, B38, B57, B63a–B63b
Also see Discover the Wonder ExploraCenter

Family/School Partnership
Teacher's Edition, pages B4, B20, B42, B63
Explorer's Activity Guide, pages 83–84

Multicultural Connections
Teacher's Edition, pages B16, B24, B44
Interactive Videodisc Software Activity

Module B
Links to Literature

Introducing the Literature Library Selection

The literature library selection for this module is *Time Train* by Paul Fleischman, illustrated by Claire Ewart (HarperCollins, 1991). In this selection, Miss Pym takes her class on a field trip from New York to Dinosaur National Monument. They board a very strange train that not only carries them to the park, but also takes them back in time. The class has wonderful adventures among real dinosaurs.

In addition to the module literature selection, each chapter has a companion book.

- In *My Visit to the Dinosaurs* by Aliki (Harper Trophy, 1985), a boy shares what he learned about dinosaurs on a museum visit. He describes characteristics and habitats of fourteen dinosaurs.
- *Let's Go Dinosaur Tracking!* by Miriam Schlein (HarperCollins, 1991) tells what an older gentleman and several children learned about dinosaurs when they explored many different kinds of dinosaur tracks.
- *What Happened to the Dinosaurs?* by Franklyn M. Branley, illustrated by Marc

Simont (Crowell, 1989), points out that we know what happened to the dinosaurs: they disappeared. But we don't know why. Several theories are presented. Along with each theory is a simple explanation of its strong and weak points.

Activity Corner

Cross-Curricular Activities

Language Arts
- **Retelling a Story** Review important vocabulary words in the story. Then have children retell the story using the words.

Fine Arts
- **Dramatizing a Scene** Have children act out a scene from the story, such as the children setting up camp in Utah, cooking a meal, or studying the dinosaurs.

Encourage children to speak loudly and clearly.

Art
- **Drawing a Picture** Have children draw a picture of a dinosaur doing something such as eating. Then have children dictate or write a sentence describing their picture. If necessary, assist children in writing their sentence.

Beginning with the Bulletin Board

Have children match clue cards with pictures of various prehistoric animals, an activity inspired by the literature library selection *Time Train* by Paul Fleischman.

You will need:

 construction paper

 drawing paper

 safety scissors

 pushpins

 envelope

 note cards

 markers

Preparing the Bulletin Board

Use drawings and construction paper cutouts to create a prehistoric setting: mountains, trees, a swamp, and so on. Include areas of sea and sky. In appropriate places around the scene, attach drawings or cutout pictures of various prehistoric animals as suggested in the story.

Attach an envelope to the bottom of the board. In the envelope, place note cards containing

simple clues for children to match with the pictures of prehistoric animals. Include the name of each animal.

Make the clues visual "give-aways," such as the following: *I am the biggest dinosaur of all. I am even heavier than ten elephants.* (Brachiosaurus [bra′ke ə sor′əs]); *I use my three horns to protect myself against larger dinosaurs.* (Triceratops [tri ser′ ə tops]); *I am called "the roofed lizard."* (Stegosaurus [steg′ sor′əs])

Bulletin Board Activity

Have a volunteer take a clue card from the envelope and read it aloud. Then ask the volunteer to attach the clue card by the corresponding animal picture on the bulletin board. Write the name of the animal on the chalkboard and help children pronounce it. Repeat this procedure until all the animals and clue cards have been matched.

Extend the Activity

Have children share additional information about the displayed picture. Invite volunteers to read aloud appropriate excerpts from grade-level books about prehistoric animals.

Changes Over Time

The world of long ago looked much different from the world you live in today. The earth is always changing. Changes happen to animals and plants too.

Chapter 1

Discovering Dinosaurs

What were dinosaurs really like? You might be surprised to find out how many kinds of dinosaurs lived. Page **B 4**

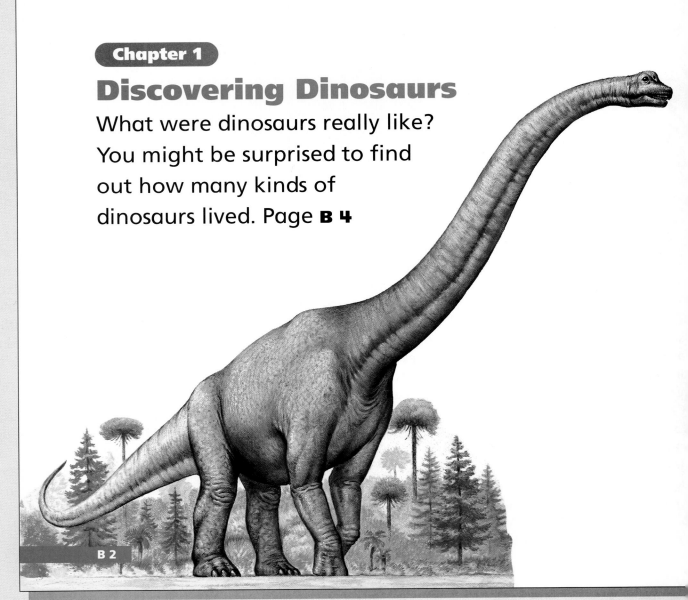

B 2

Dinosaur Detectives

Dinosaurs do not live on the earth any more. How do people know so much about dinosaurs and the way they lived? Page **B 20**

A Changing World

Even a small change on the earth can make a difference to plants and animals. What kinds of changes can help animals and plants? Page **B 42**

Chapter 1 Planning Guide
Discovering Dinosaurs

Lessons / *Skills*	Materials (per group)

Lessons / *Skills*

Lesson 1
Discover Activity: **How did dinosaurs look?** pp. B4–B5
(making physical models)

Lesson 2
How big were dinosaurs? pp. B6–B7
(comparing)

Lesson 3
Let's Explore: **How long were some dinosaurs?** pp. B8–B9
(measuring, comparing, making analogies)

Lesson 4
What did dinosaurs eat? pp. B10–B11
(listing, classifying, comparing)

Lesson 5
How were dinosaurs named? pp. B12–B13
(observing, naming)

Lesson 6
How fast did dinosaurs move? pp. B14–B15
(contrasting, listing, ordering)

Lesson 7
Let's Solve It!: **How are dinosaurs alike and different?**
pp. B16–B17
(organizing information, solving problems)

Lesson 8
Chapter Review: **What did you learn?** pp. B18–B19
(making physical models, applying information)

Materials (per group)

Lesson 1 Activity: *How did dinosaurs look?*
Module Kit Items: assorted buttons; craft sticks; clay
School Supplied Items: construction paper; white paper; pencils; scissors

Lesson 3 Activity: *How long were some dinosaurs?*
Module Kit Items: yarn; meter stick
School Supplied Items: masking tape
Advance Prep: Precut the yarn to equal the lengths of the dinosaurs. Attach a piece of masking tape with the name and length of the dinosaur to each piece of yarn.

Lesson 4 Activity: *Sort dinosaurs by their foods.*
Module Kit Items: 6 index cards; 2 pieces yarn *(1 m long)*
School Supplied Items: markers

Lesson 8 Activity: *Make a dinosaur museum.*
Module Kit Items: index card; pipe cleaners *(3 or more)*; craft sticks *(2 or more)*
School Supplied Items: paper; shoe box; dinosaur model *(from Discover Activity on B5)*; crayons
Safety Kit Items: cover goggles *(1/child)*

Assessment Options	Content	Performance	Portfolio
Teacher's Assessment Package			
Chapter Test, pp. 27–28	✓		✓
Group Interview Assessment, p. 29	✓	✓	✓
Performance Strategies, p. 30	✓	✓	✓
Explorer's Activity Guide			
Activity worksheets, pp. 41–49		✓	✓
Chapter Review, pp. 50–51	✓		✓
Interactive Transparency Package			
Transparency 6 and BLM	✓	✓	✓
Teacher's Guide, pp. 16–17	✓	✓	
Hands-on activity for second-language learners	✓	✓	✓
Science Literature Library			
My Visit to the Dinosaurs		✓	✓
Interactive Videodisc Software			
Teacher's Guide, pp. 53–61			
Computer-based Activity	✓	✓	
Journal Presentations	✓	✓	✓
Videodisc Classroom Guide, pp. 17–24, **or**			
Video Reader			
Hands-on activity	✓	✓	✓
ExploraCenter Teacher's Guide, pp. 9, 14, 22			
ExploraCenter			
Science activity cards 4, 9, 17	✓	✓	✓
ScottForesman Online Service			
Online field trips	✓	✓	✓

Chapter Overview

Children begin this chapter by making a model of what they think a dinosaur looked like. Children discover that dinosaurs were different in many ways—size, diet, speed, and other characteristics. Their exploration of dinosaurs culminates when they make a dinosaur museum.

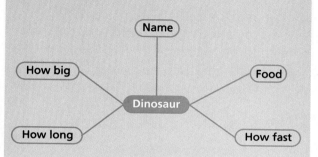

Lesson Objective

Children use prior knowledge to show how they think a dinosaur might have looked.

Introduce

Invite Learning

Show the videodisc segment for this chapter. Bar codes and a description of this segment are given below on page B5.

Make Connections

To **assess prior knowledge,** provide illustrations of dinosaurs for children to observe and compare. Listen to what children say about the dinosaurs. Some children may have the idea that all dinosaurs were of a particular size or shape.

Teach

Discover Activity

Children make a model of a dinosaur with art materials. **Skill:** Making a physical model

Materials (per group)
Module Kit Items: assorted buttons; 2 craft sticks; clay *(1/2 stick)*
School Supplied Items: construction paper; white paper; pencils; scissors

---

Chapter 1

Discovering Dinosaurs

Pretend you are on a trip to the past. You go back a long time ago. You visit the world in the picture. No people were living then. But dinosaurs lived in many places on the earth. What were dinosaurs really like? Let's take a closer look!

B 4

 Science Idea Exchange

Collaborative Learning: Small Groups

Assign specific children to gather and clean up materials. All children in the Discover Activity group should plan the design of the dinosaur model, construct the model, and be involved in sharing results.

Science and Literature

Have children use the literature selection *My Visit to the Dinosaurs* by Aliki (Harper Trophy, 1985) to prepare an oral report about their favorite dinosaur. Encourage children to make a visual aid to accompany their report. It could be a drawing or a clay model of the dinosaur.

Family/School Partnership: Family Support

Encourage families to be active partners in learning by suggesting that they and their children:
- observe models or pictures of dinosaurs,
- describe the dinosaur models or the dinosaurs in the pictures, an◦
- talk about how the dinosaurs we◦ alike and different.

How did dinosaurs look?

1. Make a model of a dinosaur body.
2. Shape different body parts for your model.
3. Add these body parts to your dinosaur.
4. **Tell about it.** Write a story about your dinosaur. What does it eat? How does it move? What is its name?

Ask me what else I want to find out about dinosaurs.

B 5

Helpful Hints

- Use the models as a **baseline assessment** for the entire chapter. You can follow up on this assessment in the Chapter Review activity.
- *See Equipment Kit Teacher's Guide for additional hints.*

What to Expect

Children may tend to create models of large, fierce-looking dinosaurs.

Close

Check for Understanding

- Ask children what information they used to create their models.
- **Answers to Tell about it** Children's stories will vary, but the physical traits of the models should match the traits and abilities described in the stories.

What Else Do You Want to Find Out?

Stimulate interest by using a **constructivist** approach. Ask: *What do you know about the sizes of dinosaurs? What questions do you have about dinosaurs? How can we find answers to your questions?* Record questions on chart paper. Invite children to look for the answers as they explore the chapter.

Connecting Lessons

In the next lesson, children will learn that dinosaurs varied greatly in size. ▶

Explorer's Activity Guide

The **Discover Activity recording sheet** on page 43 of the Explorer's Activity Guide can be used by children to record their activity results.

Visual Literacy

Discover the Wonder Videodisc, Grade 2, Module B, invites children to discover the prehistoric world of dinosaurs through literature and to apply mathematical skills by comparing the sizes of dinosaurs with other animals.

Bar Codes

Chapter 10: Stills

Step

Interactive Software

DISCOVER THE WONDER

Lesson 2

Introduce

Invite Learning

Have children describe the overall size of their favorite dinosaur. Have them compare their dinosaur's size with something they see every day.

Make Connections

To **assess prior knowledge,** ask children how big they think the biggest dinosaur was and how small they think the smallest dinosaur was. Record their answers as a **baseline assessment** that you can refer to in Check for Understanding.

Teach

Helpful Hint

Help children pronounce the names of the dinosaurs in this lesson: *Brachiosaurus* (brā´kē ə sôr´əs), *Allosaurus* (al´ə sôr´əs), and *Compsognathus* (komp sog´nə thəs).

Observe and Listen

● Divide the class into small groups to **compare** the dinosaurs shown on pages B6 and B7.

How big were dinosaurs?

Were all dinosaurs giants? The answer may surprise you. Dinosaurs were many sizes.

The biggest dinosaur in the picture was taller than most school buildings. This dinosaur was heavy too. It was heavier than ten elephants.

Imagine standing next to the middle dinosaur in the picture. It was about the size of a school bus. You would not even reach its knee!

Brachiosaurus

B 6

Science Idea Exchange

Science Background

The names of dinosaurs are usually based on Greek or Latin words that describe a characteristic of the dinosaur. For example, the name *Brachiosaurus* means "arm lizard." It refers to the fact that the front limbs of this dinosaur were longer than its hind limbs. Other names are explained in Lesson 5.

Science and Language Arts

Ask children how their lives would be different if they were as large as *Brachiosaurus.* Encourage children to sit in a circle and build an oral story that **describes** something they would be able to do that they cannot do at their present size.

Special Education

To help children conceptualize differences in height, help them use a meter stick to measure a distance of 12 m (40 ft). Then have them measure a distance of 5 m (16 ft). Develop the idea that *Brachiosaurus* was as tall as the first measure, while *Allosaurus* wa as tall as the second measure.

You would be taller than the small dinosaur in the picture. This dinosaur was only about the size of a chicken.

Checkpoint

Draw a picture of a dinosaur next to another object. Let your picture show how big your dinosaur is.

Allosaurus

Compsognathus

B 7

- Encourage children to ask and answer each other's questions about how the dinosaurs were alike and different.

Act as a Consultant
Suggest that children consider some things that a large dinosaur, like *Brachiosaurus*, could do that a smaller one couldn't. (Answers may include eating food from trees and having a clear view of the area.) Have them consider problems that a large dinosaur might have. (Answers may include not being able to hide from an enemy or move quickly.)

Close

Check for Understanding
- As a follow-up to the **baseline assessment,** refer to children's responses from Make Connections. Ask if they would like to change their answers about the sizes of dinosaurs.
- **Answers to Checkpoint** Children's drawings should demonstrate an understanding that *Brachiosaurus* was about 12 m (40 ft) tall, *Allosaurus* was about 5 m (16 ft) tall, and *Compsognathus* was about 30 cm (1 ft) tall.

Connecting Lessons
In the next lesson, children will learn about the length of some dinosaurs. ▶

Explorer's Activity Guide
Use Explorer's Activity Guide page 44 with this lesson to help children answer the text question, "How big were dinosaurs?" with a hands-on activity.

Achieving English Proficiency
Help children understand comparisons by having them choose other children to represent someone who is tall, someone who is taller, and someone who is the tallest. Avoid using short, shorter, and shortest as comparisons. Children can also compare heights of crayons, pencils, or other objects for this activity.

Science Themes
By **comparing** the different shapes and sizes of various dinosaurs, children develop their understanding of the themes of **diversity** and **scale and structure.**

Lesson 3

Lesson Objective
Children learn about the lengths of some dinosaurs.

Introduce

Invite Learning
Play a measurement guessing game. Ask children to show how long they think 60 cm (2 ft) is by standing that distance from a classroom wall. Then ask them to demonstrate 2 m (6 1/2 ft) and finally 4 m (13 ft).

Make Connections
To **assess prior knowledge,** ask children to walk the length they think a small dinosaur might have been, then a long dinosaur. Measure the distance using a piece of string. Save the string as a **baseline assessment** that you can follow up on later in Check for Understanding.

Teach

Activity
Children try to locate objects in the school or classroom that are the same length as were some dinosaurs.
Skills: Measuring, comparing, making analogies

Materials (per group)
Module Kit Items: yarn; meter stick
School Supplied Item: masking tape

How long were some dinosaurs?

Could dinosaurs have fit in your classroom? You might guess that some dinosaurs could have fit in it. You can use yarn to find out how long some dinosaurs were.

You will need:

 yarn

 masking tape

meter stick

Find out about it.

1. Tape one end of the yarn your teacher gives you to a corner of your classroom wall.

2. Stretch out your yarn.

3. Tape down the other end of the yarn.

4. Measure the yarn.

B 8

Science Idea Exchange

Science Anecdote
One of the longest dinosaurs was *Diplodocus* (di plod'ə kəs), which is thought to have been about 27 m (88 ft) long, about the length of three school buses. The tallest dinosaur may have been *Brachiosaurus*, which rose to a height of 12 m (40 ft), more than twice as tall as a giraffe.

Math/Science Connection
Challenge the children in each group to determine the longest dinosaur string in the group. Then have them find the shortest dinosaur string in the group. Finally, have the children in each group sequence the strings from the longest to the shortest.

Collaborative Learning: Cooperative Learning
All children in the Let's Explore group should record and share results. Also, each child in the group can be assigned a specific role:
- one who stretches out the yarn;
- one who tapes one end of the yarn to the corner of the wall;
- one who tapes down the other end of the yarn;
- one who measures the yarn.

Write about it. ✏️

Make a chart like this. Write the name of your dinosaur. Write how long it was. Draw a picture of an object or place that is about as long as your dinosaur.

name	how long	object or place

Checkpoint

1. How long was your dinosaur?

2. Take Action! Find other objects or places in your school that might be as long as your dinosaur.

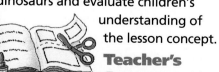

Helpful Hints

- Pre-cut the yarn to equal the lengths of some dinosaurs. Dinosaurs may include: *Compsognathus:* 60 cm (2 ft); *Bactrosaurus* (bak trə sôr′əs): 4 m (13 ft); *Oviraptor* (ō və rap′tôr): 2 m (6 1/2 ft); *Stegoceras* (steg ə ser′əs): 2.5 m (8 ft); *Allosaurus:* 9 m (30 ft); *Tyrannosaurus:* 12 m (40 ft); *Apatosaurus* (ap′ ə tō sôr′ əs): 21 m (70 ft). Use masking tape to label each piece of yarn with the name and length of the dinosaur.
- Children may wish to choose their own dinosaur, investigate its length, and cut a piece of yarn the same length.
- *See Equipment Kit Teacher's Guide for additional hints.*

Close

Check for Understanding

- As a follow-up to the **baseline assessment,** ask children to compare the lengths they measured for the dinosaurs with the lengths of string from Make Connections.
- **Answers to Checkpoint** 1. Answers should reflect the lengths of the dinosaurs. 2. **Take Action!** Answers will vary but might include a chalkboard, desk, flag pole, and room.

Connecting Lessons

In the next lesson, children will learn that dinosaurs' diets varied. ▶

Explorer's Activity Guide

Use Explorer's Activity Guide hands-on activity on page 45 to explore dinosaurs and evaluate children's understanding of the lesson concept.

Teacher's Assessment Package

A **scoring rubric** to assess student performance is provided on page 25 of the Teacher's Assessment Package.

Activity Results

Children should find objects that are about the same length as each dinosaur or that combine to form a certain length. Children should get an idea of the various lengths of some dinosaurs.

Science and Art

Have children use reference books to **observe** drawings of one of the types of dinosaurs they learned about in the activity. Ask them to make their own drawing of the dinosaur. Children's drawings may reflect how children feel about dinosaurs as well as what they observe in other drawings.

Lesson 4

Lesson Objective
Children learn that the diets of dinosaurs varied.

Introduce

Invite Learning
Ask children to name some foods they've seen animals eat. Encourage them to think of pets, zoo animals, and animals they've seen on TV.

Make Connections
To **assess prior knowledge,** ask children what they think dinosaurs ate. Record their answers as a **baseline assessment.**

Teach

Activity
Children study visuals that show what some dinosaurs ate. Then children classify the pictured dinosaurs as meat eaters or plant eaters. **Skills:** Listing, classifying, comparing

Materials (per group)
Module Kit Items: 6 index cards; 2 pieces yarn *(each 1 m long)*
School Supplied Item: marker

Helpful Hints
- Help children pronounce these dinosaur names: *Triceratops* (trī sər′ə tops), *Compsognathus* (komp sog′nə thəs), *Tyrannosaurus* (ti ran′ə sôr′əs), and *Stegosaurus* (steg′ə sôr′əs).

What did dinosaurs eat?

What are some of your favorite foods? Did dinosaurs eat the same kinds of foods you do?

Some dinosaurs had long, sharp teeth for eating meat. Other dinosaurs had big, flat teeth for eating plants. The pictures tell about the kinds of foods some dinosaurs ate.

Triceratops

Compsognathus

Tyrannosaurus

Stegosaurus

B 10

Science Idea Exchange

Science Anecdote
Ornithomimus (ôr nə thə mī′məs), an ostrichlike dinosaur, had a birdlike beak and no teeth. Though its eating habits are a source of controversy, this dinosaur might have eaten buried dinosaur eggs, using its beak to crack open an egg and drink the contents.

Collaborative Learning: Cooperative Learning
All children in the Activity group should be involved in deciding where to place the cards and then in sharing results. Also, each child in the group can be assigned a specific role:
- one who makes yarn circles on the floor;
- one who writes the words *meat* and *plants* on index cards;
- one who writes dinosaur names on index cards;
- one who places cards in the appropriate circle as the group makes its decisions.

Sort dinosaurs by their foods.

You will need: 🧶 yarn

📇 note cards ✏️ markers

1. Make a circle on the floor.
2. Write the word *meat* on a card. Put the card in the circle.
3. Make another circle with yarn.
4. Write the word *plant* on a card. Put the card in the circle.
5. Look at the dinosaurs on the last page. Write each dinosaur name on a card. Notice if each dinosaur ate meat or plants.
6. Put each card in the correct circle.

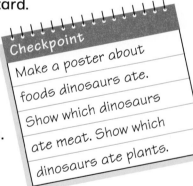

Checkpoint

Make a poster about foods dinosaurs ate. Show which dinosaurs ate meat. Show which dinosaurs ate plants.

B 11

- *See Equipment Kit Teacher's Guide for additional hints.*

Raise Questions

Before children begin the activity, you may want to ask: *What type of teeth did meat-eating dinosaurs have?* (long, sharp teeth) *What type of teeth did plant-eating dinosaurs have?* (big, flat teeth) *Where did meat-eating dinosaurs get their food?* (other animals) *What type of food did plant-eating dinosaurs eat?* (bushes, trees, shrubs)

Ask for Evidence

Have children explain why they classified the cards as they did.

Close

Check for Understanding

- As a follow-up to the **baseline assessment,** refer to children's responses to the questions in Make Connections. Ask if they would like to change their answers.
- **Answers to Checkpoint** Posters should show that *Triceratops* and *Stegosaurus* were plant eaters, while *Tyrannosaurus* and *Compsognathus* were meat eaters.

Connecting Lessons

In the next lesson, children will learn that some dinosaurs were named according to their distinguishing characteristics. ▶

Explorer's Activity Guide

Use Explorer's Activity Guide hands-on activity on page 46 to help children answer the question, "What did dinosaurs eat?"

Teacher's Assessment Package

A **scoring rubric** to assess student performance is provided on page 25 of the Teacher's Assessment Package.

Activity Results

Triceratops and *Stegosaurus* cards should be in the plant circle. *Tyrannosaurus* and *Compsognathus* cards should be in the meat circle.

Extend the Activity

Make a list of other types of living things on the chalkboard. Ask children to **classify** each organism listed as a meat eater, a plant eater, or a plant and meat eater.

Lesson 5

Lesson Objective
Children learn that some dinosaurs were named according to their characteristics.

Introduce

Invite Learning
Give children the opportunity to **observe** pictures of dinosaurs. Ask what names they would give to the dinosaurs.

Make Connections
To **assess prior knowledge**, ask: *What dinosaur's name means "king of the terrible lizards"?* (Children are likely to respond *Tyrannosaurus rex* because of their familiarity with this name.) *How do you think scientists name dinosaurs?* Record their answers as a **baseline assessment**.

Teach

Helpful Hint
Help children pronounce these dinosaur names: *Oviraptor* (ō və rap′tôr), *Deinonychus* (dī non′i kəs).

Observe and Listen
- Discuss with children the names and traits of the dinosaurs shown.
- Have them ask each other if they can think of other names that describe the dinosaurs.

How were dinosaurs named?

Suppose you need to name an animal. You might name the animal by the way it looks. You might name it by the way it acts.

The name dinosaur means "terrible lizard." What does the name tell about dinosaurs? Look at these dinosaurs and their names. What do names tell about the dinosaurs?

Checkpoint
Paint a picture of a dinosaur. Give your dinosaur a name that tells about it.

B 12

Oviraptor means "egg stealer."

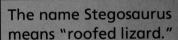

The name Stegosaurus means "roofed lizard."

💡 Science Idea Exchange

Science Anecdote
The first *Oviraptor* fossil was found in the Gobi Desert in 1923. It was thought that the *Oviraptor* died while eating the eggs of another animal. However, recent discovery of the fossil of an *Oviraptor* embryo suggests that the *Oviraptor* may actually have been protecting its own eggs.

Science and Language Arts
Children may enjoy making up a dinosaur name for a classmate. Tell them to think of good ways in which their friend is special. Then have children use these traits in naming their friend. For example, a kind friend might be called a "Kindasaurus," while a funny pal might be a "Laughasaurus."

Explore Further
Supply pictures of three or four different dinosaurs that have distinctive physical traits. Have children work in groups to come up with names for these dinosaurs. Have groups compare the names they have chosen. As an extension, suggest that groups combine traits from different dinosaurs to create a new kind of dinosaur.

Triceratops means "three-horned face."

Deinonychus means "terrible claw."

B 13

Raise Questions

Ask: *What word part ends many dinosaur names?* ("-saurus") *This word part means "lizard". Does the name "saurus" fit all types of dinosaurs?* (yes) *It would have been easy to name all dinosaurs simply "saurus." Why didn't scientists do this?* (to be more specific and describe only one kind of dinosaur)

Close

Check for Understanding

- As a follow-up to the **baseline assessment,** ask children to explain what kind of information is contained in a dinosaur name. (The name tells about a special trait—physical or behavioral—of that dinosaur.)
- **Answers to Checkpoint** Names should reflect a trait or traits of the dinosaur.

Ask Open-ended Questions

To guide children into the next lesson, ask: *What body parts do you think scientists look at to identify and name fast-moving dinosaurs?* (Answers may include overall size and size of legs.)

Connecting Lessons

In the next lesson, children will learn how fast some dinosaurs moved. ▶

Explorer's Activity Guide

Use Explorer's Activity Guide page 47 with this lesson to help children answer the text question, "How were dinosaurs named?" with a hands-on activity.

Visual Literacy

To enhance the **visual literacy** connection, use the interactive overhead transparency that correlates with the above two pages. The transparency will help your students understand the key concepts presented on these pages.

Your Ideas

_____

_____

_____

_____

_____

Lesson 6

Lesson Objective
Children learn how fast some dinosaurs moved.

Introduce

Invite Learning
Ask children to **list** five animals that they could beat in a race across the classroom. Then have children list five animals that would win the race. Record all responses on the chalkboard.

Make Connections
To **assess prior knowledge,** ask children if they think they could win a race against a dinosaur. Record their answers as a **baseline assessment** that you can refer to in Check for Understanding.

Teach

Act as a Consultant
- Encourage children to work in groups to study the illustrations. Have them try to identify some physical traits that might make a dinosaur a fast or a slow runner.
- Observe children and listen to their discussion. Listen especially for comments concerning the size and weight of the dinosaur discussed and whether its legs appear strong.

How fast did dinosaurs move?

Did dinosaurs move slowly like turtles do? Or were they fast like tigers? You may guess that some dinosaurs moved faster than others.

Imagine that you live in the world of dinosaurs. You watch the dinosaur in the first picture take big, slow steps. A fast runner might win a race with this dinosaur!

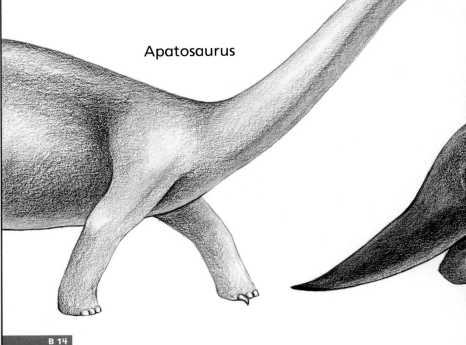

Apatosaurus

B 14

Science Idea Exchange

Science Background
Small dinosaurs that moved quickly tended to have hollow, lightweight bones. Long shin bones imply that the *Ornithomimus* could sprint. Dinosaur tracks give information about dinosaurs' speed. For example, the long strides of some small meat eaters show that they ran fast.

Collaborative Learning: Role-Playing
Divide the class into groups. Invite children to use their stories from Checkpoint to develop a group story. Then have each group act out the story for the rest of the class. Be sure that everyone in the group has a part in the story. Children may need to add characters to their story to allow everyone to participate.

Gifted and Talented
Children may enjoy making up a new kind of dinosaur that is faster than all the others. Encourage them to draw a picture of their dinosaur and to **name** it. Ask them to explain what makes their dinosaur fast.

Suppose the dinosaur with the horns ran by. Could you catch it? No, it moved fast. It could run faster than you can ride a bicycle.

This small dinosaur was the fastest one of all. Its strong legs helped it run. It could run almost as fast as a car can move.

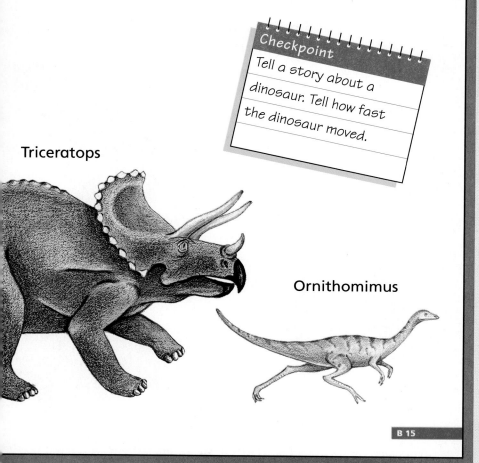

Checkpoint

Tell a story about a dinosaur. Tell how fast the dinosaur moved.

Triceratops

Ornithomimus

B 15

Ask for Evidence

Suggest that children **contrast** fast dinosaurs with slow dinosaurs. Ask them to list the physical traits of each. Then have children use the models they made in the Discover Activity to show how fast their dinosaur might have moved. Ask them to tell how big they imagine their dinosaur to be and to think about this size as they move their models.

Close

Check for Understanding

• As a follow-up to the **baseline assessment,** ask children to **order** the three dinosaurs shown in the pictures from slowest to fastest. Ask children if they could win a race against any of these dinosaurs.

• **Answers to Checkpoint** Children's stories should demonstrate an understanding that dinosaurs moved at varying rates of speed. Size and structure of the animal played a role in determining the rate at which it moved.

Connecting Lessons

In the next lesson, children will compare the lengths of some dinosaurs. ▶

Explorer's Activity Guide

Use Explorer's Activity Guide page 48 to help children answer the text question, "How fast did dinosaurs move?" with a hands-on activity.

Science Themes

By discussing the different speeds at which some dinosaurs moved and the relationship between body structure and speed, children develop their understanding of the themes of **modeling** and **systems and interactions.**

Your Ideas

_____

_____

_____

_____

_____

Lesson 7

Lesson Objective
Children compare the lengths of some dinosaurs. **Skills:** Organizing information, solving problems

Introduce

Invite Learning
Show three or four different lengths of string. Invite children to **compare** the lengths to see which is longest and which is shortest. Have them tape the strings to a wall horizontally from shortest to longest.

Make Connections
To **assess prior knowledge,** ask children how long the longest dinosaur was and how short the shortest dinosaur was. They may compare the lengths to something familiar, such as a bus.

Teach

Helpful Hints
- Help children pronounce *Iguanodon* (i gwä′nə don′).
- Tell children that the dinosaurs are drawn to scale. *Apatosaurus* is drawn four times longer than *Stegosaurus* because *Apatosaurus* was about four times longer than *Stegosaurus* in real life. If four *Stegosaurus* were lined up, they would be as long as one *Apatosaurus*.

B 16

Let's Solve It!

How are dinosaurs alike and different?

One way to compare dinosaurs is by looking at how long they were. The drawings show how long four dinosaurs were.

1. Look at the drawings of dinosaurs. Apatosaurus was the longest dinosaur. Which was the shortest dinosaur?

Tyrannosaurus
12 meters long

Stegosaurus
6 meters long

Science Idea Exchange

Science Background
Scientists can make inferences about dinosaurs by looking at their bones. The discovery of a 2 m (6 1/2 ft) upper leg bone of a *Brachiosaurus,* for example, gave an idea of how large this dinosaur was. Hip bones can give clues as to whether the animal walked on two legs or four legs.

Math/Science Connection
The chart children draw is a bar graph. Provide further practice with bar graphs by suggesting children work in groups to graph the lengths of common classroom objects.

Multicultural Connection
Dinosaurs could be found all over the world. Chinese researchers, for example, have found that many dinosaurs once roamed there, including *Omeisaurus* (ō′mā sôr′əs) a plant eater 14 m (45 ft) long; *Yangchuanosaurus* (yäng chwän′e sôr′es), a meat eater 8 m (26 ft) tall; and *Huayangosaurus* (hwä yäng′e sôr′es), a stegosaur 4 m (13 ft) long.

2. Draw a chart like this one.

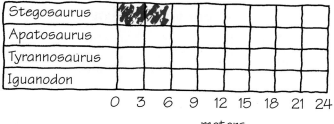

Stegosaurus								
Apatosaurus								
Tyrannosaurus								
Iguanodon								

0 3 6 9 12 15 18 21 24

meters

3. The chart shows how long the Stegosaurus was. Color your chart to show how long the other dinosaurs were.

Checkpoint

1. Which dinosaurs were longer than the Stegosaurus?

2. Write the names of the dinosaurs in order from the shortest to the longest.

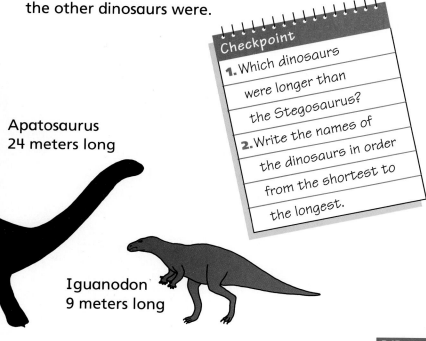

Apatosaurus
24 meters long

Iguanodon
9 meters long

B 17

Observe and Listen
- Divide the class into small groups to **compare** the dinosaur drawings.
- Allow children to work in groups to answer the question on page B16 and to complete the chart and Checkpoint on page B17.

Ask for Evidence
Ask: *How did you decide which dinosaur was the shortest?* (by comparing the lengths of the drawings, by comparing the labels, by observing the chart)

Close

Check for Understanding
- Have children use their graphs to answer these questions: *How many* Stegosaurus *equal the length of one* Tyrannosaurus? (two) *How many* Tyrannosaurus *equal the length of one* Apatosaurus? (two)
- **Answers to Checkpoint** 1. *Iguanodon, Tyrannosaurus,* and *Apatosaurus* were all longer than *Stegosaurus*. 2. *Stegosaurus, Iguanodon, Tyrannosaurus, Apatosaurus*

Connecting Lessons
In the next lesson, children will draw upon the concepts they learned in the chapter to make a model of a museum exhibit. ▶

Explorer's Activity Guide
Use Explorer's Activity Guide page 49 to help children solve the question of how dinosaurs were alike and different. You can also use this hands-on activity page to evaluate how well children understand the concept of this lesson.

Science and Social Studies
Numerous dinosaur remains were discovered in England more than 300 years ago. At that time, people believed the remains were bones of human giants. Scientists later came to understand that the bones and teeth unearthed in England were actually those of prehistoric animals.

Extend the Activity
You may wish to extend the activity by having children add the lengths of the following dinosaurs to their graphs: *Deinonychus*: 4 m (13 ft); *Sinosaurus* (sī nə sôr′əs): 2.5 m (8 ft); *Anatosaurus* (ə nat′ə sôr′əs): 13 m (42 ft); *Diplodocus*: 27 m (88 ft).

Lesson Objective

Children make a model of a museum exhibit to show the concepts they learned in this chapter.

Introduce

Invite Learning

Review the **baseline assessment** activities you used in this chapter. Choose one or more to do again that you think will help children understand the chapter concepts.

Teach

Performance Assessment Activity

Children make a model of a museum exhibit to show the concepts they learned in the chapter. **Skills:** Making physical models, applying information

Materials (per group)

Module Kit Items: index card; pipe cleaners (*3 or more*); craft sticks (*2 or more*)

School Supplied Items: paper; shoe box; dinosaur model (*from Discover Activity on page B5*); crayons

Safety Kit Items: cover goggles (*1/child*)

Helpful Hints

- With children, brainstorm a list of dinosaur facts and concepts. Write children's suggestions on the chalkboard.

Chapter Review

What did you learn?

Look again at the dinosaur you made at the beginning of this chapter. How can you make it more like a dinosaur that really lived?

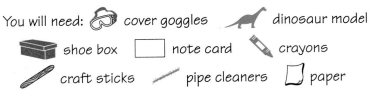

You will need: cover goggles   dinosaur model   shoe box   note card   crayons   craft sticks   pipe cleaners   paper

Make a dinosaur museum.

1. Make your dinosaur look more like a real dinosaur. You can use what you learned to change your model.
2. Use a shoe box to make a home for your dinosaur. Decorate the box to show how the land looked.
3. Make a card like the one in the picture. Write what your dinosaur was like.
4. Draw a picture of your dinosaur on the back of the card.

B 18

 # Science Idea Exchange

Teacher's Assessment Package

Use the pages from the Teacher's Assessment Package at this time to promote **performance assessment** opportunities for your children.

Collaborative Learning: Cooperative Learning

All children in the Chapter Review group should decide what changes should be made to the dinosaur model, contribute ideas to the design of the diorama, and share in answering questions. Also, each child in the group can be assigned a specific role:

- one who makes changes to the dinosaur;
- one who completes the diorama;
- one who draws a picture of the dinosaur on the index card;
- one who writes information about the dinosaur on the back of the index card.

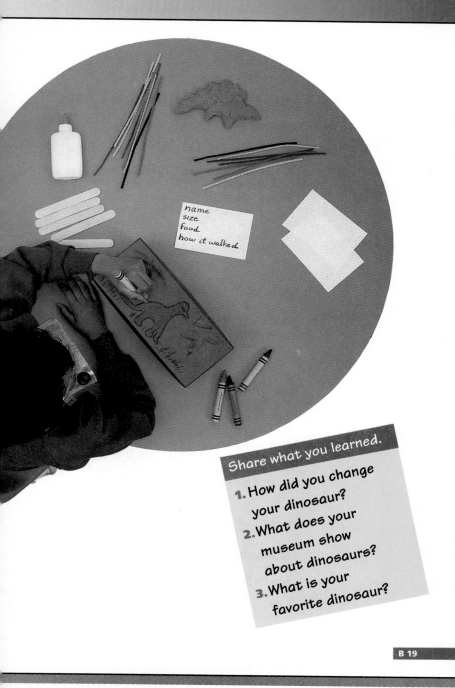

Share what you learned.

1. How did you change your dinosaur?

2. What does your museum show about dinosaurs?

3. What is your favorite dinosaur?

- Since children will be working with models they developed in the Discover Activity, try to assign them to the same groups.

Encourage Student Definitions
Encourage the whole class to use their finished models to come up with a definition for "dinosaur."

Close
Check for Understanding
- Ask children to explain what they have learned about dinosaurs that led them to change the model they made in the Discover Activity.
- **Answers to Share what you learned**
1. Answers will vary, depending on new insights gained by children. They might change the shape of teeth and the size and shape of limbs, for example. 2. Answers will depend on the level of detail in children's models and in the description on their cards. 3. Favorite dinosaur choices will vary among children.

Connecting Chapters
In the next chapter, children will discover that most of the current information about dinosaurs is gained from studying fossils. ▶

Explorer's Activity Guide
Use Explorer's Activity Guide pages 50–51 as a hands-on activity to evaluate how well children understand the concepts covered in this chapter.

Activity Results
Children's models should depict a dinosaur that looks like what they have described on their cards. It should also show any dinosaur characteristics learned in this chapter such as height, length, diet, and speed.

Science Background
Organisms that eat plants are called herbivores; those that eat meat are carnivores; those that eat both plants and animals are omnivores. The *Struthiomimus* (strü thē ō mī′ məs) was probably an omnivore that ate fruits, seeds, and small animals. Human beings are classified as omnivores.

Chapter 2 Planning Guide
Dinosaur Detectives

Lessons / *Skills*

Lesson 1
Discover Activity: **What can objects tell about a person?**
pp. B20–B21
(observing, making inferences)

Lesson 2
How do we learn about dinosaurs? pp. B22–B23
(making physical models, inferring)

Lesson 3
Let's Explore: **How can you make a fossil?** pp. B24–B25
(making physical models)

Lesson 4
How do fossils form? pp. B26–B27
(observing, describing)

Lesson 5
How do we get fossils? pp. B28–B29
(observing, describing, visualizing)

Lesson 6
What can dinosaur fossils show? pp. B30–B31
(comparing, observing)

Lesson 7
How do dinosaur bones fit together? pp. B32–B33
(making physical models)

Lesson 8
What else can fossils show? pp. B34–B35
(observing, describing)

Lesson 9
What was life like long ago? pp. B36–B37
(observing, comparing, contrasting)

Lesson 10
Let's Solve It!: **How can you measure fossils?** pp. B38–B39
(organizing information, solving problems)

Lesson 11
Chapter Review: **What did you learn?** pp. B40–B41
(observing, organizing information, comparing, contrasting)

Materials (per group)

Lesson 1 Activity: *What can objects tell about a person?*
Module Kit Item: paper bag
School Supplied Items: assorted small objects *(small toys, pictures related to sports, objects that reflect hobbies, and so on)*
Advance Prep: Prepare a bag for each group. Each bag should contain objects that give clues about a person's interests, hobbies, age, and so on.

Lesson 2 Activity: *Make a shoe print.*
Module Kit Items: 2 pieces of plastic wrap; 2 sticks clay
School Supplied Item: shoe
Advance Prep: Encourage children to wear or bring sneakers to class the day of the activity. The patterned sole of a sneaker will make the print easier to identify.

Lesson 3 Activity: *How can you make a fossil?*
Module Kit Items: petroleum jelly *(for thin layer on shoe print);* 1 cup plaster of Paris; plastic knife
School Supplied Items: cardboard strip; masking tape; container of water *(about 1/2 cup);* clay shoe print *(from Activity on B23);* container for plaster
Advance Prep: Cut cardboard strips to fit around the shoe print. Strips 5 cm x 50 cm should be large enough.

Lesson 5 Activity: *Dig for fossils.*
Module Kit Items: paintbrush; cup; sand; spoon; modeling clay
School Supplied Items: none

Lesson 7 Activity: *Make a model of a dinosaur skeleton.*
Module Kit Items: pipe cleaners *(at least 6)*
School Supplied Items: none
Safety Kit Items: cover goggles *(1/child)*
Advance Prep: To increase the number of pipe cleaners, you can cut them into various lengths ahead of time. Give children a variety of lengths to use.

Lesson 11 Activity: *Make a fossil game.*
Module Kit Items: none
School Supplied Items: crayons; construction paper *(2 sheets/child);* scissors

Assessment Options

	Content	Performance	Portfolio
Teacher's Assessment Package			
Chapter Test, pp. 33–34	✓		✓
Group Interview Assessment, p. 35	✓	✓	
Performance Strategies, p. 36	✓	✓	✓
Explorer's Activity Guide			
Activity worksheets, pp. 53–68		✓	✓
Chapter Review, pp. 69	✓		✓
Interactive Transparency Package			
Transparency 7 and 8 and BLMs	✓	✓	✓
Teacher's Guide, pp. 18–21	✓	✓	
Hands-on activity for second-language learners	✓	✓	✓
Activity for second-language learners	✓	✓	✓
Science Literature Library			
Let's Go Dinosaur Tracking!		✓	✓
Interactive Videodisc Software Teacher's Guide, pp. 53–61			
Computer-based Activity	✓	✓	
Journal Presentations	✓	✓	✓
Videodisc Classroom Guide, pp. 17–24, or **Video Reader**			
Hands-on activity	✓	✓	✓
ExploraCenter Teacher's Guide, pp. 9, 14, 22			
ExploraCenter			
Science activity cards 4, 9, 17	✓	✓	✓
ScottForesman Online Service			
Online field trips	✓	✓	✓

Chapter Overview

In this chapter, children discover how fossils form and that people study fossils to learn about plants and animals that lived long ago. Children make a footprint fossil and measure plant fossils. They make a model dinosaur skeleton to see how scientists put together dinosaur fossils.

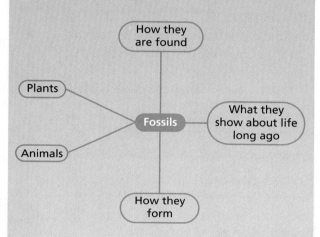

Lesson 1

Lesson Objective
Children learn they can study evidence to make inferences.

Introduce

Invite Learning
Show the videodisc or videotape segment for this chapter. Bar codes and a description of this segment are given below on page B21.

Make Connections
To **assess prior knowledge,** place an item into a covered box. Let children guess what is in the box without looking inside. Let them tilt or shake the box. As a **baseline assessment,** make a list of the clues they use that you can refer to in Check for Understanding.

Teach

Discover Activity

Children observe items that represent a person and make inferences about traits and interests of that person. **Skills:** Observing, making inferences

Materials (per group)
Module Kit Item: paper bag
School Supplied Item: assorted small objects *(small toys, pictures related to sports, objects that reflect hobbies, and so on)*

Chapter 2

Dinosaur Detectives

Can you solve this mystery? You find an object on your desk. You did not see anyone. But the object is a clue that tells you that someone was near your desk.

People have never seen dinosaurs. How do we know that they lived? We learn about dinosaurs by looking at the clues they left behind. Let's find out more.

B 20

Science Idea Exchange

Collaborative Learning: Small Groups
Assign specific children to gather and clean up materials. All children in the Discover Activity group should study the objects in the bag, make suggestions about what the clues tell, and be involved in discussing what clues can tell them about things they cannot see.

Science and Literature
Read the literature selection *Let's Go Dinosaur Tracking!* by Miriam Schlein (Harper Collins, 1991). Help children use a potato, ink pad, and paper to make dinosaur tracks. Make a stamp by drawing a footprint on a potato half and carving away the surrounding potato with a spoon.

Family/School Partnership: Family Support
Encourage families to be active partners in learning by suggesting that they and their children:
- describe an object in their home,
- talk about clues the object might give about their family, and
- talk about old objects in their home that might give clues about the past.

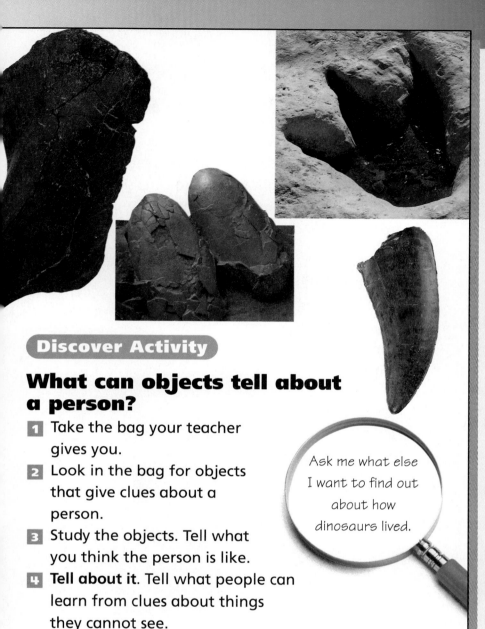

Discover Activity

What can objects tell about a person?

1. Take the bag your teacher gives you.
2. Look in the bag for objects that give clues about a person.
3. Study the objects. Tell what you think the person is like.
4. **Tell about it**. Tell what people can learn from clues about things they cannot see.

Ask me what else I want to find out about how dinosaurs lived.

B 21

Safety Tip
Do not place sharp objects in the bags.

Helpful Hints
- Before the activity, prepare a bag for each group.
- *See Equipment Kit Teacher's Guide for additional hints.*

What to Expect
Children should tell about a person who might use these objects.

Close

Check for Understanding
- As a follow-up to the **baseline assessment,** show children the list of clues made in Make Connections and ask how they would change it.
- **Answers to Tell about it** Responses might refer to how something looks, how it is used, or how it might relate to an event.

What Else Do You Want to Find Out?
Record children's questions about dinosaurs on chart paper. Use the questions to invite exploration of the chapter topics.

Connecting Lessons
In the next lesson, children will discover that people learn about dinosaurs by studying evidence and making inferences. ▶

Explorer's Activity Guide
The **Discover Activity recording sheet** on page 53 of the Explorer's Activity Guide can be used by children to record their activity results.

Visual Literacy
Discover the Wonder Videotape or *Videodisc,* Grade 2, Module B, follows a group of young explorers as they examine dinosaur fossils and investigate how scientists make inferences about the characteristics and behaviors of these prehistoric animals.

Bar Codes

Chapter 8: Video, English

Chapter 8: Video, Spanish

Play

Interactive Software

Lesson 2

Lesson Objective
Children learn that people find out about dinosaurs by studying evidence and making inferences.

Introduce

Invite Learning
Invite children to **observe** a clean chicken bone and a leaf. Challenge the class to **describe** the kind of animal or plant each might have come from.

Make Connections
To **assess prior knowledge,** ask children what footprints can tell about a living thing. Record their responses on chart paper and use them as a **baseline assessment.** You can follow up on the assessment in Check for Understanding.

Teach

Activity
Children make their own shoe print in clay and infer which shoe left another print in clay. **Skills:** Making physical models, inferring

Materials (per group)
Module Kit Items: 2 pieces of plastic wrap; 2 sticks clay
School Supplied Items: shoe

How do we learn about dinosaurs?

Imagine that you are taking a walk. You step in soft, wet mud. Look! You can see your footprints. What might your footprints show about your size? What else might your footprints show about you?

Long ago, this dinosaur walked through mud. How are its footprints different from yours? What might footprints show about the dinosaur?

Tyrannosaurus

B 22

Science Idea Exchange

Science Background
One way to study ancient life is to study fossils. A fossil is any evidence of ancient life preserved in rock or some other material. Some fossils form when the hard parts of organisms such as shells, teeth, or bones become buried in mud, clay, or other sediment. As this sediment hardens into rock, the body part dissolves, leaving an impression, or mold, in the rock. Later, water may fill the mold with minerals. The minerals form a solid shape called a cast, which resembles the original hard part. Fossils of soft body parts are more rare because these parts are usually eaten or decayed before they have a chance to become fossils.

Science and Language Arts
Let children be footprint detectives. Have them keep a log in which they draw footprints of real or imaginary creatures and describe what that animal is probalbly like based on the footprint.

Make a shoe print.

You will need:  clay · plastic wrap · shoe

1. Roll a piece of clay out flat. Put the piece of clay between two pieces of plastic wrap.
2. Step carefully with one foot on the clay. Take the plastic wrap off of your print.
3. Take off your shoe. Put it in a pile with those of your classmates.
4. Match the shoe prints with the shoes.

Checkpoint
Tell what your shoe print shows.

B 23

Helpful Hints
- Be sure to save all shoe prints for use in the next lesson.
- Help children pronounce the name of the dinosaur in the lesson: *Tyrannosaurus* (ti ran'ə sôr'əs).
- *See Equipment Kit Teacher's Guide for additional hints.*

Ask for Evidence
Ask: *How might you figure out which shoe made which shoe print?* (Try to fit the shoes into the shoe prints to see which shoe fits best.) *What else might you look for?* (markings on the bottom of the shoe)

Close

Check for Understanding
- As a follow-up to the **baseline assessment,** let children review their responses about what footprints can tell about a living thing from Make Connections. Ask if they would like to add to or subtract anything from their responses.
- **Answers to Checkpoint** The shoe print shows the size, the shape, and perhaps the brand of the shoe.

Connecting Lessons
In the next lesson, children will learn what a fossil is and make models of fossils. ▶

Explorer's Activity Guide
Use Explorer's Activity Guide hands-on activity on page 55 to help children answer the question, "How do we learn about dinosaurs?"

Teacher's Assessment Package
A **scoring rubric** to assess student performance is provided on page 31 of the Teacher's Assessment Package.

Activity Results
Each print will show the size and shape of the shoe. Children should be able to **infer** which shoes made which prints.

Collaborative Learning: Small Groups
Assign specific children to gather and clean up materials. All children in the Activity group should decide which shoe to use for an imprint, participate in preparing the clay and making the imprint, place their shoes in a pile with classmates, and share in matching shoes with imprints.

Lesson 3

Lesson Objective
Children learn what a fossil is and that some dinosaur footprints became fossils.

Introduce

Key Term
fossil

Invite Learning
Have children choose an object and make a print in a tray of sand and another print in a tray of damp soil.

Make Connections
To **assess prior knowledge,** ask children which print tells them more about the object that made it. Then ask how we can know what dinosaur footprints were like.

Teach

Encourage Student Definitions
Encourage children to give their own definition of the word "fossil." Save this definition to use as a **baseline assessment.**

Activity
Children use plaster of Paris and their shoe print from the previous activity to make a model of a fossil. **Skill:** Making physical models

---

How can you make a fossil?

What happened to the footprints dinosaurs left behind? Some footprints became **fossils.** A fossil can be a part or a mark from an animal or plant. How can your clay shoe print become a fossil?

You will need:

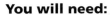 clay shoe print

 cardboard strip

 masking tape

 plaster of Paris

 plastic knife

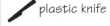 petroleum jelly

Find out about it.

1 Cut around the shoe print you made.

2 Coat the shoe print with petroleum jelly.

3 Tape the cardboard strip around your shoe print.

4 Fill the shoe print with plaster of Paris. Let it dry.

5 Take away the cardboard. Carefully peel away the clay from your fossil.

B 24

 ## Science Idea Exchange

Science Background
The activity in this lesson shows two of the most common types of fossils—molds and casts. Compare the formation of molds and casts in the Science Background of the previous lesson to this activity. The clay shoe print is the mold. The plaster of Paris model is the cast.

Science and Art
Children may enjoy making a crayon rubbing of their fossil. Have them place a piece of paper on top of the fossil and gently rub the side of a crayon across the paper. In addition to showing the size and shape of the fossil, the rubbing will also show its texture.

Multicultural Connections
People have found evidence of dinosaurs throughout the world and through the centuries. Dr. Dong Zhiming, a dinosaur expert in Beijing, China, has reported that fossil dinosaur teeth—called "dragon's teeth" by the Chinese— were found as long ago as the 1500s B.C.

Write about it.

Make a chart like this one. Draw what your fossil shows.

what my fossil looks like

Checkpoint

1. What does your fossil show about your shoe?

2. Take Action! List the things your fossil shows about you.

B 25

Materials (per group)

Module Kit Items: petroleum jelly *(for thin layer on shoe print);* 1 cup plaster of Paris; plastic knife

School Supplied Items: cardboard strip; masking tape; container of water *(about 1/2 cup);* clay shoe print *(from Activity on page B23);* container for plaster

Helpful Hints

● Be sure children cut an oval shape around the shoe print.

● *See Equipment Kit Teacher's Guide for additional hints.*

Close

Check for Understanding

● As a follow-up to the **baseline assessment,** show children the definition they gave of the word "fossil." Ask if they would change it now. If so, how? Ask them to write a sentence if they have changed their definition.

● **Answers to Checkpoint** 1. The fossil shows the size, shape, and possibly the patterns on the bottom of the shoe. 2. **Take Action!** Possible answers include the following: the kind of shoe I sometimes wear, how big my feet are, and maybe my age.

Connecting Lessons

In the next lesson, children will learn how fossils were formed. ▶

Explorer's Activity Guide

Use Explorer's Activity Guide hands-on activity on page 56 to explore fossils and evaluate children's understanding of the lesson concept.

Teacher's Assessment Package

A **scoring rubric** to assess student performance is provided on page 31 of the Teacher's Assessment Package.

Activity Results

Children should fill in the chart to reflect their shoe size (as measured with a ruler or as marked on the shoe print); the shape of their shoe (whether the toe is pointed, rounded, or squared); any distinguishing marks on the bottom of the shoe (unusual or distinct tread pattern); and the kind of shoe (sneaker, boot, dress shoe).

Collaborative Learning: Small Groups

Assign specific children to gather and clean up materials. All children in the Let's Explore group should participate in making the fossil and then record data and share results.

Lesson 4

Lesson Objective
Children learn how some fossils were formed.

Introduce

Invite Learning
If you can, obtain a fossil from a nearby high school, university, or rock shop. Let children observe and feel the fossil. Record children's questions about the fossil and return to their questions throughout the lesson. If real fossils are unavailable, use lumps of clay to represent rocks and make impressions in them with the threads of a screw or veins of a leaf.

Make Connections
To **assess prior knowledge,** ask children to draw a series of pictures showing how they think a fossil forms. Save their drawings to use as a **baseline assessment.**

Teach

Act as a Consultant
- Suggest that small groups work together to make simple flip books that show how they think a fossil forms from a plant or an animal.
- Ask children to suggest how the mark may have formed in the rock. Listen to children's descriptions of the process by which fossils form.

How do fossils form?

Did you ever see a mark like the one on this rock? How did the mark get there?

Long ago, an animal died. It became covered with mud. The mud dried and became hard. The body of the animal rotted away. The shell of the animal was left. Then the shell wore away. Only the animal's mark stayed in the rock. The mark had become a fossil.

B 26

Science Idea Exchange

Science Background
Fossils form in several different ways. A plant or animal may become petrified, or turned into stone. Wood that is dissolved by groundwater and replaced by minerals in the water is known as petrified wood. Sometimes whole organisms are found preserved in ice and frozen ground.

Science and Language Arts
Have children make up a story that tells how they discovered a dinosaur fossil. Children should describe how the fossil of their dinosaur formed over time. They might also wish to imagine certain clues about the appearance or behavior of their dinosaur that they could gain by examining the fossil.

Science Themes
By investigating how fossils form, children develop their understanding of the theme of **systems and interactions.**

If you go on a fossil hunt, you might find fossils like these. Point to the fossil that came from an animal. Point to the fossil that came from a plant. What can fossils show about animals and plants that lived long ago?

Checkpoint

Make a picture book that shows how a fossil forms.

Ask for Evidence

Ask: *What can you look for in a fossil to tell whether it is a plant fossil or an animal fossil?* (Animal fossils may have bones or skeletons; plant fossils do not.)

Ask Open-ended Questions

Ask children to tell what they think fossils show about animals and plants of long ago. (Fossils show what the animals and plants looked like, how big they were, and what kinds they were.)

Close

Check for Understanding

- As a follow-up to the **baseline assessment,** have children look at their pictures and talk about how their ideas may have changed.
- **Answers to Checkpoint** Books might show plant or animal remains being covered with mud, layers of mud building up on the remains, fleshy parts of the organism rotting away, hard parts of the organism wearing away, and finally a mark in a rock that resembles some portion of the organism.

Connecting Lessons

In the next lesson, children will learn that workers dig into the ground to uncover fossils. ▶

Explorer's Activity Guide

Use Explorer's Activity Guide page 57 with this lesson to help children answer the text question, "How do fossils form?" with a hands-on activity.

Math/Science Connection

Have children work in small groups. Provide each group with drawings or pictures showing different stages of fossil formation. You may use the drawings children made for Make Connections. Challenge children to place the drawings in the correct order. Then have children number the drawings in order.

Your Ideas

_____

_____

_____

_____

_____

Introduce

Invite Learning
Get children involved in discovery by letting them dig for "treasures." Gather magazine pictures of various objects. Cut or tear each picture into 2 or 3 pieces. Bury the pieces at different levels in a bucket of peanuts with shells. Challenge groups of children to find the pieces. Have children match the pieces to reconstruct the pictures.

Make Connections
To **assess prior knowledge,** ask children what they would have to do to find a fossil. Save their responses on chart paper as a **baseline assessment.**

Teach

Activity
Children imitate the process of digging for a fossil by uncovering a mystery fossil buried in sand. **Skills:** Observing, describing, visualizing

Materials (per group)
Module Kit Items: paintbrush; cup; sand; spoon; modeling clay
School Supplied Items: newspaper

How do we get fossils?

You pick up a handful of dirt. You know that fossils are buried in rocks and dirt. If fossils were here, how would you get them?

Digging for fossils is a hard job. Workers use tools to dig deep into the ground. These workers uncover fossils. They gently brush away some of the dirt. Workers need to be very careful not to break any fossils.

B 28

Science Idea Exchange

Science Background
Paleontologists use a variety of methods to remove fossils. Sturdy fossils such as bones, shells, and teeth are generally removed directly from rock with a trowel or shovel. More delicate fossils are wrapped in plastic. Then they are wrapped in layers of cloth soaked with wet plaster. The hard plaster serves to protect the fossils from damage as they are chipped away from the rock and transported back to museums. To chip away the plaster, paleontologists use electric saws, picks, dental tools, and brushes. Even after finding a fossil, it can take months to remove it from the rock.

Science and Language Arts
Suggest children create a help-wanted advertisement for a fossil hunter. Tell them to keep in mind what this person might have to do in the job when writing the advertisement. The ad should include information on what kinds of tools are needed and what kinds of things the person should know about.

Dig for fossils.

You will need: cup  spoon clay sand paintbrush

1. Use clay to make a model of a fossil.
2. Bury your fossil in a cup of sand.
3. Trade cups with someone in your group.
4. Dig through the sand until you uncover the fossil.
5. Take the fossil out and clean it.

Checkpoint
Write a story about a fossil hunt. Tell how workers take a fossil out of the ground.

B 29

- Instead of or in addition to clay, children could use such items as pasta, raisins, and pretzels for fossils.
- Children may want to break their fossil model into 2 or 3 pieces before burying it. Partners can put the pieces together to reconstruct the whole fossil.
- Remind children to handle the fossil model gently in order to avoid damaging it.

Close

Check for Understanding

- As a follow-up to the **baseline assessment,** show children their responses from Make Connections. Ask if there are any changes they would like to make.
- **Answers to Checkpoint** Stories should describe looking for fossils deep in the ground, uncovering a fossil, removing it from rock, and carefully cleaning it.

Connecting Lessons

In the next lesson, children will learn that people make inferences about dinosaurs by studying fossils of dinosaur bones. ▶

Explorer's Activity Guide

Use Explorer's Activity Guide hands-on activity on page 58 to help children answer the question, "How do we get fossils?"

Teacher's Assessment Package

A **scoring rubric** to assess student performance is provided on page 32 of the Teacher's Assessment Package.

Activity Results

Children should work slowly and carefully so that they do not damage their fossil. They should be able to uncover the entire fossil without breaking it. Guide them in understanding what a slow, careful process it is to uncover real fossils.

Collaborative Learning: Small Groups

Assign specific children to gather and clean up materials. All children in the Activity group should participate in making a model fossil, burying it, uncovering another child's fossil, and sharing results.

Lesson 6

Lesson Objective

Children learn that people make inferences about dinosaurs by studying fossils of dinosaur bones.

Introduce

Invite Learning

Let children examine two very different kinds and sizes of bones, such as chicken wing bones and the cross-section of bone from a round steak. Boil the bones first to clean them. Allow children to **compare** the bones and make discoveries about them.

Make Connections

To **assess prior knowledge**, record children's inferences about the bones they examined in Invite Learning. Use this list as a **baseline assessment**.

Teach

Helpful Hint

Help children pronounce the name of the dinosaur in this lesson: *Iguanodon* (i gwä′nə don).

Observe and Listen

- Have groups of three or four children draw pictures of dinosaur skeletons.

What can dinosaur fossils show?

Imagine finding these giant bones. You probably would ask "What kind of animal had bones like these?" These bones were from a dinosaur.

The dinosaur bones were buried in mud for many years. Slowly the mud and the bones hardened. The bones became fossils. What can these fossils show about dinosaurs?

The Iguanodon was taller than a house — and as long as a house too.

The Iguanodon probably lifted its tail when it ran.

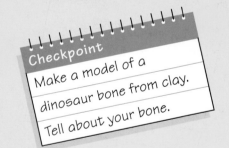

> **Checkpoint**
> Make a model of a dinosaur bone from clay.
> Tell about your bone.

B 30

Science Idea Exchange

Science Background

Scientists have changed their views of dinosaurs over the years. Today, they are still looking for evidence to answer questions about whether dinosaurs were warm-blooded creatures, if they lived in groups, and how they cared for their young. Recent evidence shows that certain young dinosaurs' bones were too weak to support a walking animal, and that the young therefore had to stay in the nest and be cared for by adults. Evidence also suggests that birds are the closest living relatives of dinosaurs. In fact, most dinosaurs structurally resemble birds more than they resemble lizards.

Math/Science Connection

The longest *Iguanodon* was probably 9 m (30 ft) long. Have children use a meter stick and string to demonstrate this length. They can compare the length of this dinosaur with a familiar object, such as a bus or building.

Iguanodon

The Iguanodon had big, flat teeth for eating plants.

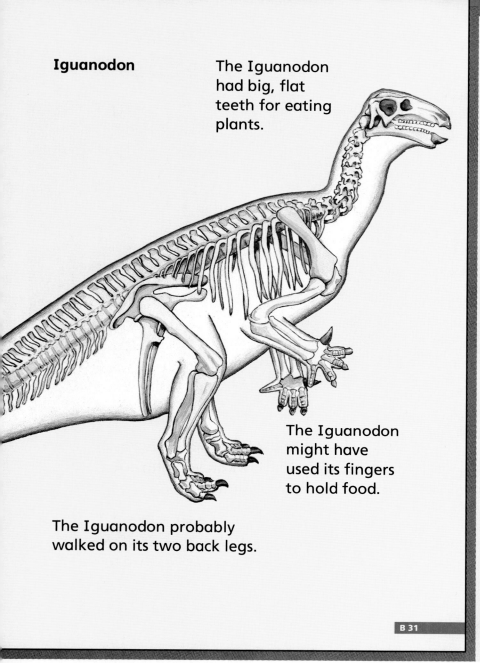

The Iguanodon might have used its fingers to hold food.

The Iguanodon probably walked on its two back legs.

- Invite groups of children to exchange drawings, list physical characteristics, and **infer** possible behavioral traits of each dinosaur shown as they **observe** the illustrations.

Raise Questions

After children have observed the illustrations and the captions have been read, ask: *What clue tells scientists that a dinosaur was a plant eater?* (flat teeth) *What type of teeth would a meat-eating dinosaur have?* (sharp, pointed teeth)

Close

Check for Understanding

- As a follow-up to the **baseline assessment,** have children examine the bones from Invite Learning again. Ask them if there is anything else about the bones they would like to add to their list.

- **Answers to Checkpoint** Descriptions should include how the particular bone enabled the dinosaur to do a specific task or was part of a particular physical trait.

Connecting Lessons

In the next lesson, children will learn that people put fossils of dinosaur bones together to make a model of a dinosaur skeleton. ▶

Explorer's Activity Guide

Use Explorer's Activity Guide page 59 with this lesson to help children answer the text question, "What can dinosaur fossils show?" with a hands-on activity.

Visual Literacy

To enhance the **visual literacy** connection, use the interactive overhead transparency that correlates with the above two pages. The transparency will help your students understand the key concepts presented on these pages.

Your Ideas

_____

_____

_____

_____

_____

Lesson Objective
Children learn that people put fossils of dinosaur bones together to make a model of a dinosaur skeleton.

Introduce

Invite Learning
Have children draw a picture of a dinosaur skeleton on a piece of paper and cut the picture into ten pieces. Children should exchange puzzles with a classmate and reassemble the pieces.

Make Connections
To **assess prior knowledge,** show children a picture of a dinosaur skeleton. Ask how they think the bones were arranged when they were found. Record their responses as a **baseline assessment.**

Teach

Activity
Children imitate the process of assembling a dinosaur skeleton by making a model with pipe cleaners.
Skill: Making physical models

Materials (per group)
Module Kit Items: pipe cleaners *(at least 6)*
School Supplied Items: none
Safety Kit Items: cover goggles *(1/child)*

How do dinosaur bones fit together?

Do you like puzzles? Suppose you have many puzzle pieces. How can you find out what the whole puzzle shows?

Fitting together dinosaur bones is like putting together a puzzle. Workers need to figure out where each bone belongs. Then they put the bones together.

B 32

Science Idea Exchange

Science Background
Paleontologists often display a dinosaur skeleton as a free mount, where the skeleton appears to be standing on its own. A small model of the entire skeleton is completed first. Then a framework of steel or plastic is constructed. Replicas of the fossilized bones are then attached to this framework.

Science and Language Arts
Invite children to imagine they are museum workers making a new display for a dinosaur skeleton. Help them write a letter to a friend describing a typical day at work.

Science Themes
By making models of a dinosaur skeleton, children develop their understanding of the themes of **modeling** and **scale and structure.**

Make a model of a dinosaur skeleton.

You will need:  cover goggles   pipe cleaners

1. Twist two pipe cleaners together to make one long piece.
2. Bend one end of the long piece to make the head of the dinosaur. Bend the rest of the piece to make the back and the tail.
3. Use pipe cleaners to make front and back legs.
4. Use pipe cleaners for ribs. Twist the ribs around the back.

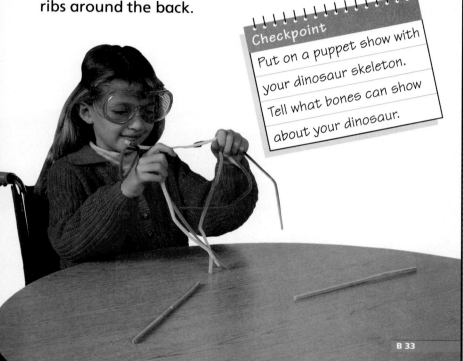

Checkpoint
Put on a puppet show with your dinosaur skeleton. Tell what bones can show about your dinosaur.

B 33

Helpful Hints
- Have children draw a picture of the dinosaur skeleton they wish to build before they begin the activity.
- Provide children with shorter pieces of pipe cleaner for the ribs.
- *See Equipment Kit Teacher's Guide for additional hints.*

Ask for Evidence
Have children carefully disassemble their model skeletons, leaving the shape of each bone intact. Then have children mix the pieces together and exchange them with classmates for reassembly.

Close

Check for Understanding
- As a follow-up to the **baseline assessment,** show children their responses to the Make Connections question and ask if they would like to change or add to them.
- **Answers to Checkpoint** Puppet shows may describe how the dinosaur moves, what it eats, and what its size and shape were.

Connecting Lessons
In the next lesson, children will learn how people make inferences about how some dinosaurs cared for their young. ▶

Explorer's Activity Guide
Use Explorer's Activity Guide hands-on activity on pages 60–61 to help children answer the question, "How do dinosaur bones fit together?"

Teacher's Assessment Package
A **scoring rubric** to assess student performance is provided on page 32 of the Teacher's Assessment Package.

Activity Results
Dinosaur skeletons should reflect what children have learned about dinosaurs' sizes and shapes as well as how they might have been able to walk or support themselves.

Collaborative Learning: Small Groups
Assign specific children to gather and clean up materials. All children in the Activity group should participate in making the model of a dinosaur skeleton and planning the puppet show and then share results.

Lesson 8

Lesson Objective

Children learn how people use fossils to make inferences about how some dinosaurs cared for their young.

Introduce

Invite Learning

Invite children to play the animal game suggested in the text. Tell children you are going to give three clues about a particular type of animal. They should use these clues to name the animal. For example: "I move from place to place by hopping. I carry my babies inside a pouch. I live in Australia." After the correct response (kangaroo) is given, have volunteers continue the games.

Make Connections

To **assess prior knowledge,** use the **constructivist** approach. Ask children: *What do you know about young dinosaurs? What questions do you have about how young dinosaurs were cared for? How can we find the answers to your questions?* Use their responses to the second question as a **baseline assessment.**

Teach

Helpful Hint

Help children pronounce the name of the dinosaur in the illustration: maiasaur (mā′ ə sôr)

What else can fossils show?

Let's play a "guess the animal" game. This animal laid eggs in nests. Babies hatched from the eggs. The babies probably stayed near their nests for a long time. What animal was it? You can find the answer in the picture.

How do we know about these dinosaurs? People digging for fossils found nests. In the nests, they found pieces of eggshells. Fossils of dinosaur babies were in the nests too.

Maiasaur and babies

B 34

Science Idea Exchange

Science Background

The maiasaur nest described in the text was discovered in Montana in 1978. The remains of 15 baby dinosaurs indicated that the mother probably cared for her young until their bones developed and they were able to live on their own.

Science Themes

By exploring how scientists use fossils to develop theories about dinosaurs, children are developing their own understanding of the theme of **modeling.**

Science and Language Arts

Have children imagine they have discovered a fossil nest of maiasaurs. Invite them to create a short skit in which they describe what they found and what they learned from their discovery.

Fossils of young dinosaurs were near the nests. The teeth were worn from eating. How did the young dinosaurs get food? Near one nest, people found fossils of a grown dinosaur. Dinosaurs probably brought food to their babies.

Checkpoint

Act out a play about dinosaurs. Show how dinosaurs took care of their babies.

B 35

Ask Open-ended Questions

- Ask children how they think some baby dinosaurs were like baby birds (hatched from eggs, lived in nests, were brought food by adults).
- Ask children what would not be known about dinosaurs if nests had not been found and studied.
- Challenge children to change or make up new evidence about dinosaurs and state new conclusions. For example, children might ask each other: *What could it mean if no grown dinosaur fossils were ever found near nests?* (maybe that baby dinosaurs were left to get food on their own)

Close

Check for Understanding

- As a follow-up to the **baseline assessment**, ask children if all the questions they asked in Make Connections have been answered. Help them determine how to find answers to any other questions they still have.
- **Answers to Checkpoint** Plays should show the parent dinosaurs providing their offspring with food, a safe place to sleep, and protection from enemies.

Connecting Lessons

In the next lesson, children will learn how people make inferences about animals and plants that lived long ago by studying fossils. ▶

Explorer's Activity Guide

Use Explorer's Activity Guide pages 63–64 with this lesson to help children answer the text  question, "What else can fossils show?" with a hands-on activity.

Science and Art

Invite children to **make models** of dinosaur eggs. While wearing cover goggles, children can inflate oval balloons up to 30 cm (1 ft) long and 25 cm (10 in.) across. They can then cover the balloons with strips of newspaper dipped in papier-mâché and paint their models.

Math/Science Connection

Full-grown maiasaurs were about 9 m (30 ft) long, while one-year-old maiasaurs were about 1 m (3 1/3 ft) long. Encourage children to measure objects to find something that represents the length of a one-year-old maiasaur and a full-grown maiasaur.

Chapter 2
Dinosaur Detectives **B 35**

Lesson Objective
Children learn that by studying fossils, people can tell much about animals and plants that lived long ago.

Introduce

Invite Learning
Read the literature selection *Time Train* by Paul Fleischman (HarperCollins, 1991) aloud. Then ask children to look out the window or, if possible, take the class outdoors. Have children look for examples of living things. Keep a list of the things they see in the air, on the ground, or in the water. Ask how their world compares to the world they saw in the story.

Make Connections
To **assess prior knowledge,** have children draw a picture of what the world looked like when dinosaurs lived. Save their pictures to use as a **baseline assessment.**

Teach

Observe and Listen
Encourage children to explain to each other what they think the picture is illustrating. Suggest that they **compare** and **contrast** the world shown in the picture with the world they observed outside their classroom.

What was life like long ago?

Look at the world of the dinosaurs shown on these two pages. Does it look the way you imagined it? How is it the same as what you imagined? How is it different?

You may be surprised to see so many animals and plants. How do we know so much about life long ago? If you said that we learned from fossils, you are right!

Checkpoint
Make a diorama. Show some animals and plants that lived long ago.

B 36

 # Science Idea Exchange

Science Anecdote
Plant life during the time dinosaurs roamed the earth did not include grass but did include ferns, mosses, and giant tree ferns. Besides dinosaurs, other land animals included frogs, lizards, turtles, and insects. Some were similar to those seen today, while others were much larger.

Science and Language Arts
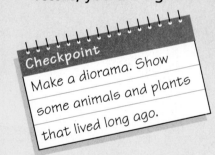
Suggest that children imagine they are "time-travelers." They have just stepped out of a time machine and into the world shown in the illustration. Invite them to make up and act out a story describing what they find on their journey. Children may want to work in groups.

Save the Earth
A fossil fuel is a hydrocarbon fuel derived from living matter of a previous geologic time. Coal, oil, and natural gas are fuels that come from underground deposits formed millions of years ago from the remains of plants and animals. About 97 percent of the energy people use today comes from fossil fuels.

Raise Questions

As children **observe** the illustration, have them use visual clues to **compare** animals in different ways. Ask questions to inspire visual learning and help children make distinctions. For example, ask: *What is the largest dinosaur shown in the picture?* (*Apatosaurus,* in background) *What animal is eating plants?* (*Stegosaurus*) *Which are meat eaters?* (*Allosaurus,* to the right) *Do you see any animals that look like animals alive now?* (yes, the turtle, lizard, and small mammals near the lizard)

Close

Check for Understanding

- As a follow-up to the **baseline assessment,** have children look at their pictures and at the illustration on pages B36–B37. Encourage them to discuss any additions or changes they might make to their pictures.
- **Answers to Checkpoint** Dioramas should depict a prehistoric scene comparable to that shown in the illustration on these pages.

Connecting Lessons

In the next lesson, children will learn they can make inferences about certain plants by comparing the fossils of these plants. ▶

Explorer's Activity Guide

Use Explorer's Activity Guide pages 65–67 with this lesson to help children answer the text

question, "What was life like long ago?" with a hands-on activity.

Visual Literacy

To enhance the **visual literacy** connection, use the interactive overhead transparency that correlates with the above two pages. The transparency will help your students understand the key concepts presented on these pages.

Your Ideas

_____

_____

_____

_____

_____

Lesson Objective

Children learn that they can make inferences about plants by comparing the fossils of plants.

Skills: Organizing information, solving problems

Introduce

Invite Learning

Have groups of children simulate a fossil by pressing a leaf, up to 12 cm (4 1/2 in.) tall, into clay so that an imprint is made.

Make Connections

To **assess prior knowledge,** have children tell about the attributes of their group's fossil. Then have the groups **compare** and **contrast** their fossils.

Teach

Observe and Listen

- Have children work in small groups as in Invite Learning and Make Connections. Have children explain to one another how the chart shows which fossil is the longest.
- Encourage children to ask and answer one another's questions as they complete the information in the chart. Discuss any unanswered questions that arise.

How can you measure fossils?

You learned that many kinds of plants lived long ago. Now you might see fossils of some of these plants. You can measure these fossils.

1. Look at the fossils of the plants. The yew is the shortest fossil. Which is the tallest fossil?

fern

cycad

Science Idea Exchange

Science Background

Ferns are among the oldest living land plants. In fact, huge ferns were common on parts of the earth in prehistoric times. Each of the plants measured in the activity—fern, cycad, and yew—is a nonflowering plant. Flowering plants evolved much later in geologic time.

Science and Language Arts

Suggest that children make up a news report about finding one of the fossils in the picture. Children should explain how the fossil was found and describe what the fossil shows about the plant.

Math/Science Connection

The chart in the text is a bar graph. Provide further practice with bar graphs by suggesting children work in groups to graph other information. For example, children might make a bar graph of pencil lengths or the lengths of plant leaves in their neighborhood.

2. Draw a chart like this one.

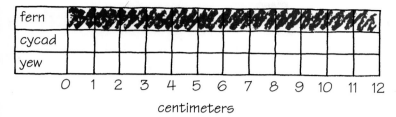

centimeters

3. The chart shows how tall the fern fossil is. Color your chart to show how tall the other fossils are.

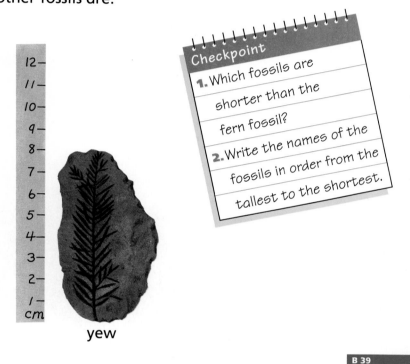

yew

Checkpoint

1. Which fossils are shorter than the fern fossil?

2. Write the names of the fossils in order from the tallest to the shortest.

Encourage children to fill in the blanks: The _____ (fern) is longer than the cycad, and the cycad is longer than the _____ (yew).

Close

Check for Understanding

• Draw a bar graph on the chalkboard like the one on page B39. Have the groups measure their fossil from Invite Learning and record the measurement on the graph.

• **Answers to Checkpoint** 1. The yew fossil and the cycad fossil are each shorter than the fern. 2. fern, cycad, yew

Connecting Lessons

In the next lesson, children will make a game to show the concepts they learned in this chapter. ▶

Explorer's Activity Guide

Use Explorer's Activity Guide page 68 to help children solve the question of how you can measure fossils. You can also use this hands-on activity page to evaluate how well children understand the concept of this lesson.

Achieving English Proficiency

Give children further practice with comparisons by encouraging them to demonstrate the concepts of "long," "longer," and "longest." Have them order three objects they see in their classroom according to length.

Special Education

Invite children to find and **measure** six objects in the classroom. Three objects should be measured with a centimeter ruler, and three objects should be measured with a meter stick. Help develop the idea that the meter stick is suitable for measuring greater lengths than the centimeter ruler.

Lesson 11

Lesson Objective
Children make a game to show the concepts they learned in this chapter.

Introduce

Invite Learning
Review the **baseline assessment** activities you used in this chapter. Choose one or more to do again that you think will help children understand the chapter concepts.

Teach

Performance Assessment Activity
Children match pictures with fossils based on what they have learned in this chapter. **Skills:** Observing, organizing information, comparing, contrasting

Materials (per group)
Module Kit Items: none
School Supplied Items: crayons; construction paper *(2 sheets/child);* scissors

Helpful Hints
- You may want children to review Chapter 2 if they need assistance generating ideas for their drawings.
- *See Equipment Kit Teacher's Guide for additional hints.*

What did you learn?

You know that fossils tell us about animals of long ago. You found out that fossils tell about plants too. You can make a game about fossils.

You will need:  paper   crayons   scissors

Make a fossil game.
1. Draw pictures of three animals or plants from long ago.
2. Draw fossils that tell about each animal or plant.
3. Cut your pictures apart.
4. Trade pictures with a classmate.
5. Match each picture of an animal or a plant with its fossil.

 Science Idea Exchange

Teacher's Assessment Package
Use the pages from the Teacher's Assessment Package at this time to promote **performance assessment** opportunities for your children.

Managing Groups
Assign specific children to gather and clean up materials. Each child in the Chapter Review group should draw three plants or animals on one piece of paper and three corresponding fossils on another piece of paper, cut the pictures apart, trade pictures, match pictures of plants and animals with their fossils, and share results.

Your Ideas

_____

_____

_____

_____

_____

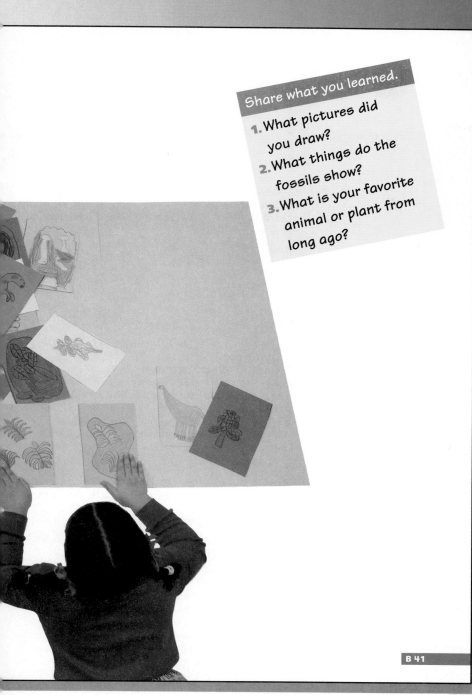

Share what you learned.

1. What pictures did you draw?
2. What things do the fossils show?
3. What is your favorite animal or plant from long ago?

Ask for Evidence

As children are working on their drawings, ask them to point out what things about the plant and animal can be seen in its fossil (size, shape, whether or not it had bones).

Ask Open-ended Questions

Ask children what things about the animals and plants are similar to animals and plants they might see in their everyday life.

Close

Check for Understanding

- Invite children to tell why fossils are important in helping people know about life long ago.
- **Answers to Share what you learned**
1. Answers will vary but should include organisms observed in this lesson.
2. Fossils provide clues to the structure and behavior of types of organisms we may have never seen. 3. Answers about children's favorite animal or plant will vary. Have children tell why it is their favorite.

Connecting Chapters

In the next chapter, children will discover how changes in habitats can affect plants or animals. ▶

Explorer's Activity Guide

Use Explorer's Activity Guide page 69 as a hands-on activity to evaluate how well children understand the concepts covered in this chapter.

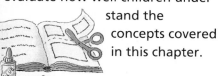

Activity Results

There should be a recognizable trait evident in children's pictures that is also evident in their drawing of the fossil.

Extend the Activity

After children match their pictures and fossils, have them **classify** the drawings according to similar traits. For example, fossils may be classified as either plants or animals.

Chapter 3 Planning Guide
A Changing World

Lessons / *Skills*

Lesson 1
Discover Activity: **What happened to dinosaurs?** pp. B42–B43
(describing, formulating hypotheses, drawing conclusions)

Lesson 2
How did dinosaurs disappear? pp. B44–B45
(recognizing cause and effect)

Lesson 3
What else became extinct? pp. B46–B47
(describing, observing)

Lesson 4
What living things are in danger? pp. B48–B49
(observing, recognizing cause and effect)

Lesson 5
Let's Explore: **What else can change living things?** pp. B50–B51
(observing, recording, comparing)

Lesson 6
How does air become polluted? pp. B52–B53
(observing, comparing)

Lesson 7
How can people help living things? pp. B54–B55
(making physical models)

Lesson 8
Let's Solve It!: **How do zoos help endangered animals?**
pp. B56–B57
(organizing information, solving problems)

Lesson 9
Chapter Review: **What did you learn?** pp. B58–B59
(describing, restating ideas)

Materials (per group)

Lesson 1 Activity: *What happened to dinosaurs?*
Module Kit Items: none
School Supplied Items: paper *(3 sheets/child);* crayons or markers; pencils

Lesson 5 Activity: *What else can change living things?*
Module Kit Items: 2 clear plastic cups
School Supplied Items: 2 plant cuttings; container of vinegar *(about 150 mL);* container of water *(about 300 mL)*
Safety Kit Items: cover goggles *(1/child)*
Advance Prep: Prepare the polluted water ahead of time by mixing one-half vinegar and one-half water.

Lesson 6 Activity: *Find out what is in the air.*
Module Kit Items: petroleum jelly; plastic slide; hand lens
School Supplied Item: paper towel

Lesson 7 Activity: *Make a bird feeder.*
Module Kit Items: handful of birdseed; dowel *(or use stick);* string *(30 cm)*
School Supplied Items: milk carton; crayons; scissors
Safety Kit Items: cover goggles *(1/child)*
Advance Prep: Begin collecting clean milk cartons a week before the activity. Poke a hole in the cartons so children have a starting point for their cutting. Cut a 30-cm piece of string for each group.

Lesson 9 Activity: *Make a book.*
Module Kit Items: none
School Supplied Items: construction paper *(2 sheets/child);* white paper *(4 sheets/child);* crayons; pencils

Assessment Options	Content	Performance	Portfolio
Teacher's Assessment Package			
Chapter Test, pp. 39–40	✓		✓
Group Interview Assessment, p. 41	✓	✓	
Performance Strategies, p. 42	✓	✓	✓
Explorer's Activity Guide			
Activity worksheets, pp. 70–79		✓	✓
Chapter Review, pp. 81–82	✓		✓
Interactive Transparency Package			
Transparency 9 and BLM	✓	✓	✓
Teacher's Guide, pp. 22–23	✓	✓	
Hands-on activity for second-language learners	✓	✓	✓
Science Literature Library			
What Happened to the Dinosaurs?		✓	✓
Interactive Videodisc Software Teacher's Guide, pp. 53–61			
Computer-based Activity	✓	✓	
Journal Presentations	✓	✓	✓
Videodisc Classroom Guide, pp. 17–24, or **Video Reader**			
Hands-on activity	✓	✓	✓
ExploraCenter Teacher's Guide, pp. 9, 14, 18			
ExploraCenter			
Science activity cards 4, 9, 13	✓	✓	✓
ScottForesman Online Service			
Online field trips	✓	✓	✓

Chapter Overview

This chapter begins with possible explanations for the disappearance of dinosaurs. Children learn that plants and animals can become endangered or extinct when their habitats change. Pollution of air and water is discussed, as are ways people can help living things.

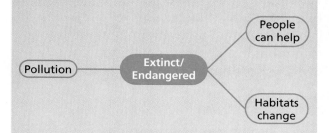

Lesson 1

Lesson Objective
Children use prior knowledge to present an explanation of what they think might have happened to dinosaurs.

Introduce

Invite Learning
Show the videodisc segment for this chapter. Bar codes and a description of this segment are given below on page B43.

Make Connections
To **assess prior knowledge**, ask children to explain why they have never seen a living dinosaur. Some children might think that live dinosaurs still exist in some remote regions of the world.

Teach

Discover Activity

Children draw a picture and tell a story about what might have happened to a dinosaur. **Skills:** Describing, formulating hypotheses, drawing conclusions

Materials (per group)
Module Kit Items: none
School Supplied Items: paper
(3 sheets/child); crayons or markers; pencils

Chapter 3

A Changing World

Has your neighborhood changed since last year? Maybe some new stores are being built. Maybe new neighbors have moved in. The world around you is always changing.

When dinosaurs lived, the world was changing too. But the dinosaurs were not able to live in this changing world. People have different ideas about how the world changed. Maybe you have your own ideas.

B 42

Science Idea Exchange

Managing Groups
Assign specific children to gather and clean up materials. Each child in the Discover Activity group should draw a dinosaur and depict what happened to it, write a story, and share the story with the group.

Science and Literature
After reading the literature selection *What Happened to the Dinosaurs?* by Franklyn M. Branley (Crowell, 1989), allow groups to discuss the different theories. Have children make a mural entitled "What Happened to the Dinosaurs?" that illustrates each theory.

Family/School Partnership: Family Support
Encourage families to be active partners in learning by suggesting that they and their children:
- name animals that live in their area
- describe plants that live in their area, and
- talk about how changes in their area might affect the animals and plants.

What happened to dinosaurs?

1 Draw a picture of a dinosaur on one side of a paper.

2 Draw a picture on the other side of your paper. Show what you think might have happened to the dinosaur.

3 **Tell about it.** Write a story about your dinosaur. Tell what might have happened to it.

Ask me what else I want to find out about the changing world.

Helpful Hints

● Save children's drawings to use as a **baseline assessment** for the chapter.

● *See Equipment Kit Teacher's Guide for additional hints.*

What to Expect

Drawings might show that the dinosaurs suddenly got sick and died or that something from space struck the earth, killing off all living things. Accept all answers and explanations. Guide children to understand that since humans didn't live when dinosaurs did, humans did not cause the extinction of dinosaurs.

Close

Check for Understanding

● Ask children to explain why dinosaurs are not found in a zoo.

● **Answers to Tell about it**   Stories will vary but could describe an event so severe that no dinosaurs survived. Accept all explanations.

What Else Do You Want to Find Out?

Record children's questions and invite them to look for answers as they explore the chapter topics.

Connecting Lessons

In the next lesson, children will learn some theories about what caused the extinction of dinosaurs. ▶

Explorer's Activity Guide

The **Discover Activity recording sheet** on page 70 of the Explorer's Activity Guide can be used by children to record their activity results.

Visual Literacy

Discover the Wonder Videodisc, Grade 2, Module B, introduces children to a wide range of endangered animals and encourages them to consider the importance of saving these animals from possible extinction.

Bar Codes

Chapter 9: Video and Stills

Play

Step

Interactive Software

DISCOVER THE WONDER

Lesson Objective
Children learn some theories about what caused the extinction of dinosaurs.

Introduce

Key Term
extinct

Invite Learning
Share the illustrations of Dinosaur National Monument from the literature selection *Time Train* by Paul Fleischman (HarperCollins, 1991). Then show pictures of the actual park. Ask which pictures show the park as it appears now—those with dinosaurs or those without.

Make Connections
To **assess prior knowledge,** invite children to share their ideas of what happened to dinosaurs from the Discover Activity. Record their ideas on chart paper and save them as a **baseline assessment** that you can follow up in Check for Understanding.

Teach

Observe and Listen
Invite groups of children to make dinosaur puppets from paper bags or cutouts mounted on straws. Listen as children use their puppets to act out the theories presented in the lesson.

How did dinosaurs disappear?

Dinosaurs lived on the earth for many years. Now dinosaurs are **extinct.** Extinct animals are kinds of animals that no longer live on the earth.

Nobody really knows what happened to dinosaurs. But the weather became colder at about the same time dinosaurs became extinct. Maybe dinosaurs could not live in the cold weather.

B 44

Science Idea Exchange

Science Background
A new theory concerning the extinction of dinosaurs has been presented by paleontologist Robert Bakker. He suggests that as dinosaurs migrated across land bridges, they spread diseases that eventually caused their extinction. A similar fate happened to many of the Native Americans of Central and South America. Diseases brought by the Europeans, such as smallpox, killed many native people. In some cases, whole groups of people were wiped out.

Multicultural Connection
People from around the world have developed myths about the presence of fossils. In Australia, the aborigines believed that creatures called Kadimakara lived in trees. One day when the Kadimakara were on the ground looking for food, the trees were destroyed. The Kadimakara were forced to remain on the ground and died, leaving their bones in the earth as fossils.

Many people think that a big rock from space crashed into the earth. Maybe dust from the crash blocked sunlight. Without sunlight, plants could not grow. Then dinosaurs could not live.

New kinds of animals began to live on the earth. Maybe these animals ate plants the dinosaurs needed for food. Maybe these animals even ate dinosaur eggs.

Checkpoint

Do a TV news show. Tell how you think dinosaurs became extinct.

Raise Questions

Without sunlight, plants could not grow. Ask: *What effect would this have on dinosaurs with big, flat teeth like* Stegosaurus? (The plant eaters would not have plants to eat and might die.) *If plant eaters died out, what would happen to dinosaurs with sharp, pointed teeth like* Tyrannosaurus? (Meat eaters that fed on plant eaters could also die.)

Encourage Student Definitions

Ask children to explain what they think the word "extinct" means. Have them write a sentence using the word and post their sentences on the chalkboard.

Close

Check for Understanding

- As a follow-up to the **baseline assessment,** ask children if there are any ideas about what happened to the dinosaurs they want to add to or remove from the list.
- **Answers to Checkpoint** News programs will vary but should describe a theory of extinction that children have discussed from the lesson.

Connecting Lessons

In the next lesson, children will learn that changes in habitat can cause other animals and plants to become extinct. ▶

Explorer's Activity Guide

Use Explorer's Activity Guide page 71 with this lesson to help children answer the text question, "How did dinosaurs disappear?" with a hands-on activity.

Visual Literacy

To enhance the visual literacy connection, use the interactive overhead transparencies of the above two pages with children. These transparencies will help them understand the key concepts presented on these pages.

Your Ideas

_____

_____

_____

_____

_____

Lesson 3

Lesson Objective
Children learn that changes in a habitat can cause plants and animals to become extinct.

Introduce

Invite Learning
Ask if anyone can name any other animals, besides dinosaurs, that are extinct today.

Make Connections
To **assess prior knowledge,** show children a picture of a forest. Ask them what might happen to the animals that live in the forest if their habitat changed to a desert. Show children a picture of a desert. Write their responses on chart paper to use as a **baseline assessment** in Check for Understanding.

Teach

Raise Questions
Ask: *What happens when an animal cannot get the things it needs from its habitat?* (It dies out or becomes extinct.) *What could an animal do to stay alive after its habitat has changed?* (It could move to another location that has what it needs to survive.)

What else became extinct?

How are the animals in the picture like dinosaurs? These kinds of animals are extinct. There are many kinds of extinct plants and animals.

Remember that a living thing gets everything it needs from its habitat. What happens when a habitat is changed? Some plants and animals may not be able to get the things they need. They become extinct.

Quagga

B 46

 Science Idea Exchange

Science Background
Moas were large, flightless birds resembling ostriches. They lived on the grassy plains of New Zealand. A change in vegetation to a more forested habitat caused their extinction of these birds. In addition, they were hunted for food. One species may have survived until around 1785.

Science and Social Studies
The quagga and moa shown in this lesson were native to different parts of the world. Encourage children to create a symbol for each animal. Children should place their symbols at the following locations on a world map: quagga—South Africa; moa—New Zealand.

Gifted and Talented
Encourage children to choose one of the animals in the illustrations or any other extinct animal and find out when it was alive and how it became extinct. You may want to ask them to share this information with the rest of the class.

Here is what happened to the extinct bird in the picture below. This bird once lived in grassy places. Then its habitat changed. Many trees began to grow on the land.

Many of the birds could not find the food they needed to live. After a while, the birds became extinct.

Checkpoint

Draw a picture of a plant or animal. Draw its habitat. Tell what can happen if its habitat is changed.

Moa

B 47

Have pairs of children draw two pictures showing how the habitat of the birds changed. (One picture should show grassy places, and the other should show the same area filled with trees.) Ask them to explain to each other how this change might stop the birds from finding food. (Answers may include that the plants the birds used for food were unable to grow in the same place as the trees.)

Close

Check for Understanding

- As a follow-up to the **baseline assessment,** ask children if there are any other things that may happen to forest animals if their habitat changes. Add these ideas to the responses from Make Connections.
- **Answers to Checkpoint** Pictures will vary. However, it should be clear that the plant or animal can get everything it needs from the habitat that is pictured. Explanations should describe how plants and animals might be unable to get what they need to live.

Connecting Lessons

In the next lesson, children will learn that changes in habitat can cause living things to become endangered. ▶

Explorer's Activity Guide

Use Explorer's Activity Guide page 72 with this lesson to help children answer the text question, "What else became extinct?" with a hands-on activity.

Science Themes

By discussing how changes in a habitat affect living things, children develop their understanding of the themes of **systems and interactions** and **evolution.**

Save the Earth

Explain to children that many animals today are losing their homes as more and more forests are cleared and land is developed. Ask children to suggest ways they can help protect animals that are being threatened in their natural habitats.

Lesson 4

Lesson Objective
Children learn that changes in habitat can cause living things to become endangered.

Introduce

Key Term
endangered

Invite Learning
Hand out cards with pictures of trees, bushes, ground cover (grass and plants), and birds or squirrels. Most of the cards should have trees, bushes, and ground cover on them. Only three or four should be birds or squirrels. Say: *The trees get cut down.* Have children with tree cards turn them in. Do the same for bushes and ground cover by saying: *The bushes get pulled out. The grass is dug up and covered with concrete.* Ask children what cards are left.

Make Connections
To **assess prior knowledge,** ask children to **predict** what would happen to the birds and squirrels pictured on the remaining Invite Learning cards if the plants disappeared. Save their responses as a **baseline assessment.**

What living things are in danger?

Many kinds of living things are in danger of becoming extinct. These living things are **endangered.** That means that very few of these animals and plants are living. Many animals and plants become endangered when their habitats change. The plants and animals you see here are endangered.

Checkpoint

Make a poster for your classroom about an endangered plant or animal.

B 48

whooping crane

giant panda

Science Idea Exchange

Science Background
Plants and animals facing possible extinction are classified in three groups. Endangered species require direct protection to prevent extinction. Threatened species are organisms whose numbers are dwindling worldwide. Rare species have populations that remain steady yet extremely low.

Science and Social Studies
Have children cut out or draw pictures of endangered animals and attach them to a map showing where these animals live.

Your Ideas

small whorled pogonia

Hawaiian monk seal

cheetah

B 49

Teach

Observe and Listen

Have pairs of children **observe** the illustrations. Encourage them to discuss and describe the habitat of each animal to one another and how a change in habitat might harm a living thing.

Encourage Student Definitions

Ask children what word they hear in "endangered" (danger). Display and discuss pictures of endangered animals. Have children say sentences using "endangered," such as "The giant panda is endangered because it can't find the food it needs." Record and post their sentences on a bulletin board titled: "Endangered Living Things."

Close

Check for Understanding

- As a follow-up to the **baseline assessment,** show children their predictions. Ask if they would change their responses now.
- **Answers to Checkpoint** Posters will vary but should show the animal and what is causing their animal to become endangered.

Connecting Lessons

In the next lesson, children will learn that polluted water can harm plants. ▶

Explorer's Activity Guide

Use Explorer's Activity Guide pages 73–74 with this lesson to help children answer the text question, "What living things are in danger?" with a hands-on activity.

Science Themes

By discussing how plants and animals are endangered by changes in their habitats, children develop their understanding of the theme of **patterns of change**.

Visual Literacy

To enhance the **visual literacy** connection, use the interactive overhead transparency that correlates with the above two pages. The transparency will help your students understand the key concepts presented on these pages.

Lesson 5

Lesson Objective
Children learn what polluted water is and that it can harm plants.

Introduce

Key Term
polluted

Invite Learning
Show children a jar with clean water in it and another jar with soapy water in it. Invite children to **predict** which jar of water would be better for a plant.

Make Connections
To **assess prior knowledge,** have children draw a picture showing what polluted water is. Save their drawings as a **baseline assessment.**

Teach

Activity
Children experiment to find out how a water pollutant (vinegar) can harm a plant. **Skills:** Observing, recording, comparing

Materials (per group)
Module Kit Items: 2 clear plastic cups
School Supplied Items: 2 plant cuttings; container of vinegar *(about 150 mL);* container of water *(about 300 mL)*
Safety Kit Items: cover goggles *(1/child)*

What else can change living things?

Living things get water from their habitats. Plants get some of this water from rain. But suppose the rain water is **polluted.** Polluted water is dirty water. Can polluted water harm a plant?

You will need:

 cover goggles

 clean water

 polluted water

plant cuttings

Find out about it.

1 Get a cup of clean water from your teacher. Get a cup of polluted water from your teacher.

2 Look carefully at the plant cuttings.

3 Put one plant cutting into the clean water. Put the other plant cutting into the polluted water.

4 Wait a few hours. Look again at the plant cuttings.

Science Idea Exchange

Science Background
Pollution is a change in the quality of the environment that can be harmful or unpleasant for living things. Some sources of water pollution are chemical wastes from homes, cities, and factories, and erosion and sediment deposits from farms and construction sites. By the year 2020, the United States may produce three times as much sewage as it did in 1970. Most harmful substances are removed from sewage at sewage treatment plants before being piped into bodies of water. Before the water from those bodies is safe to drink, the water must go through a water purification plant.

Science and Language Arts
Ask children to consider all the different ways they use clean water. Have them think about what life would be like if they were unable to obtain clean water. Suggest that children write sentences, naming at least three things they would not be able to do without clean water.

Write about it. ✏️

Make a chart like this one. Draw what you found out.

clean water	polluted water

Checkpoint

1. What happened to the plant cuttings?

2. Take Action! Draw what might happen to plants if rain water is polluted.

Safety Tips
- If children have plant allergies, adapt the activity as needed.
- Be sure children do not drink any of the water samples in the activity.

Helpful Hints
- Prepare the polluted water before the activity by making a solution of one-half vinegar and one-half water.
- You may want to have children record their results the next day when results should be more visible.
- See Equipment Kit Teacher's Guide for additional hints.

Close

Check for Understanding
- As a follow-up to the **baseline assessment,** have children draw another picture of polluted water. Direct children to **compare** their two pictures. Look for an understanding that polluted water doesn't always look dirty.
- **Answers to Checkpoint** 1. The plant cuttings in the polluted water wilted. 2. **Take Action!** Drawings should show that polluted rainwater can harm plants.

Connecting Lessons

In the next lesson, children will learn that living things need clean air and that many things people do today pollute the air. ▶

Explorer's Activity Guide
Use Explorer's Activity Guide hands-on activity on page 75 to explore change and evaluate children's understanding of the lesson concept.

Teacher's Assessment Package

A **scoring rubric** to assess student performance is provided on page 37 of the Teacher's Assessment Package.

Activity Results
The clean water cutting should show no change, while the polluted water cutting should be wilting or beginning to turn brown.

Collaborative Learning: Small Groups

Assign specific children to gather and clean up materials. All children in the Let's Explore group should work together to set up the plant cuttings in the cups and should observe the cuttings, record results, and share results.

Lesson 6

Lesson Objective
Children learn that living things need clean air and that many things people do pollute the air.

Introduce

Invite Learning
Have children take turns pantomiming different ways they move from place to place. Other children should guess what mode of transportation is being presented, then tell whether it contributes to air pollution.

Make Connections
To **assess prior knowledge,** ask children to suggest ways in which they might reduce air pollution (riding on a bike instead of in a car). List children's responses on chart paper, and save the list as a **baseline assessment.**

Teach

Activity
Children construct a simple device for checking the amount of dust and dirt in the air. **Skills:** Observing, comparing

Materials (per group)
Module Kit Items: petroleum jelly; plastic slide; hand lens
School Supplied Item: paper towel

How does air become polluted?

Take in a big breath. Now let it out. You are breathing air. You need air to stay alive. Clean air is important for all living things.

Polluted air is dirty. It can harm living things. Polluted air can have dust and dirt in it. Polluted air can have smoke. Find things in the picture that can make air polluted. Can you always see what is in the air? You can find out.

B 52

 # Science Idea Exchange

Collaborative Learning: Small Groups
Assign specific children to gather and clean up materials. All children in the Activity group should participate in preparing and observing the slide and then share results.

Science and Art
Suggest that children design a poster to encourage people to help keep the air clean by walking and by riding bicycles more, rather than driving. Display posters on a classroom bulletin board or in a school hallway.

Science and Language Arts
Help children write a class letter to officials of the local, state, or federal government, asking what steps are taken to keep the air they breathe as clean as possible.

Find out what is in the air.

You will need: ___ plastic slide 🫙 petroleum jelly

📜 paper towels 🔍 hand lens

1. Dip a paper towel in petroleum jelly.
2. Spread a very thin layer of petroleum jelly on the slide.
3. Place the slide outside.
4. Wait four days. Use a hand lens to look at your slide. Tell what you see.

Checkpoint

Tell if the air outside has dirt in it. How do you know?

Helpful Hints

- For best results, instruct children to use a thin, smooth layer of petroleum jelly.
- Suggest that groups place their slides in different places such as near a parking lot, on a windowsill, and attached with masking tape to a tree.
- *See Equipment Kit Teacher's Guide for additional hints.*

Ask for Evidence

Ask: *What did the petroleum jelly show about the air?* (There is dust and dirt in the air.) Have children label their samples "inside" and "outside" and place them side by side. Then have children examine them to determine where the air contained the most dust and dirt.

Close

Check for Understanding

- As a follow-up to the **baseline assessment,** ask children if they would like to add anything to their list of ways to reduce air pollution.
- **Answers to Checkpoint** The presence of dirt particles in the petroleum jelly shows that the outdoor air has dirt in it.

Connecting Lessons

In the next lesson, children will learn how people can help other things survive. ▶

Explorer's Activity Guide

Use Explorer's Activity Guide hands-on activity on page 76 to help children answer the question, "How does air become polluted?"

Teacher's Assessment Package

A **scoring rubric** to assess student performance is provided on page 37 of the Teacher's Assessment Package.

Activity Results

The slide should have dirt and dust particles stuck in the petroleum jelly.

Extend the Lesson

Have children check the jar lids after a week. They can check the lids again after two weeks. Ask children whether there has been a change in the number of particles collected in the lids.

Lesson 7

Lesson Objective
Children learn how people can help other living things survive.

Introduce

Invite Learning
Take the class outdoors if weather permits, or have children look out the window. Invite them to **list** all the living things with which they share their environment.

Make Connections
To **assess prior knowledge**, ask children how they can help plants and animals survive. Have children make a poster showing their suggestions as a **baseline assessment**.

Teach

Activity
Children make a bird feeder. **Skill:** Making physical models

Materials (per group)
Module Kit Items: handful of birdseed; dowel (*or use stick*); string (*about 30 cm*)
School Supplied Items: milk carton; crayons; scissors
Safety Kit Items: cover goggles (*1/child*)

Safety Tip
Caution children to be careful when cutting holes in the milk carton.

How can people help living things?

How are these people helping the earth? When you keep the earth clean, you are helping protect the habitats of living things.

How else can people help plants and animals? People can make parks. Plants and animals can live in the parks.

Here is something you can do to help living things. You can help birds get enough food.

B 54

Science Idea Exchange

Science Background
Many state and federal laws help protect wildlife in the United States. The Endangered Species Act of 1973 protects rare wildlife from being hunted, collected, or otherwise threatened. It also prohibits some federal projects that would destroy an area where an endangered species lives.

Collaborative Learning: Cooperative Learning
Assign specific children to gather and clean up materials. All children in the Activity group should contribute to the construction of the bird feeder and tell a story. Also, each child in the group can be assigned a specific role:

- one who draws and cuts out a circle on the carton;
- one who places a dowel in the carton and attaches a string to the carton and ties it;
- one who puts birdseed in the carton;
- one who selects a location and hangs the bird feeder.

Make a bird feeder.

You will need:  cover goggles milk carton crayons scissors stick  birdseed  string

1. Draw a circle on one side of the carton. Cut out the circle.
2. Put a small hole below the opening you made. Push the stick through the hole.
3. Put two holes through the top of the carton. Pull string through the holes.
4. Put birdseed in your feeder.
5. Tie the string. Hang your bird feeder outside.

Checkpoint
Tell a story about an animal or plant. Tell how people have helped it live.

B 55

- Some children may need assistance tying a knot at the end of the string.
- You may want to poke a hole in the milk carton so that children have a starting point to cut their circles.
- *See Equipment Kit Teacher's Guide for additional hints.*

Raise Questions

Ask: *How can your bird feeders help birds survive?* (by providing food) Encourage children to think of other ways they could help birds survive. (Answers might include building a birdhouse or protecting the trees where birds build nests.)

Close

Check for Understanding

- As a follow-up to the **baseline assessment,** ask children if there is anything they want to add to or change on their poster.
- **Answers to Checkpoint** Stories should describe situations in which people helped the living thing by protecting its habitat, providing a habitat, or adding needed things to its habitat.

Connecting Lessons

In the next lesson, children will learn the snow leopard, an endangered animal, is being helped by zoos. ▶

Explorer's Activity Guide

Use Explorer's Activity Guide hands-on activity on pages 77–78 to help children answer the question, "How can people help living things?"

Teacher's Assessment Package

A **scoring rubric** to assess student performance is provided on page 37 of the Teacher's Assessment Package.

Activity Results

Children should make a bird feeder that is sturdy and practical. Children can watch for birds like cardinals, chickadees, and finches to come to their feeders. Remind children that it may take a few days for birds to find the feeder.

Extend the Lesson

Encourage children to observe their bird feeders at scheduled times over a two-week period. Have children keep journals of their observations. Information they should **record** includes the number of birds they see at the feeder and how often the birdseed needs to be replenished.

Lesson 8

Lesson Objective

Children learn that the snow leopard is an endangered animal and that its numbers are increasing in zoo habitats. **Skills:** Organizing information, solving problems

Introduce

Invite Learning

Invite children to pantomime how their favorite animal at the zoo acts. Other children can try to guess the animal. Ask if anyone knows how a snow leopard acts. Ask how the class could find out.

Make Connections

To **assess prior knowledge,** ask children to name reasons that we have zoos. Accept all reasonable answers. Make a list of their reasons on chart paper and save it as a **baseline assessment.**

Teach

Observe and Listen

- Divide the class into small groups to study the chart on page B56.
- Have children discuss what information the chart shows. Encourage children to ask and answer one another's questions.
- Allow children to work in their groups to complete the chart and answer any questions they might have.

How do zoos help endangered animals?

The snow leopard is endangered. People took some snow leopards to live in zoos. In zoos, snow leopards get everything they need to live. Baby snow leopards are born at zoos. The number of snow leopards is getting bigger.

1. Look at the chart. It shows about how many snow leopards were born in zoos for four years. How many snow leopards were born in zoos in 1990?

year	number of snow leopards born in zoos
1990	30
1991	20
1992	50
1993	60

Science Idea Exchange

Science Background

The coat of the snow leopard helps camouflage the animal in its snowy habitat, making the leopard less noticeable to its prey. However, this unusual coat has made the animal a target of fur traders. Because so many snow leopards have been killed for their fur, the species is endangered.

Science and Language Arts

Have children imagine they are a snow leopard that was just placed in a zoo. Challenge them to create a story describing what it is like to live there.

Science and Art

Suggest that children make a poster encouraging people to come to the zoo to see the snow leopards. Children may want to include information on the poster about how people in zoos help snow leopards. Display the posters in the classroom or school hallway.

2. Draw a chart like this one.

year	number of snow leopards born in zoos
1990	░░░░░░░░░░░░░░░░░░░░░░░
1991	
1992	
1993	

0   5   10   15   20   25   30   35   40   45   50   55   60

3. The chart shows about how many snow leopards were born in zoos in 1990. Fill in the chart for 1991, 1992, and 1993.

Checkpoint

1. In which year were the most snow leopards born?

2. How can taking endangered animals to zoos help the animals?

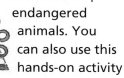

B 57

Ask for Evidence

Invite children to study their finished graphs and to **contrast** 1990 with 1991, 1992, and 1993. Ask: *How are they different?* (1991 has the shortest bar.) *What does this mean?* (The fewest number of snow leopards were born in 1991.) Have children **order** the years from fewest number of snow leopard births to the largest number of births. (1991, 1990, 1992, 1993)

Close

Check for Understanding

- As a follow-up to the **baseline assessment**, ask children if there are any reasons they would like to add to or subtract from the list they made in Make Connections.
- **Answers to Checkpoint** 1. 1993 2. A zoo provides the animals with a safe habitat to live in and food to eat.

Connecting Lessons

In the next lesson, children will make a book to show the concepts they learned in this chapter. ▶

Explorer's Activity Guide

Use Explorer's Activity Guide page 79 to help children solve the question of how zoos help endangered animals. You can also use this hands-on activity page to evaluate how well children understand the concept of this lesson.

Math/Science Connection

Provide further practice with charts by suggesting children work in groups to chart other information. For example, children might make a chart of the number and kinds of animals that class members have as pets.

Explore Further

You could call a nearby zoo to find out if they have any endangered animals there. You might also wish to invite a zookeeper to speak to the class about how zoos help animals.

Lesson 9

Lesson Objective
Children make a book to show the concepts they learned in this chapter.

Introduce

Invite Learning
Review the **baseline assessment** activities you used in this chapter. Choose one or more to do again that you think will help children understand the chapter concepts.

Teach

Performance Assessment Activity
Children make a book illustrating the concepts they have learned.
Skills: Describing, restating ideas

Materials (per group)
Module Kit Items: none
School Supplied Items: construction paper *(2 sheets/child);* white paper *(4 sheets/child);* crayons; pencils

Helpful Hints
- You may wish to have children look back to previous lesson illustrations to identify an extinct or endangered plant or animal.
- *See Equipment Kit Teacher's Guide for additional hints.*

What did you learn?

You know that the world of dinosaurs changed. The world of other animals and plants changes too. You read about some of these changes. You can make a book that shows what you learned.

You will need: 4 sheets of paper pencil crayons  construction paper

Make a book.
1. Draw a picture of an extinct animal.
2. Draw an endangered animal or plant.
3. Draw a picture that shows polluted air or polluted water.
4. Draw a picture of one way people can help living things.
5. Make a cover for your book. Put the pages inside the cover.

B 58

 # Science Idea Exchange

Teacher's Assessment Package

Use the pages from the Teacher's Assessment Package at this time to promote **performance assessment** opportunities for your children.

Collaborative Learning: Cooperative Learning
Assign specific children to gather and clean up materials. All children in the Chapter Review group should be involved in planning the book and in sharing answers. Also, each child in the group can be assigned a specific role:
- one who draws an extinct animal and an endangered plant or animal;
- one who draws a picture showing pollution;
- one who draws a picture showing people helping living things;
- one who uses the construction paper to make a book cover and places the pages inside.

Share what you learned.

1. What living things did you draw?

2. What does your book show about habitats?

3. How might the world look when you grow up?

Ask for Evidence

Have children describe their books to their classmates and answer any questions they may have.

Ask Open-ended Questions

Ask children for their thoughts on why more than 50 species of birds and over 75 species of mammals have become extinct during the last 200 years. (Answers may include pollution, loss of habitat, or hunting.)

Close

Check for Understanding

● As a follow-up to the **baseline assessment** in the Discover Activity, have children look at their drawings of what they think happened to the dinosaurs. Based on what they have learned in the previous lessons, ask them how they might change their drawings.

● **Answers to Share what you learned**
1. Answers will vary but may include living things discussed in the chapter.
2. The book should show that changes in a living thing's habitat can have a negative effect on that living thing.
3. Accept all answers, but ask for reasons. For example, some children may say fewer trees because of construction. But other children may say more trees because people will want to plant trees.

Explorer's Activity Guide

Use Explorer's Activity Guide pages 81–82 as a hands-on activity to evaluate how well children understand the concepts covered in this chapter.

Activity Results

Children's books should show an understanding of concepts covered in the chapter, including how plants and animals become extinct, what causes plants or animals to become endangered species, causes of water and air pollution, and the ways that people can help protect living things.

Your Ideas

_____

_____

_____

_____

_____

People at Work

Nature of work

At many museums, conservators are in charge of the museum's collections; conservators prepare the collections for exhibition and give lectures and demonstrations. Other museum workers, called preparators, prepare the actual exhibits. These workers might repair fossil bones, make fossil casts, build the steel understructure to support a fossil skeleton, construct the background needed for an exhibit, and paint any necessary scenery.

Places of Work

Because most museums are located in cities, most jobs for museum workers are also in cities. However, sometimes preparators for a museum of natural history visit digs.

Training

A museum can specialize in an area such as natural history, science and technology, art, history, or horticulture. An outdoor museum may specialize in horticulture. At a museum of natural history, the preparators are often skilled craftspeople, graphic designers, or artists.

Preparation

Children who are interested in working with fossils and other artifacts can begin by building a collection of fossils, rocks, shells, or leaves.

People at Work

A visit to a museum

You walk into the museum. A dinosaur skeleton is there. Wire holds the bones together. But who put the bones together?

Scientists sometimes find fossils of bones in rock. They send the rock to a museum. Then a **museum worker** digs the fossils out of the rock. Workers may use drills to dig out the fossils. At last, the fossils are out of the rock. Then museum workers put the skeleton together.

Science Idea Exchange

Examine the Career

Ask children to suggest qualities a museum worker would need (patience while working with small objects, an ability to solve problems, and a good imagination).

Explore Further

For children interested in learning more about museum work, you might invite someone from a local museum to speak to the class. Perhaps the guest could bring a rock containing a fossil and demonstrate how the fossil is removed from the rock.

How does a drill work?

1 Air moves in and out through tubes.

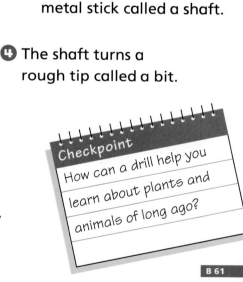

2 The air pushes against the blades and turns them.

3 The blades turn a long metal stick called a shaft.

4 The shaft turns a rough tip called a bit.

5 The bit scrapes away small pieces of rock.

Checkpoint

How can a drill help you learn about plants and animals of long ago?

B 61

Science Background

You may wish to share with children some of the following information about museum work.

- Museum workers sometimes use an X ray to help them locate a fossil that is completely embedded in a rock.
- Sensitive tools, similar to dental tools, can be used to reveal a fossil. For instance, extremely small drill bits are used to cut through rock. An air jet or air brush can be used to blow away the excess stone.
- Depending on the material, it can take several hours or even several days to safely remove a small, delicate fossil from a stone or rock.
- At the site of a fragile fossil find, a form might be built around the rock or material containing the fossil. The form is filled with plaster and the entire block of plaster, containing the rock and its fossil, may be shipped to a laboratory or museum for study. The plaster package protects both the rock and the fossil in it until workers are ready to remove the fossil for study.

Discussion

If possible show children several different tools such as drills, brushes, scalpels, and tweezers. Ask children what workers might use each tool for and what problems might occur when using the tool.

Answers to Checkpoint

A drill can be used to remove the rock from around plant and animal fossils. The fossils are then studied in order to understand more about the plants and animals that the fossils are formed from and to find out how the fossils formed.

Collaborative Learning: Small Groups

Have groups of three children prepare and present a brief play about museum workers trying to dig dinosaur bones from their rocky bed. Encourage children to talk about the problems they encounter in trying not to damage the bones.

Show What You Know

- You might want to share *Dinosaurs, Dragonflies, and Diamonds* by Gail Gibbons (Four Winds Press, 1988) before the lesson. This book tells about exhibits in natural history museums.

- You can use the first paragraph in the text to begin assessing what children know about dinosaurs and fossils. Children can generate a list of items they might include in the museum as you record their ideas on the chalkboard.

- Help children understand that a museum of natural history displays accurate models and real-life objects for people to see and sometimes to touch.

Plan Your Museum

Have children list their steps verbally or in writing before doing their projects. Ask how they will share their projects. Some children may prefer visual presentations, while others prefer oral presentations.

Assessment Projects

- **Make an exhibit** Suggest that children pretend that their fossils are from long ago. Have them describe methods of searching for fossils and how fossils help tell about the past.

Module Review

Show what you know.

Where can you find fossils? Where can you learn about dinosaurs? You can go to a museum. A museum has objects that tell about life long ago. You can make a museum in your classroom. What can you put in your museum?

Plan a museum.

1. Pick a project you would like to do.
2. Find things you need to do your project.
3. Think about how to describe your project to someone else.

Make an exhibit.

Make your own fossil for the museum. Write a story about your fossil. Tell how your fossil formed. Display your fossil and the story.

B 62

Science Idea Exchange

Develop a Project

Children may choose to do one of the projects in the book, or they may be able to develop one of the ideas from the class list suggested above in Show What You Know into a project for the museum.

Explorer's Activity Guide

For a **Home/School Connection,** use Explorer's Activity Guide pages 83–84. This letter home describes the concepts children have learned in this module and also provides a hands-on activity that the family can do together.

Using Multiple Intelligences (See page T5.)

The projects presented on these pages provide the opportunity for children to show their understanding of concepts using their strongest individual problem-solving abilities, or intelligences. The chart at right shows which of the seven intelligences are developed within each project and which chapter concepts each project assesses.

Act out a story.

Act out a story about a dinosaur. Show how your dinosaur moved. Show other things about your dinosaur. How will you show why there are no more dinosaurs?

Tape-record a story.

Tape-record a story for the museum. Tell how living things can become endangered or extinct. Tell how people can help protect living things. Draw pictures for your story.

Share what you know.
1. Share your project about dinosaurs with your classmates.
2. What was fun about doing your project?

B 63

Assessment Projects (cont'd.)

- **Act out a story** Invite children to make a dinosaur model or use one they made in an earlier lesson to act out the story. They can also act as dinosaurs themselves. They should show what their dinosaur ate. Encourage children to include sound effects.
- **Tape-record a story** Children's stories should explain how changes in habitats affect living things and how this sometimes leads to the endangering or extinction of organisms. Children's pictures should illustrate their tape recordings.

Share What You Know

1. Encourage children to share their projects in a format that is comfortable for them: large group, small group, or one-on-one.
2. Encourage children to think about what they liked about their projects. Invite them to share their thoughts with the class. Ask them if they would have done any part of their project differently.

Performance Assessment

The module assessment projects can be used as performance assessment activities.

Museum

Project	Intelligence	Chapters Covered
Exhibit	visual/spatial verbal/linguistic	1, 2, 3
Acting out a story	body/kinesthetic visual/spatial verbal/linguistic	1, 2, 3
Tape recording	verbal/linguistic visual/spatial	3

Family/School Partnership: Progress Report

Share with families their child's progress in the following areas:
- makes and records observations
- compares and contrasts objects
- classifies in more than one way
- experiments to solve problems
- asks questions and communicates information

Math/Science Connection

Calculate Footprints Across the Classroom

Review with the children different kinds of dinosaurs they learned about. Invite children to discuss how dinosaurs varied in size. How did dinosaur footprints vary in size? How might dinosaur footprints compare in size to children's own shoeprints?

PROBLEM
Challenge children to compare the footprints of a theropod such as *Tyrannosaurus* with their own shoeprints. Children will find out how many dinosaur footprints it takes to go across the classroom. Then they will compare this number to the number of their own shoeprints it takes to go across the classroom.

Materials (per group)
cover goggles, 8 sheets construction paper, theropod dinosaur footprint pattern, glue, scissors

Advance Preparation: Tape 4 sheets of construction paper together to use as a base for the pattern. Prepare patterns for dinosaur theropod footprints by drawing a footprint like the one shown here, 1 meter in length.

SOLVE THE PROBLEM
- Have each team of children glue a dinosaur footprint pattern on construction paper. Have them follow the pattern to cut out the construction-paper footprint.

- Guide teams as they place their dinosaur footprints end-to-end across the room. Have children count and record the number of footprints it takes to go across the classroom.

- Have each team member trace around his or her shoe on a piece of construction paper. Then have them cut out the construction paper shoeprints.

- Ask each team to predict how many of their shoeprints it will take to go across the classroom. Then have children place the shoeprints end-to-end across the classroom. Have them count and record the number of shoeprints it takes to reach across the room.

Share the Solutions
Help children organize their information about the numbers of footprints and shoeprints it takes to reach across the classroom. Then help them record the information on a class bar graph or table. Encourage children to compare the number of theropod footprints that it takes to go across the room with the number of their shoeprints it takes to go the same distance. Then discuss the following questions:
- Does it take more of the dinosaur footprints or your shoeprints to go across the classroom?

- How many more of one kind of print did it take to go across the room?

- When you are an adult, will it take the same number of your shoeprints to reach across the room as it does now? Why or why not?

Assess for Success

Observe how well students:

✓ count the total number of dinosaur footprints and shoeprints placed end-to-end across the classroom,

✓ help make a bar graph or table that shows the relationship between the number of dinosaur footprints and shoeprints,

✓ calculate the difference between the number of shoeprints and dinosaur footprints, and

✓ draw inferences on how the changing size of their foot as they grow will change the number of their shoeprints that would fit in the same space.

EXTEND THE PROBLEM

Review the numbers of dinosaur footprints and shoeprints from each team that fit across the classroom. Then have children add the numbers from all the groups for each category.

Ask children to name objects in the classroom that are about the same size as the dinosaur footprints. Then have children measure the footprints and the objects and compare the measurements.

Students may use handprint patterns. Invite them to predict how many handprints placed end-to-end it will take to go across the classroom. Compare the number of handprints to the number of dinosaur footprints. Then compare the number of handprints to the number of shoeprints.

Your Ideas

Making Things Move

Module C

C 1

Module C Planning Guide
Making Things Move

Module At-a-Glance

Lessons/Concepts

Themes: *Systems and Interactions, Energy*

In this module, children discover that in order for an object to be moved, a force must be applied. Children also learn about some properties and uses of magnets and that machines can make moving objects easier.

Activity Opportunities

Pupil's Edition	Teacher's Edition/Ancillaries

Discover Activity p. C5
Activity p. C11
Activity p. C13
Let's Explore pp. C14–C15
Activity p. C17
Let's Solve It! pp. C18–C19
Chapter Review pp. C20–C21
	Explorer's Activity Guide
	  pp. 85–99
	ExploraCenter Teacher's Guide
	  pp. 19, 21, 23, 34, 35
	Videodisc Classroom
	  Guide pp. 25–32
	Interactive Transparency
	  Guide pp. 24–25
	Interactive Videodisc Software
	  Teacher's Guide pp. 62–70

Discover Activity p. C23
Let's Explore pp. C26–C27
Let's Explore pp. C30–C31
Activity p. C33
Activity p. C35
Let's Solve It! pp. C36–C37
Chapter Review pp. C38–C39
	Explorer's Activity Guide
	  pp. 101–110
	ExploraCenter Teacher's Guide
	  pp. 10, 21, 23
	Videodisc Classroom
	  Guide pp. 25–32
	Interactive Transparency
	  Guide pp. 26–27
	Interactive Videodisc Software
	  Teacher's Guide pp. 62–70

Discover Activity p. C41
Activity p. C45
Activity p. C47
Let's Explore pp. C48–C49
Let's Explore pp. C54–C55
Let's Solve It! pp. C56–C57
Chapter Review pp. C58–C59
	Explorer's Activity Guide
	  pp. 111–124
	ExploraCenter Teacher's Guide
	  pp. 8, 10, 11, 19, 21, 23,
	  33, 34, 35
	Videodisc Classroom
	  Guide pp. 25–32
	Interactive Transparency
	  Guide pp. 28–29
	Interactive Videodisc Software
	  Teacher's Guide pp. 62–70

	Explorer's Activity Guide • Family letter pp. 125–126 **Teacher's Edition** • Math/Science Connection pp. C63a–C63b

Assessment Opportunities
(CONTENT • PORTFOLIO • PERFORMANCE)

Pupil's Edition	Teacher's Edition/Ancillaries

Checkpoint pp. C7, C8, C11,
  C13, C15, C17, C19
Chapter Review
  Performance Assessment
  Activity pp. C20–C21
	Teacher's Edition
	 • Check for Understanding
	  pp. C5, C7, C9, C11, C13,
	  C15, C17, C19, C21
	Teacher's Assessment Package
	 • Activity Rubrics pp. 47–48
	 • Chapter Test pp. 49–50
	Explorer's Activity Guide
	 • Chapter Review pp. 97–99

Checkpoint pp. C25, C27–C28,
  C31, C33, C35, C37
Chapter Review
  Performance Assessment
  Activity pp. C38–C39
	Teacher's Edition
	 • Check for Understanding
	  pp. C23, C25, C27, C29,
	  C31, C33, C35, C37, C39
	Teacher's Assessment Package
	 • Activity Rubrics pp. 53–54
	 • Chapter Test pp. 55–56
	Explorer's Activity Guide
	 • Chapter Review p. 110

Checkpoint pp. C43, C45, C47,
  C49, C51, C52, C55, C57
Chapter Review
  Performance Assessment
  Activity pp. C58–C59
	Teacher's Edition
	 • Check for Understanding
	  pp. C41, C43, C45, C47,
	  C49, C51, C53, C55, C57,
	  C59
	Teacher's Assessment Package
	 • Activity Rubrics pp. 59–60
	 • Chapter Test pp. 61–62
	Explorer's Activity Guide
	 • Chapter Review pp. 123–124

Module Review pp. C62–C63	**Teacher's Assessment Package** • Performance Assessment Test pp. 65–66

Module C Event
Moving Circus

Planning

A Moving Circus, showing various methods of moving things, can be a stimulating performance assessment for this module.

To prepare for this event, you might want to accumulate the drawings and other products from activities children do throughout the module.

Getting Started

Motion is everywhere around us—people and objects move or are moved from one place to another. The Discover Activities in chapters 1, 2, and 3 focus children's attention on moving objects and the pushes or pulls that move those objects. The children's charts comparing motion across surfaces, their electromagnets, and their models of muscles can form the basis of rings in the circus.

Activity Options

Language Arts Connection

The activity in Chapter 3 showing how muscles work can be a springboard for a circus exhibit. Suggest children make additional cardboard-and-balloon muscle models to demonstrate the motions they might see at a circus. Encourage children to provide a one-word description for each model. Suggest they use action verbs, such as "walking," "jumping," "swinging," "running," "turning," or "leaping." Children can place the muscle models in the center ring of the Moving Circus.

Multicultural Connection

Many of the kinds of animals you see in a circus were trained centuries ago to carry heavy loads. The horse, elephant, and camel moved ancient Egyptians, Romans, and Asians across deserts and mountains. Asiatic elephants were used to move tree trunks and other heavy objects in some Asian countries. Elephants are still used today for these purposes. Invite children to draw pictures or to collect magazine photographs showing these forms of work or transportation. Have children write a short story to explain how and why many of these animals could help set up the tents of a traveling circus.

Social Studies Connection

Help children recognize that the methods used to move objects and people may depend on the landscape, the weather, and the needs of the people. For example, some Inuit of Canada use dog sleds; others use snowmobiles. Encourage children to choose a location such as a mountainous region or a dense forest. Have them draw or make a model of a method of transportation, using either machines or animals, that could be used to move a circus to that location. Place these drawings and models along a path between the rings of the Moving Circus.

The activities on these pages provide the opportunity for students to use their strongest individual problem-solving abilities, or intelligences. The chart shows which of the seven intelligences are developed within each activity option. In addition, all students can develop interpersonal intelligence as they participate in the Module Event, Moving Circus.

Activity	Intelligences
Language Arts Connection	body/kinesthetic
Multicultural Connection	verbal/linguistic
Social Studies Connection	visual/spatial
Art Connection	visual/spatial

Art Connection

Invite children to design several pieces of circus equipment for acrobats, trapeze artists, or clowns. Help children recognize that each piece of equipment may include a machine, such as a springboard, a ramp, or a unicycle. Allow children to build a model or draw equipment that uses a combination of machines. Encourage children to show which parts of the equipment are ball bearings, wheels, ramps, or levers. Post the artwork at the entrance to the Moving Circus.

Let Parents Try It

Set up a side table or booth at the circus where parents and guardians can try their hand at magnetic fishing. Children can make a variety of fish from construction paper and attach a small magnet to each. Visitors to the booth would use a stick and string fishing line, with a magnet attached, to catch the fish. To attract more interest, have children write a point value on each of the fish and encourage visitors to catch the most valuable fish in the pond.

The Big Event

Set up tables, booths, or areas in your room to fit the choices you made from the Activity Options. Place a yarn or construction-paper circle on each of three or four tables to make "circus rings" for the display.

Place children's artwork in a side ring or near the entrance to the Moving Circus. Volunteers can monitor this exhibit and answer any questions the visitors might have. Children can take turns monitoring the center ring and demonstrating the movements shown in the models of how muscles work. Invite visitors to the event to duplicate the motions.

Encourage children to take turns at each exhibit explaining to visitors how the items in the exhibit help people and objects move.

Module C
Across the Curriculum

Science Background

Newton's Laws

Born in 1642, Isaac Newton wrote the laws of physics that describe motion today. His first law, the law of inertia, explains that an object at rest, or in motion in a straight line at constant speed, tends to maintain that state unless compelled to change by forces exerted upon it.

Newton's second law states that the acceleration produced by moving an object depends not only on the force (push or pull) exerted, but on the mass of the object as well. For example, a person would have to push harder to make a grocery cart move when it is full of groceries than when it is empty.

Newton's third law explains that whenever one object exerts a force on a second object, the second object exerts an equal and opposite force on the first object. Forces occur in pairs in every interaction. One force is called action force, and the other is called reaction force. An example of this is when a swimmer interacts with water.

Electromagnets at Work

An electromagnet is a piece of metal wound with a wire that becomes magnetized when a current flows through the wire. There are two basic principles of electromagnetism. One is that electricity in motion creates a magnetic field. The second is that a magnetic field that moves across an electric field produces an electromotive force.

Electromagnets have many industrial uses. One of the latest technological advances is the maglev, or magnetically elevated train, that moves over, not on, rails at speeds faster than 200 km per hour. Scientists and transportation specialists from all over the world are interested in how this train will make travel by rail safer, faster, and more energy efficient.

Science Across Cultures

Animals and Moving

Many different animals help people move and carry objects in different parts of the world. Some of the first Europeans trying to reach the South Pole used ponies to pull their sleds through the Antarctic wilderness. These explorers were unsuccessful in reaching their goal. Other explorers, who followed the example of the people living in arctic areas by relying on teams of dogs to pull the sleds, reached the South Pole. In some regions of Alaska and Canada, teams of dogs are still used to pull sleds over the snow. In other snow-covered regions, such as Siberia, teams of reindeer pull sleighs over snow.

In many regions of the world, including parts of Africa and India, people rely on oxen for riding. They also use oxen as pack animals. In these areas, oxen pull the plows of many local farmers. In the desert regions of Egypt and the Middle East, camels carry people and goods, pull carts, and even race.

In mountainous regions, where roads and paths are often steep and narrow, people use mountain-dwelling animals to carry goods. For example, shepherds in Tibet rely on the yak and Andean farmers rely on the llama.

Goats probably were tamed more than 9,000 years ago by people who lived in Asia and the Eastern Mediterranean region. Today, goats are important farm animals throughout the world, especially in mountainous areas.

Cross-curricular Activities

The activities in this module provide many opportunities to make connections between science and other areas of the elementary curriculum.

In addition, the wide variety of cross-curricular activities helps make learning both interesting and fun!

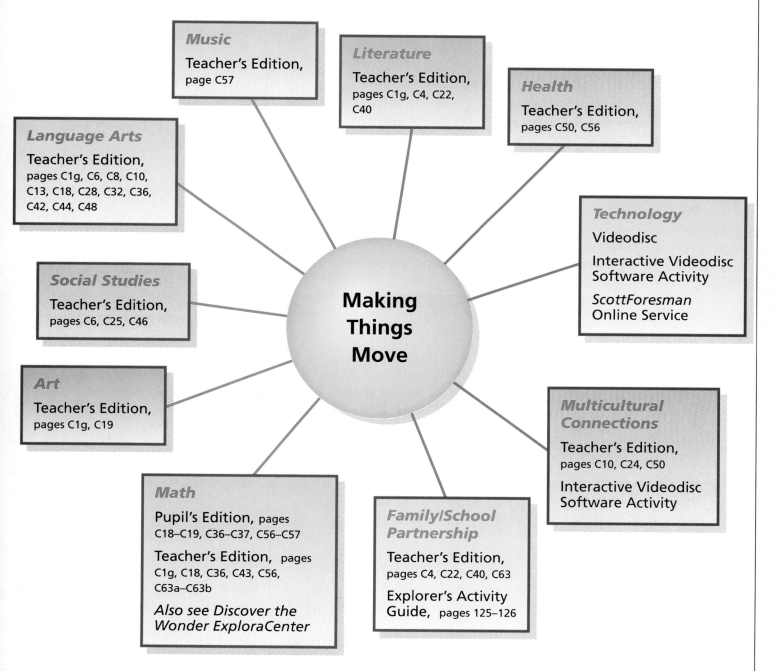

Music
Teacher's Edition, page C57

Literature
Teacher's Edition, pages C1g, C4, C22, C40

Health
Teacher's Edition, pages C50, C56

Language Arts
Teacher's Edition, pages C1g, C6, C8, C10, C13, C18, C28, C32, C36, C42, C44, C48

Social Studies
Teacher's Edition, pages C6, C25, C46

Art
Teacher's Edition, pages C1g, C19

Making Things Move

Technology
Videodisc

Interactive Videodisc Software Activity

ScottForesman Online Service

Multicultural Connections
Teacher's Edition, pages C10, C24, C50

Interactive Videodisc Software Activity

Math
Pupil's Edition, pages C18–C19, C36–C37, C56–C57

Teacher's Edition, pages C1g, C18, C36, C43, C56, C63a–C63b

Also see Discover the Wonder ExploraCenter

Family/School Partnership
Teacher's Edition, pages C4, C22, C40, C63

Explorer's Activity Guide, pages 125–126

Module C
Links to Literature

Introducing the Literature Library Selection

The literature library selection for this module is *Ferryboat* by Betsy and Giulio Maestro (Crowell, 1986). In this story, a family crosses a river on a ferryboat and observes how the ferry operates. During their trip they see many machines in action, including a loading ramp, a lever, and wheels (on cars, a bicycle, and a baby carriage).

In addition to the module literature selection, each chapter has a companion book.

- *Cars and How They Go* by Joanna Cole, illustrated by Gail Gibbons (Crowell, 1983), offers simple text to explain the parts of a car. Friendly illustrations present automotive systems in a "how it works" and a "where it's located" format.
- *Switch On, Switch Off* by Melvin Berger (Crowell, 1989) tells about the use of magnets in electricity. It explains how children can use a magnet and wire to make electricity.
- In *Machines at Work* by Byron Barton (Crowell, 1987), simple illustrations and minimal text present a busy day at a construction site. Workers use a variety of heavy equipment to knock down an old building and begin construction of a new one.

Activity Corner

Cross-Curricular Activities

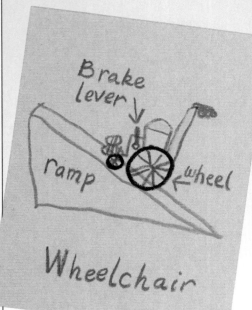

Math

- **Sorting and Counting**
  Write on the chalkboard the names of the following simple machines: a wheel, a ramp, a lever. Then have children name as many objects for each category as they can. Help children total the number of objects in each group. Then ask children to determine which category has the largest number of objects and which has the fewest.

Language Arts

- **Retelling a Story** Review the kinds of pushes and pulls children see in action in the story; then have them retell the story using the words to describe the motions they observe.

Art

- **Drawing Pictures** Have children draw pictures of objects with wheels, ramps, and levers. Have them write the name of the machine at the bottom of their picture.

Beginning with the Bulletin Board

Making Connections

Have children discuss the objects that are in motion in each picture in *Ferryboat* by Betsy and Giulio Maestro. Then have children make their own drawings of each object.

You will need:

 index cards

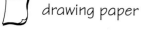 drawing paper

 safety scissors

 crayons

 pushpins

tape

Preparing the Bulletin Board

Label the top of the bulletin board *Motion* and provide a background that shows a ferryboat crossing a body of water. Label the left side of the bulletin board *Strong push or pull*; label the right side of the board *Weak push or pull.*

Bulletin Board Activity

Have children draw, color, and then cut out pictures of moving

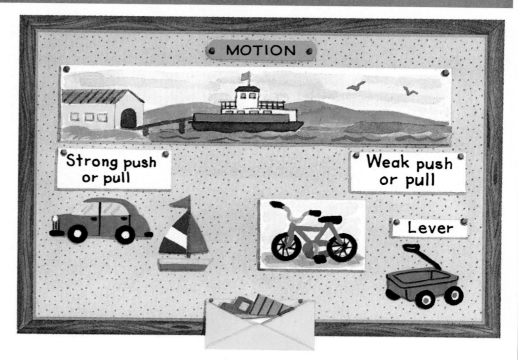

things that were seen on the ferryboat trip. Encourage them to include any moving cars, sailboats, trucks, bicycles, baby carriages, gates, elevators, rowboats, oars, pulleys, wheels on cars, and the different movements of people at work and play. Place the drawings and cutouts in a large envelope attached to the bulletin board.

Invite children to take pictures from the envelope and attach them to the appropriate section of the bulletin board. Have children decide whether an object would require a strong force or a weak force to move it. Have them analyze which objects require pulls and which require

pushes. Allow children to discuss any pictures that can be placed in more than one section of the bulletin board. Invite children to give reasons for the placements they chose. Ask if they can classify in any other ways the movements of the objects.

Extend the Activity

Write the names of machines such as a lever, wheel, and ramp on several index cards. Invite volunteers to attach the labels to the machines shown on the bulletin board. Allow children to discuss any picture that could have more than one machine label.

Making Things Move

You can move your body in different ways. You can make objects move too. Sometimes moving things is not as easy as it looks. Can you make moving things easier?

Chapter 1

How Things Move

It might be easy for you to move a small toy. But you might need to use a strong force to move something heavy. Page **C 4**

C2

Chapter 2
Magnets

How can one object push some things away and pull other things closer? Welcome to the amazing world of magnets! Page **C 22**

Chapter 3
Moving and Machines

You probably know how to use some kinds of machines. How do machines make moving things easier? Page **C 40**

C 3

Chapter 1 Planning Guide
How Things Move

Lessons / *Skills*

Lesson 1
Discover Activity: **How can you make a boat move?** pp. C4–C5
(recognizing cause and effect, solving problems)

Lesson 2
What makes things move? pp. C6–C7
(observing, describing)

Lesson 3
Where are the pushes and pulls? pp. C8–C9
(observing, classifying)

Lesson 4
How can you move something farther? pp. C10–C11
(comparing, drawing conclusions)

Lesson 5
What do different forces do? pp. C12–C13
(measuring, recording, comparing, drawing conclusions)

Lesson 6
Let's Explore: **How does force move heavy things?** pp. C14–C15
(measuring, recording, predicting)

Lesson 7
Where is it easier to pull things? pp. C16–C17
(comparing)

Lesson 8
Let's Solve It!: **What surfaces make moving things easier?**
pp. C18–C19
(organizing information, solving problems)

Lesson 9
Chapter Review: **What did you learn?** pp. C20–C21
(recognizing patterns and relationships, summarizing)

Materials (per group)

Lesson 1 Activity: *How can you make a boat move?*
Module Kit Items: craft stick; piece of clay; plastic pan; wood block
School Supplied Items: paper square; container of water *(about 4 L)*; glue

Lesson 4 Activity: *Push the can.*
Module Kit Items: masking tape *(at least 5 short pieces)*
School Supplied Item: soup or juice can

Lesson 5 Activity: *Use different forces.*
Module Kit Items: large rubber band; wooden ruler
School Supplied Items: paper; pencil
Safety Kit Items: cover goggles *(1/child)*

Lesson 6 Activity: *How does force move heavy things?*
Module Kit Items: piece of string *(about 1 m)*; large rubber band; wooden ruler
School Supplied Items: 3 small books; mural paper
Safety Kit Items: cover goggles *(1/child)*
Advance Prep: Cut string into 1-m lengths ahead of time.

Lesson 7 Activity: *Slide the book.*
Module Kit Item: piece of string *(about 1 m)*
School Supplied Items: small book; rug *(or carpeted area)*
Advance Prep: Cut string into 1-m lengths ahead of time.

Lesson 9 Activity: *Make a poster.*
Module Kit Items: none
School Supplied Items: scissors; crayons; glue; old magazines; flip chart paper or poster board
Advance Prep: You will need to collect a good supply of old magazines for this activity. Child-centered publications work best.

	Content	Performance	Portfolio

Assessment Options

Teacher's Assessment Package
Chapter Test, pp. 49–50 — Content ✓, Portfolio ✓
Group Interview Assessment, p. 51 — Content ✓, Performance ✓
Performance Strategies, p. 52 — Content ✓, Performance ✓, Portfolio ✓

Explorer's Activity Guide
Activity worksheets, pp. 85–96 — Performance ✓, Portfolio ✓
Chapter Review, pp. 97–99 — Content ✓, Portfolio ✓

Interactive Transparency Package
Transparency 10 and BLM — Content ✓, Performance ✓, Portfolio ✓
Teacher's Guide, pp. 24–25 — Content ✓, Performance ✓
Hands-on activity for second-language learners — Content ✓, Performance ✓, Portfolio ✓

Science Literature Library
Cars and How They Go — Performance ✓, Portfolio ✓

Interactive Videodisc Software
Teacher's Guide, pp. 62–70
Computer-based Activity — Content ✓, Performance ✓
Journal Presentations — Content ✓, Performance ✓, Portfolio ✓

Videodisc Classroom Guide, pp. 25–32, or
Video Reader
Hands-on activity — Content ✓, Performance ✓, Portfolio ✓

ExploraCenter Teacher's Guide, pp. 19, 21, 23, 34, 35

ExploraCenter
Science activity cards 14, 16, 18, 29, 30 — Content ✓, Performance ✓, Portfolio ✓

ScottForesman Online Service
Online field trips — Content ✓✓, Performance ✓✓, Portfolio ✓✓

Chapter Overview

Children begin this chapter by thinking about what makes things move. They learn that a force is a push or pull that makes something move and that different strengths of forces are needed to do different things. As a culminating activity, children make a poster that shows pushes and pulls.

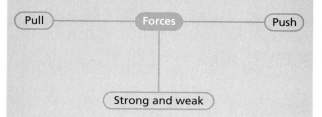

Pull — Forces — Push

Strong and weak

Lesson Objective
Children explore different ways to make objects move.

Introduce

Invite Learning
Show the videodisc segment for this chapter. Bar codes and a description of this segment are given below on page C5.

Make Connections
To **assess prior knowledge,** ask children to place a small common object, such as a pencil, on their desks. Have them list as many ways as they can to make the object move. Suggest they try them out. Children's lists can serve as a **baseline assessment** that you can use as a follow-up in Check for Understanding.

Teach

Discover Activity

Children demonstrate different ways to move a small boat. **Skills:** Recognizing cause and effect, solving problems

Materials (per group)
Module Kit Items: craft stick; piece of clay; plastic pan; wood block
School Supplied Items: paper square *(1/child)*; container of water *(about 4 L)*; glue

Chapter 1

How Things Move

Things are moving all around you. The leaves on a tree move. Clouds move across the sky. Cars, buses, and trains move on land. Airplanes move through the air.

Have you ever wondered what makes things move? Wind pushes these sailboats over the water. A person can use oars to pull the rowboat through the water. What makes the other boat move?

C 4

Science Idea Exchange

Collaborative Learning: Small Groups
Assign specific children to gather and clean up materials. All children in the Discover Activity group should be involved in making the boat, testing ways to move the boat, and sharing results.

Family/School Partnership: Family Support
Encourage families to be active partners in learning by suggesting that they and their children:
- observe objects being moved in different ways, and
- access the *Young America* electronic field trip presented by ScottForesman and Delphi Internet.

Science and Literature
Children may read *Cars and How They Go* by Joanna Cole (Crowell, 1983) to find out how a car's engine makes the car move. Invite children to push a toy car across their desk. Explain that their hand provides the push that moves the toy car.

Discover Activity

How can you make a boat move?

1. Use the objects you get from your teacher to make a boat.
2. Float your boat in a large pan of water.
3. Try different ways to make your boat move in the water.
4. Exchange boats with someone in your group.
5. **Tell about it.** Name two ways you can make your boat move.

Ask me what else I want to find out about how things move.

Helpful Hints

- A sailboat can be made by taping or gluing paper to the craft stick and placing this "sail" in clay that has been pressed onto the wood block.
- *See Equipment Kit Teacher's Guide for additional hints.*

What to Expect

Children may blow on the sail or pull and push the boat in a variety of ways.

Close

Check for Understanding

- As a follow-up to the **baseline assessment,** ask children to think of other ways to move their objects.
- **Answers to Tell about it** Post a class list of the words children used to **describe** how each boat was moved. Help children **classify** similar methods. (For example, blowing on the sail and pushing with the hand are both pushing.)

What Else Do You Want to Find Out?

Using a **constructivist** approach, ask: *What else would you like to know about how objects move? How can we find out?* Use the questions throughout the chapter to invite exploration.

Connecting Lessons

In the next lesson, children will learn that anything that moves needs a force—a push or a pull—to start it. ▶

Explorer's Activity Guide
The **Discover Activity recording sheets** on pages 87–88 of the Explorer's Activity Guide can be used by children to record their activity results.

Visual Literacy
Discover the Wonder Videodisc, Grade 2, Module C, provides video clips and stills to illustrate a variety of ways in which people use and change forces to move objects. Show these images to help children identify forces they use in their daily lives.

Bar Codes

Chapter 13: Video and Stills

Play

Step

Interactive Software

DISCOVER THE WONDER

Lesson Objective

Children discover that in order to move an object, they must push it or pull it and that a push or a pull is called force.

Introduce

Key Term

force

Invite Learning

Invite children to **name** all the objects that move in the literature selection *Ferryboat* by Betsy and Giulio Maestro (Crowell, 1986). On chart paper, record all the objects children name.

Make Connections

To **assess prior knowledge,** encourage children to identify whether each object on the list is being pushed or pulled. Record their responses as a **baseline assessment.** You can follow up on this assessment in Check for Understanding.

Teach

Observe and Listen

Invite children to bring in an object that moves or that they can make move, such as a toy. Have them work in small groups to **describe** to each other how their objects move. Listen to their choice of words, especially "push" and "pull."

What makes things move?

What did you do to make your boat move? You may have pulled it over the water with your fingers. Maybe you blew on the sail so that your breath pushed the boat. Your boat did not move by itself. You used a push or pull to make it move.

C 6

 ## Science Idea Exchange

Science Background

A force is a push or a pull that actually tends to cause movement. The word "tends" is important because a force can be exerted and no visible movement may occur. You can push against a solid wall, for example, and exert a force even though the wall does not appear to move.

Science and Language Arts

Invite children to write or tell a short story about their favorite thing to do at the school playground. Ask them to **describe** how it feels to climb a jungle gym, to swing high, to ride a seesaw, or to play games such as jump rope, tag, and hopscotch.

Science and Social Studies

Until about A.D. 800, farmers used oxen to pull their plows. Horses could not safely be used because the yoke straps cut across the horse's windpipe. Once the across-the-shoulder horse collar was designed, horses were able to pull with five times more power. They replaced oxen as field animals in most countries.

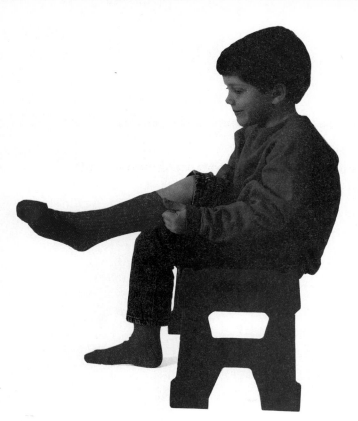

A push or pull that makes something move is a **force**. You might push a grocery cart. You might pull on your sock. What else can you push or pull?

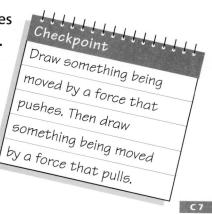

Checkpoint

Draw something being moved by a force that pushes. Then draw something being moved by a force that pulls.

C 7

Ask for Evidence

Ask: *Are any objects in the pictures moving by themselves?* (No, all are being pushed or pulled by someone.) *Could any of these objects ever move by themselves?* (No, they require a force to start them moving.)

Encourage Student Definitions

Invite children to demonstrate at their desks the meaning of the word "force." They might push against their desks or pull and push something on their desks.

Act as a Consultant

Help children recognize that they push or pull many objects during a day. Invite them to name objects they push or pull as they get ready for school.

Close

Check for Understanding

● As a follow-up to the **baseline assessment**, ask children to review the list they made in Make Connections. If children wish to make any changes, ask them what they learned that made them change their list.

●**Answers to Checkpoint** Children's drawings should show a clear distinction between a push and a pull.

Connecting Lessons

In the next lesson, children will identify a variety of pushing and pulling forces. ▶

Explorer's Activity Guide

Use Explorer's Activity Guide page 89 with this lesson to help children answer the text question,

"What makes things move?" with a hands-on activity.

Achieving English Proficiency

Have children demonstrate a push and a pull by alternately pushing and pulling a moderately heavy object, such as a box of books, across the room. Encourage them to say "push" or "pull" aloud as they apply force to the object.

Your Ideas

_____

_____

_____

_____

_____

Lesson 3

Lesson Objective
Children study a picture of a playground scene and identify the various pushing and pulling forces.

Introduce

Invite Learning
Invite children to examine an assortment of pictures that show a variety of movements such as people swimming, running, sailing, ice skating, or roller blading. Children might want to pantomime some of the movements.

Make Connections
To **assess prior knowledge,** ask children to apply self-stick notes marked "push" or "pull" on things they often move in the classroom by pushing and pulling. Examples might be desks, chairs, closet doors, windows, and erasers. Let the notes remain in place during the lesson as a **baseline assessment.**

Teach

Observe and Listen
Divide the class into small groups and suggest that each group **describe** the way each child on the playground moves an object. Encourage children to ask questions of each other and answer their questions themselves.

Where are the pushes and pulls?

Pretend you are at this playground. You can see pushes and pulls all around you. Find the girl playing in the sandbox. How is she using a push or pull?

How will the boys make the swings move? They could use a push or a pull to get them started. Find two other pushes and two other pulls.

Checkpoint
Tell about another push or pull you might see at a playground.

C 8

Science Idea Exchange

Science Background
Objects move only when acted on by a force. Once set in motion, an object will keep moving until another force stops it. This opposing force may be friction (resistance caused by the surface over which the object moves), air resistance (a form of friction), or gravity (when a ball is thrown).

Science and Language Arts
Dr. Doolittle's Circus by Hugh Lofting (J.B. Lippincott Company, 1967) describes the adventures of a two-headed animal named Pushmi-Pullyu. Show children a picture of the animal. Ask children how the animal got its name. Have them create their own imaginary animal and write or tell a short story about it.

Science Themes
By discussing different kinds of pushes and pulls, children develop an understanding of the themes of **energy** and **systems and interactions.**

C 9

Raise Questions

Have children consider answers to the following questions: *Would you move the objects on the playground in the same way as the children shown here? If not, how would you move them?* (Point out that no matter how they moved these objects, they would still use pushes and pulls.)

Act as a Consultant

Encourage children to discuss what happens if they try to move a wall or very heavy object. Help them think of several examples of pushes and pulls that do not result in movement.

Close

Check for Understanding

- As a follow-up to the **baseline assessment,** have children look at the labels they posted in Make Connections. Ask them if they would like to change any of their notes.
- **Answers to Checkpoint** Children should be able to describe another clear example of a push or a pull at a playground.

Connecting Lessons

In the next lesson, children will learn that the strength of an applied force affects how far an object will move. ▶

Explorer's Activity Guide

Use Explorer's Activity Guide page 90 with this lesson to help children answer the text question, "Where are the pushes and pulls?" with a hands-on activity.

Electronic Online Field Trip

To enhance your students' math, science, and technology literacy, access the *Young America* electronic field trip presented by ScottForesman and Delphi Internet.

Visual Literacy

To enhance the **visual literacy** connection, use the interactive overhead transparency that correlates with the above two pages. The transparency will help your students understand the key concepts presented on these pages.

Lesson 4

Lesson Objective
Children learn that the strength of an applied force affects how far an object moves.

Introduce

Invite Learning
Have children form two lines. Place a bucket about 1.5 m (5 ft) away from the first line and another bucket about 3 m (10 ft) away from the second line. Invite children to take turns trying to toss a small beanbag into the buckets. When everyone has had a turn, have the lines trade places.

Make Connections
To **assess prior knowledge,** ask children how they had to adjust their toss to get the beanbag in the bucket that was farther away. Record their answers as a **baseline assessment.**

Teach

Activity
Children demonstrate that the harder they push a can, the farther it rolls.
Skills: Comparing, drawing conclusions

Materials (per group)
Module Kit Items: masking tape *(at least 5 short pieces)*
School Supplied Item: soup or juice can

How can you move something farther?

Push a book across the floor. Use a weak push. How far does it move? What do you think will happen if you push the book using a strong push? Try it and see!

Does how hard you push the book change how far the book moves? You probably found the answer to that question. The book moves farther when you push it with a stronger force.

C 10

 Science Idea Exchange

Collaborative Learning: Small Groups
Assign specific children to gather and clean up materials. Each child in the Activity group should have an opportunity to push the can, mark where the can stops, and share observations.

Science and Language Arts
Invite children to pretend that they are sportscasters announcing the winning play of a game. Remind them to use what they have learned about forces to describe the exact movements of the players. They could use colorful but accurate speech.

Multicultural Connections
Games requiring skill in applying force are played by people all over the world. One such game is hopscotch. The patterns and the object tossed change, but the hopping motions are the same. In Aruba, in the Netherlands Antilles, the winds are so strong that stones that will not blow away must be used for tossing.

Push the can.

You will need: can  masking tape

1. Kneel at one end of your classroom. Use a weak push to roll the can toward the other side of the room.
2. Roll the can different ways. Use weak and strong pushes.
3. Mark with tape the place where your can stops each time.

Checkpoint

Tell what you did to make the can move the farthest.

C 11

Safety Tip
If empty cans are used, be sure the edges of each can are smooth, or tape any rough edges.

Hints and Tips
• Children can use full cans or empty cans for this activity.
• The distances the cans roll will depend on whether or not the classroom is carpeted.

Act as a Consultant
Help mark where the cans stop. Guide children to recognize that the distance the can rolls depends on whether they use a strong push or a weak push.

Close

Check for Understanding
• As a follow-up to the **baseline assessment,** have children explain and then demonstrate what happens when they toss a beanbag using a weak toss and then a strong toss. Ask which kind of toss uses more force.
• **Answers to Checkpoint** More force was used to make the can roll farther.

Connecting Lessons
In the next lesson, children will discover that the strength of applied forces can be varied and compared. ▶

Explorer's Activity Guide
Use Explorer's Activity Guide hands-on activity on pages 91–92 to help children answer: "How can you move something farther?"

Teacher's Assessment Package
A **scoring rubric** to assess student performance is provided on page 47 of the Teacher's Assessment Package.

Activity Results
The can moves farther when it is pushed with a stronger force.

Extend the Lesson
Challenge children to control a variable—the force of their roll. Ask them to roll the can once and then roll it again using less force. Children should say whether they're using more or less force. They can compare the distances of the rolls with the amount of force they said they used.

Lesson 5

Introduce

Invite Learning
Show pictures of a calm day, a windy day, and a day with hurricane-force winds. Allow children to share experiences of what happens to trees and other things outside when the wind's force becomes stronger.

Make Connections
To **assess prior knowledge,** have children draw pictures of someone sitting on a swing, someone swinging just a little, and someone swinging very high. Save their drawings as a **baseline assessment.**

Teach

Activity
Children compare the ways in which the strength of an applied force affects an object. **Skills:** Measuring, recording, comparing, drawing conclusions

Materials (per group)
Module Kit Items: large rubber band; metric ruler
School Supplied Items: paper; pencil
Safety Kit Items: cover goggles (1/child)

What do different forces do?

A push can be strong or weak. A pull can be strong or weak too. You can pull a swing. Will a strong pull or a weak pull make the swing move farther? How can you tell how strong a push or pull is?

C 12

Science Idea Exchange

Science Background
The greater the force used, the longer the rubber band stretches. However, the relationship is not necessarily linear because of the characteristics of the rubber band. For example, applying twice the force will not necessarily stretch the rubber band twice as far.

Collaborative Learning: Cooperative Learning
Assign specific children to gather and clean up materials. All children in the Activity group should draw their observations and share results. Also, each child in the group can be assigned a specific role:
- one who measures the unstretched rubber band;
- one who pulls the rubber band with a weak force and a strong force;
- one who measures the rubber band pulled with a weak force;
- one who measures the rubber band pulled with a strong force.

Use different forces.

You will need:  cover goggles   metric ruler

large rubber band   pencil   paper

1. Hold up the rubber band. Have a classmate measure it.
2. Pull on the rubber band with a weak force. Have a classmate measure how long the rubber band stretches.
3. Pull the rubber band with a stronger force. Have a classmate measure it.
4. Draw three lines. Show how long the rubber band was when you used no force, a weak force, and a strong force.

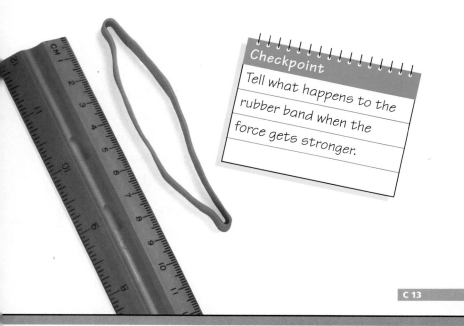

Checkpoint
Tell what happens to the rubber band when the force gets stronger.

C 13

Safety Tip
Caution children to keep the rubber bands away from their face and not to pull the rubber bands too hard.

Helpful Hints
- Have children label the lines "no force," "weak force," or "strong force" as soon as they are drawn.
- Results will vary depending on the strength of the force children use.

Ask for Evidence
Ask children to use their hands to show how long the rubber band was when pulled with a weak force and how long it was when pulled with a strong force.

Close

Check for Understanding
- As a follow-up to the **baseline assessment,** have children review their drawings and **compare** the forces that are used in sitting on a swing, swinging just a little, and swinging very high.
- **Answers to Checkpoint** The rubber band stretches farther as the force gets stronger.

Connecting Lessons
In the next lesson, children will discover that heavier objects require more force to move them. ▶

Explorer's Activity Guide
Use Explorer's Activity Guide hands-on activity on page 93 to help children answer the question, "What do different forces do?"

Teacher's Assessment Package
A **scoring rubric** to assess student performance is provided on page 47 of the Teacher's Assessment Package.

Activity Results
The rubber band should increase in length as children use more force. The three lines should show that the greater the force used, the more the rubber band stretched.

Science and Language Arts
Have children write a short poem telling how objects move farther when a greater force is applied. For example: "There was an old man from Kent. The higher he jumped, the farther he went. One day he jumped too low and had no place to go."

Lesson 6

Lesson Objective
Children learn that the heavier an object, the greater the force needed to move it.

Introduce

Invite Learning
Show children several objects such as a ball, a feather, a book, and a pumpkin. Ask whether a strong force or a weak force would be needed to push each. See if they can **order** the objects by the amount of force necessary.

Make Connections
To **assess prior knowledge,** have children draw an object that would move with a weak force and one that would require a stronger force. Save the drawings as a **baseline assessment.**

Teach

Activity
Children demonstrate the amount of force needed to move different objects.
Skills: Measuring, recording, predicting

Materials (per group)
Module Kit Items: piece of string *(about 1 m);* large rubber band; metric ruler
School Supplied Items: 3 small books; mural paper
Safety Kit Items: cover goggles *(1/child)*

How does force move heavy things?

Pretend you are pulling a wagon. A friend jumps in. The wagon is harder to move! Will you need to use more force to pull it?

Find out about it.

You will need:

 cover goggles

 large rubber band

 string

 3 small books

 mural paper

metric ruler

1 Tie one end of the string to the rubber band. Wrap the other end around the book.

2 Tie the two ends together.

3 Pull the rubber band straight. Make a mark at the end of the rubber band.

4 Pull the rubber band until the book moves. Hold the book in place. Have a classmate mark the paper to show the length of the rubber band.

5 Put two books on top of the first book. Repeat Step 4.

Science Idea Exchange

Collaborative Learning: Cooperative Learning
Assign specific children to gather and clean up materials. All children in the Let's Explore group should record data and share results. Also, each child in the group can be assigned a specific role:

- one who sets up the trials with one book and three books;
- one who pulls on the string to move one book;
- one who pulls on the string to move three books;
- one who measures how much the rubber band stretches to move one book and three books.

Explore Further
Sliding friction results when two solid surfaces slide across each other. Rolling friction, which occurs between the surface of a round object and another surface, opposes motion less than sliding friction. To demonstrate this concept, have children slide a toy wheel on its side, then roll the wheel with the same force. Suggest they compare the distances the wheel traveled.

Write about it. ✏️

Make a chart like this. Write how much the rubber band stretches to move the books.

📕	length of rubber band
before moving books	cm
moving 1 book	cm
moving 3 books	cm

Checkpoint

1. Which number of books needed the most force to be moved?

2. Take Action! Find out what will happen if you add another book.

C 15

Helpful Hints
- Books should all be the same size.
- Use thick rubber bands.
- *See Equipment Kit Teacher's Guide for additional hints.*

Act as a Consultant
Ask children to **predict:** *What would happen to the rubber band if you used heavier books?* (The rubber band would stretch more.) Then ask: *What would happen if you used lighter books?* (The rubber band would not stretch as much.) Have children test their predictions.

Close

Check for Understanding
- As a follow-up to the **baseline assessment,** ask children to add to their pictures from Make Connections showing what would happen if they tried pulling these objects with a rubber band. They should draw the changing length of the rubber band.
- **Answers to Checkpoint** 1. three 2. **Take Action!** The rubber band will stretch even more.

Connecting Lessons
In the next lesson, children will learn to compare the difference between sliding an object across a smooth surface and sliding it across a rough surface. ▶

Explorer's Activity Guide
Use Explorer's Activity Guide hands-on activity on page 94 to explore force and evaluate children's understanding of the lesson concept.

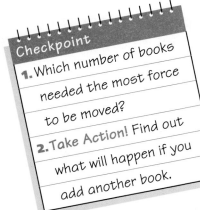

Teacher's Assessment Package
A **scoring rubric** to assess student performance is provided on page 48 of the Teacher's Assessment Package.

Activity Results
The rubber band stretches more when it is used to move heavier objects. The chart should reflect the increasing length of the rubber band.

Extend the Activity
Repeat the activity using three larger books. Ask children to predict what would happen to the length of the rubber band before they begin. (The rubber band would be stretched even longer.)

Lesson Objective

Children compare sliding a heavy object across a smooth surface with sliding the object across a rough surface.

Introduce

Invite Learning

Give children samples of smooth surfaces (tile, polished wood) and rough surfaces (sandpaper, unfinished wood) to observe and touch. Elicit descriptions of the surfaces.

Make Connections

To **assess prior knowledge,** show children a cutout of a sled. Then display pictures or simple drawings of a bumpy dirt road, a grassy lawn, and an ice-covered lake. Ask where the sled would be easiest to pull. On chart paper, record children's reasons for their choices as a **baseline assessment.** You can follow up on this assessment in Check for Understanding.

Teach

Activity

Children slide books across different surfaces and compare the amount of force needed. **Skill:** Comparing

Where is it easier to pull things?

Suppose you want to move a big box full of toys. You pull the box across a rug. Then you pull the box across a bare floor. One way is easier because you use less force. Find out which way is easier.

C 16

Science Idea Exchange

Science Background

Friction is the force that causes resistance to motion between two rubbing surfaces. The amount of friction between two surfaces depends on the kinds of surfaces and the force pressing the surfaces together. Friction is greater on rough surfaces than on smooth ones.

Special Education

To make this concept more concrete, tell children that ballet dancers often put a sticky powder on the soles of their shoes so they won't slip on the smooth stage. Encourage children to bring shoes to class and to **compare** the bottoms and the reasons for wearing them (hiking boots, shoes with cleats, sneakers, dress shoes).

Explore Further

Challenge children to **predict** what would happen in the activity if the smooth floor had just been waxed, if oil had been spilled on it, or if the floor were dirty and a sticky, syrupy liquid spilled on it. Have them try to explain their predictions.

Slide the book.

You will need:  string book rug

1. Tie one end of the string around the book.
2. Put the book on a rug. Pull the string until the book starts moving across the rug.
3. Put the book on a bare floor. Pull the string until the book moves across the floor.

Checkpoint
Tell if it is easier to move things across a rug or across a bare floor. Which time did you use less force?

C 17

Materials (per group)
Module Kit Item: piece of string *(about 1 m)*
School Supplied Items: small book; rug *(or carpeted area)*

Helpful Hint
You can use a small rug or a board with a rough surface for this activity.

Raise Questions
Have children consider what might happen if a smooth surface was turned into a rough surface or vice versa. Challenge them to think of ways this might happen. For example, a smooth surface could be cracked and cut, or a rough board could be sanded smooth.

Close

Check for Understanding
- As a follow-up to the **baseline assessment,** show the pictures from Make Connections again and ask children if they would change their answers about the easiest place to pull the sled. Have them explain why.
- **Answers to Checkpoint** It is easier to move things across a smooth floor. Less force was used on the smooth floor.

Connecting Ideas
In the next lesson, children will learn to order surfaces according to how smooth or rough they are. ▶

Explorer's Activity Guide
Use Explorer's Activity Guide hands-on activity on page 95 to help children answer the question, "Where is it easier to pull things?"

Teacher's Assessment Package
A **scoring rubric** to assess student performance is provided on page 48 of the Teacher's Assessment Package.

Activity Results
It is easier to move things across a smooth floor than across a carpet. Less force was used to move the book across the smooth floor. More force was needed to pull the book across the carpet.

Collaborative Learning: Small Groups
Assign specific children to gather and clean up materials. Each child in the Activity group should have an opportunity to move the book on the rug and bare floor, record observations, and share results.

Lesson 8

Lesson Objective
Children compare various surfaces and order them according to how smooth or rough they are. **Skills:** Organizing information, solving problems

Introduce

Invite Learning
Give children the opportunity to touch and **describe** samples of rough and smooth surfaces, such as sandpaper, wax paper, top of desk, and stones. Generate a list of characteristics named.

Make Connections
To **assess prior knowledge,** write the headings "Very Smooth," "Smooth," "Rough," and "Very Rough" on the chalkboard. Have children classify the samples from Invite Learning in these categories. Save the classifications to use as a **baseline assessment.**

Teach

Observe and Listen
- Have children work in small groups to **compare** the data on the chart and on the graph.
- Encourage each group to think of one surface they could add to the chart and graph.

What surfaces make moving things easier?

Wax paper and the top of a desk are smooth surfaces. Sandpaper and stones are rough surfaces. Is it easier to move an object across smooth surfaces or rough surfaces? You can find out. You can pull an object across each surface. You can measure how far a rubber band stretches when you pull.

1. Look at the chart. The rubber band stretched 1 cm when an object was pulled across wax paper. How far did the rubber band stretch when an object was pulled across stones?

surface	how far a rubber band stretched
sandpaper	7 cm
wax paper	1 cm
top of desk	2 cm
stones	6 cm

C 18

Science Idea Exchange

Science Anecdote
Sometimes people find it useful to deliberately make a surface rough so that moving an object across it is difficult. Examples include a doormat, bathtub strips, and hook-and-loop fastener fabric.

Math/Science Connection
Give children some practice in measurement with their metric rulers by asking them to measure the length of each bar on the graph. Have them compare their measurements with others in the class.

Science and Language Arts
Suggest that children write a story about taking an imaginary walk. Have children pretend that they are pulling an object behind them as they walk. Have children draw pictures to illustrate the surfaces over which they walk. Have them describe how easy or difficult it is to pull the object over each surface.

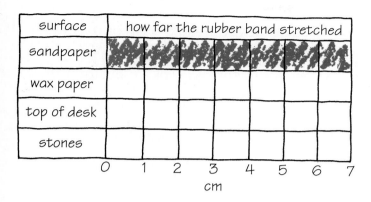

surface	how far the rubber band stretched						
sandpaper							
wax paper							
top of desk							
stones							

0　1　2　3　4　5　6　7
cm

3. The chart shows how much the rubber band stretched when sandpaper was used. Fill in the chart to show how much the rubber band stretched when other surfaces were used.

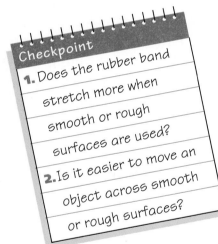

Checkpoint

1. Does the rubber band stretch more when smooth or rough surfaces are used?

2. Is it easier to move an object across smooth or rough surfaces?

C 19

Act as a Consultant
Guide children in determining what is different about each surface (the texture, how rough or smooth it is). Then help each group estimate how far a rubber band would stretch for the surface they thought of in Observe and Listen. Guide children in adding a bar to their graph.

Ask for Evidence
Ask: *How does the length of a rubber band help you tell how much force is needed to start something moving across a surface?* (It stretches more and more as greater force is needed.)

Close

Check for Understanding
- As a follow-up to the **baseline assessment,** return to the classification chart in Make Connections. Determine if children would change their groupings. If so, ask why.
- **Answers to Checkpoint** 1. The rubber band stretches more when rough surfaces are used. 2. It is easier to move objects across smooth surfaces.

Connecting Lessons
In the next lesson, children will make posters to show their understanding of the concepts in the chapter. ▶

Explorer's Activity Guide
Use Explorer's Activity Guide page 96 to help children solve the question of what surfaces make moving things easier. You can also use this hands-on activity page to evaluate how well children understand the concept of this lesson.

Save the Earth
In order to make it easier for carts to pull loads from one place to another, people built roads of smooth rocks. Today, many thousands of smooth roads cross the land to make it easier for cars and trucks to pull loads from one place to another. Ask children what they think will happen if people continue to cover the earth with roads and highways.

Science and Art
Have children draw a "Safety Tips" cartoon. Using what they have learned about rough and smooth surfaces, they can include safety warnings such as "Slippery When Wet" or "Ice Too Bumpy for Skating."

Lesson Objective
Children make a poster to identify the concepts they learned in this chapter.

Introduce

Invite Learning
Review the **baseline assessment** activities you used in the chapter. Choose one or more to do again that you think will help children understand the chapter concepts.

Teach

Performance Assessment Activity
Children create a poster collage to demonstrate that pushes and pulls of varying strength are needed to make things move. **Skills:** Recognizing patterns and relationships, summarizing

Materials (per group)
Module Kit Items: none
School Supplied Items: scissors; crayons; glue; old magazines; flip chart paper or poster board

Helpful Hints
- Encourage children to look for pictures of pushes and pulls that they use in their everyday life.
- If you have enough materials, children could do this activity individually.

What did you learn?

You found out that you need a push or a pull to make things move. Can you share what you know about forces? Make a poster that shows pushes and pulls.

You will need: paper   magazines   scissors   glue   crayons

Make a poster.
1. Cut out pictures of objects that forces can move.
2. Find pictures of someone using a force that pushes an object. Glue the pictures on one part of the paper.
3. Find pictures of someone using a force that pulls an object. Glue the pictures on the other part of the paper.

C 20

 # Science Idea Exchange

Teacher's Assessment Package
Use the pages from the Teacher's Assessment Package at this time to promote **performance assessment** opportunities for your children.

Special Education
Children can show what they have learned through pantomime. Have volunteers act out scenes involving pushes and pulls from their everyday life. (Examples may include the following: roller skating, putting on clothes, or squeezing a bottle of ketchup.) The class may guess what forces and surfaces are shown.

Collaborative Learning: Small Groups
Assign specific children to gather and clean up materials. All members of the Chapter Review group should be involved in choosing and sorting pictures for the group's poster.

Share what you learned.

1. Which picture shows a strong push?
2. Which picture shows a strong pull?
3. Which picture shows people having fun using pushes or pulls?

pushes | pulls

Act as a Consultant

Help children record a list of pushes and pulls they experience during a typical day at school. Have them label each force as strong or weak.

Raise Questions

Use a **constructivist** approach by asking: *What other questions do you have about pushing and pulling forces? How can we find the answers to your questions?*

Close

Check for Understanding

Answers to Share what you learned
Answers will vary, depending on the kind of pictures children find. Children should be able to find a wide variety of pushes, such as pushing a doorbell, a lunch tray, or a heavy object; and a wide variety of pulls, such as pulling tape on a dispenser, a sock on a foot, and a wagon.

Connecting Chapters

In the next chapter, children will discover that magnets can push and pull objects and make them move. ▶

Explorer's Activity Guide

Use Explorer's Activity Guide pages 97–99 as a hands-on activity to evaluate how well children understand the concepts covered in this chapter.

Activity Results

Pictures should include a wide variety of scenes showing strong and weak pushes and pulls. Many of the forces shown will include people, but some may not.

Alternate Activity

As a class, write a rebus story about pushes and pulls on chart paper, leaving blanks for any words that can be illustrated. Children can then draw pictures in the blanks. For example: "A person on [skates] can move easily on [ice] on a lake in winter because it has a [smooth] surface."

Chapter 2 Planning Guide
Magnets

Lessons / *Skills*

Lesson 1
Discover Activity: **What can magnets do to each other?**
pp. C22–C23
(observing, describing)

Lesson 2
What are the poles of a magnet? pp. C24–C25
(observing, comparing)

Lesson 3
Let's Explore: **What can magnets do to other things?**
pp. C26–C27
(observing, classifying)

Lesson 4
How do you use magnets? pp. C28–C29
(observing, describing, listing)

Lesson 5
Let's Explore: **What can a magnet pull through?** pp. C30–C31
(recognizing cause and effect, identifying variables)

Lesson 6
Are all magnets strong? pp. C32–C33
(identifying variables, inferring)

Lesson 7
How can you make a magnet? pp. C34–C35
(observing, recognizing cause and effect)

Lesson 8
Let's Solve It!: **How can you make a stronger magnet?**
pp. C36–C37
(organizing information, solving problems)

Lesson 9
Chapter Review: **What did you learn?** pp. C38–C39
(describing, restating or explaining ideas)

Materials (per group)

Lesson 1 Activity: *What can magnets do to each other?*
Module Kit Items: 2 bar magnets
School Supplied Items: none

Lesson 3 Activity: *What can magnets do to other things?*
Module Kit Items: 2 index cards; 2 pieces of yarn *(each about 1 m long)*; bar magnet; 20 small magnetic/nonmagnetic objects
School Supplied Items: markers
Safety Kit Items: cover goggles *(1/child)*
Advance Prep: Cut string into 1-m lengths ahead of time.

Lesson 5 Activity: *What can a magnet pull through?*
Module Kit Items: plastic wrap; cotton cloth; bar magnet; paper clip; wood block
School Supplied Items: sheet of paper *(drawing or copier paper)*; piece of cardboard
Advance Prep: Cut each piece of cloth into two equal-size pieces so each group will have a piece of cloth to test.

Lesson 6 Activity: *Find the strongest magnet.*
Module Kit Items: 3 magnets *(bar, disc, horseshoe)*; 10 paper clips
School Supplied Items: none

Lesson 7 Activity: *Make a magnet.*
Module Kit Items: D-cell battery; insulated wire *(about 60 cm)*; nail; 2 paper clips; rubber band
School Supplied Items: none
Safety Kit Items: cover goggles *(1/child)*
Advance Prep: Use sharp scissors to cut a 60-cm length of wire for each group. To strip the ends of the wire, you can use sandpaper to rub off the insulation. Or score the insulation on each end of the wire using scissors, then pull off the insulation.

Lesson 9 Activity: *Write an advertisement for magnets.*
Module Kit Items: none
School Supplied Items: paper *(1 sheet/child)*; pencil; crayons
Advance Prep: You might want to collect examples of advertisements. Children can use them as models for their magnet ads.

Assessment Options	Content	Performance	Portfolio
Teacher's Assessment Package			
Chapter Test, pp. 55–56	✓		✓
Group Interview Assessment, p. 57	✓	✓	
Performance Strategies, p. 58	✓	✓	✓
Explorer's Activity Guide			
Activity worksheets, pp. 101–109		✓	✓
Chapter Review, p. 110	✓		✓
Interactive Transparency Package			
Transparency 11 and BLM	✓	✓	✓
Teacher's Guide, pp. 26–27	✓	✓	
Hands-on activity for second-language learners	✓	✓	✓
Science Literature Library			
Switch On, Switch Off		✓	✓
Interactive Videodisc Software Teacher's Guide, pp. 62–70			
Computer-based Activity	✓	✓	
Journal Presentations	✓	✓	✓
Videodisc Classroom Guide, pp. 25–32, or **Video Reader**			
Hands-on activity	✓	✓	✓
ExploraCenter Teacher's Guide, pp. 10, 21, 23			
ExploraCenter			
Science activity cards 5, 16, 18	✓	✓	✓
ScottForesman Online Service			
Online field trips	✓	✓	✓

Chapter Overview

Children begin this chapter by experimenting with magnets. They learn what magnets can do and what they can pull through. They discover that some magnets are stronger than others. After children make a magnet, they write an advertisement to show what they have learned.

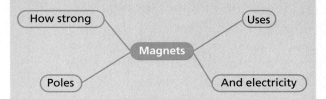

Lesson Objective
Children investigate how two magnets interact with each other.

Introduce

Invite Learning
Show the videodisc or videotape segment for this chapter. Bar codes and a description of this segment are given below on page C23.

Make Connections
To **assess prior knowledge**, provide small groups of children with two small toy cars and two bar magnets. Have them tape a magnet to the front of each car. Ask children to **predict** what will happen when the two cars are rolled slowly toward each other. Then have children check their predictions. (The cars may be attracted to each other, or may repel each other, depending on how the magnets are positioned.)

Teach

Discover Activity

Children observe magnets as they push and pull on each other. **Skills:** Observing, describing

Materials (per group)
Module Kit Items: 2 bar magnets
School Supplied Items: none

Chapter 2
Magnets

Would you like to play with some of these magnets? You could have fun picking things up and moving things around.

But magnets are more than toys. They are important parts in radios, televisions, computers, and more! What else can magnets do? Let's find out!

Science Idea Exchange

Collaborative Learning: Small Groups
Assign specific children to gather and clean up materials. All children in the Discover Activity group should have an opportunity to experiment with the magnets and share their observations.

Family/School Partnership: Family Support
Encourage families to be active partners in learning by suggesting that they and their children:
- observe objects with magnets,
- use a magnet to hold a piece of paper to an object, and
- observe what happens when they put a magnet next to various objects.

Science and Literature
Use the literature selection *Switch On, Switch Off* by Melvin Berger (Crowell, 1989) to help children understand that magnets are used to generate electricity. Ask them to draw a picture showing the materials needed to make electricity using a magnet.

Discover Activity

What can magnets do to each other?

1. Put two magnets on a table. Slowly push the magnets toward each other. What happens?
2. Turn one magnet around.
3. Push the magnets toward each other again. What happens now?
4. **Tell about it.** Tell what happened when you pushed the magnets together.

Ask me what else I want to find out about magnets.

C 23

Helpful Hints

- Mark like poles of the magnets with paint or colored marker beforehand.
- Handle magnets gently; if dropped or hit, magnets can lose some magnetism.
- *See Equipment Kit Teacher's Guide for additional hints.*

What to Expect

Children might say "push" or "pull" to describe magnets' actions and "same" or "different" to describe poles.

Close

Check for Understanding

- Invite four children to be two magnets; have them form pole pairs and choose colors to match the activity's magnets. Allow them to demonstrate the activity.
- **Answer to Tell about it** Children should be able to explain that magnets can pull and push each other.

What Else Do You Want to Find Out?

Using a **constructivist** approach, ask: *What do you think causes the push or pull of magnets? What else would you like to know about magnets?* List children's questions and refer to them throughout the chapter.

Connecting Lessons

In the next lesson, children will learn that magnets are strongest at their ends, or poles. ▶

Explorer's Activity Guide

The **Discover Activity recording sheet** on page 101 of the Explorer's Activity Guide can be used by children to record their activity results.

Visual Literacy

Dicover the Wonder Videotape or *Videodisc,* Grade 2, Module C, presents a video segment that explores the exciting and extraordinary uses of magnetism. Use this video to enhance children's understanding of magnetism as a force for moving objects.

Bar Codes

Chapter 12: Video, English

Chapter 12: Video, Spanish

Play

Interactive Software

Lesson 2

Introduce

Key Terms
magnet
pole

Invite Learning
Tell children to wear cover goggles and invite them to dip a bar magnet into a dish of small, metal paper clips. Ask them to describe where most of the paper clips stick to the magnet.

Make Connections
To **assess prior knowledge,** ask children which places on a magnet push or pull hardest. They can draw the magnet and the paper clips used in the Invite Learning activity. Save children's drawings to use as a **baseline assessment** at the close of this lesson.

Teach

Raise Questions
Ask: *How do you know where a magnet is strongest?* (where most paper clips stick)

What are the poles of a magnet?

You saw one **magnet** move another magnet. Why do you think this happens? It happens because the ends of magnets are different from each other.

The two ends of magnets are called **poles**. Look at the poles of these magnets. The N stands for north pole. The S stands for south pole. A magnet pushes or pulls hardest at its poles. The N and the S show where the magnet is strongest.

C 24

 ## Science Idea Exchange

Science Background
No matter how often a magnet is broken in two, the broken ends become new poles. If a magnet is suspended from a string, the same end will always point north. This north-seeking end is called the magnet's north pole; the other end is its south pole. Every magnet, no matter how small, has both poles.

Multicultural Connections
Over 2000 years ago, ancient Greeks knew that lodestones, composed of the mineral magnetite, had magnetic properties. Sailors from ancient China used lodestone compasses to help guide their ships. Sailors placed slivers of the magnetic rock on pieces of straw, cork, or bamboo, which they then floated in water. The slivers turned until they aligned in a north-south direction.

Your Ideas

_____

_____

_____

_____

_____

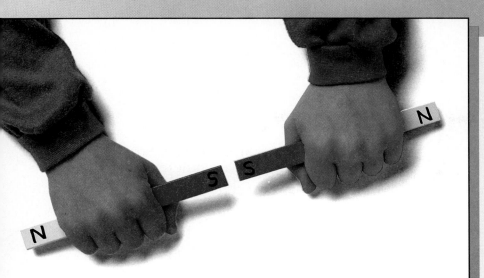

If you put poles that are the same next to each other, they push apart. Two north poles next to each other would push apart. What would two south poles do?

Two poles that are not the same will pull together. A north and a south pole are not the same. If you put them next to each other, they pull together.

Checkpoint

Tell which places on a magnet push and pull hardest.

- Invite pairs of children to hang a magnet from a string and let it swing freely. Have both children in a pair take turns using a second magnet to push or pull the hanging magnet.
- Have children explain the hanging magnet's motion to their partners.

Encourage Student Definitions

Write the following words on the chalkboard: "push," "pull," "ends," "north," "south," and "poles." Invite children to form a definition of a magnet using the words.

Close

Check for Understanding

- As a follow-up to the **baseline assessment,** review children's drawings with them. Ask if they would like to change their drawings. Have them give reasons for their changes.
- Ask children to tape the ends of one magnet so they can't see the colors or letters. Encourage them to use another magnet with marked poles to identify one end as the north pole.
- **Answers to Checkpoint** The poles of a magnet push and pull the hardest.

Connecting Lessons

In the next lesson, children will learn how magnets interact with other objects. ▶

Explorer's Activity Guide

Use Explorer's Activity Guide page 103 with this lesson to help children answer the text question,  "What are the poles of a magnet?" with a hands-on activity.

Science and Social Studies

Hang two bar magnets horizontally at different locations in the classroom. Also, place two directional compasses in the classroom (away from steel cabinets or other steel items). Inform children that the earth acts like a magnet. Let them observe that the compasses and magnets point north. This activity may work best outside.

Science Themes

By discussing the magnetic forces of pulling and pushing, children develop an understanding of the themes of **energy** and **systems and interactions.**

Lesson 3

Lesson Objective
Children learn how magnets interact with other objects.

Introduce

Invite Learning
Put an assortment of magnetic and nonmagnetic objects in a grab bag. Invite children to form teams, and ask a child from each team to pick an object. Have teams **predict** whether or not a magnet will pull the object.

Make Connections
To **assess prior knowledge,** record children's predictions from Invite Learning. Ask children to describe the materials that are pulled and those that are not pulled. Record the descriptions to use as a **baseline assessment.**

Teach

Activity
Children observe how magnets interact with different objects and demonstrate that magnets pull on many metal objects. **Skills:** Observing, classifying

Materials (per group)
Module Kit Items: 2 index cards; 2 pieces of yarn (each about 1 m long); bar magnet; 20 small magnetic/ nonmagnetic objects
School Supplied Items: markers
Safety Kit Items: cover goggles (1/child)

What can magnets do to other things?

You saw how magnets can pull together and push apart. Now find out what a magnet can do to other things.

You will need:

- strong magnet
- yarn
- markers
- 2 note cards
- 20 small objects

Find out about it.

1. Make two circles of yarn on a table.

2. Write on note cards *pulls* and *does not pull.* Put a card in each circle.

3. Put the objects on the table.

4. Hold the magnet above each object.

5. Put objects the magnet pulls in the *pulls* circle. Put objects the magnet does not pull in the *does not pull* circle.

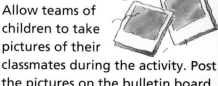

C 26

 Science Idea Exchange

Science Background
The most magnetic material is iron. Other magnetic materials are nickel, cobalt, and steel, which is a combination of iron and carbon. While tin is not attracted to magnets, tin cans usually are because most tin cans are made of steel coated with tin.

Collaborative Learning: Small Groups
Assign specific children to gather and clean up materials. Each child in the Let's Explore group should have an opportunity to try picking up at least two objects with the magnet. Also, all children in the Let's Explore group should record data and share results.

Visual Literacy

Allow teams of children to take pictures of their classmates during the activity. Post the pictures on the bulletin board as a record of each new discovery about magnets. Invite children to write captions for the pictures.

Write about it. ✏️

Make a chart like this. List the objects you placed in each circle.

pulls	does not pull

Checkpoint

1. What kinds of things do magnets pull?

2. Take Action! Find three objects that can be pulled by a magnet.

- Objects used may vary but should not be sharp and should include items made of plastic, cloth, wood, paper, magnetic metal (such as iron and nickel), and nonmagnetic metal (such as copper and aluminum).
- *See Equipment Kit Teacher's Guide for additional hints.*

Raise Questions

Ask: *How are the objects in the "pulls" circle alike?* (All are metal.) *Is there any metal in the "does not pull" circle?* (Answers may include aluminum foil.) *What could this mean?* (Magnets pick up some metals and not others.)

Close

Check for Understanding

- As a follow-up to the **baseline assessment,** ask children if they wish to revise their descriptions of what types of objects a magnet will pull. (Children should classify their objects as metal a magnet pulls, metal a magnet doesn't pull, or not a metal.)
- **Answers to Checkpoint** 1. Magnets pick up objects made of certain metals. 2. **Take Action!** Children should name three metal objects a magnet can pull.

Connecting Lessons

In the next lesson, children will learn how magnets are used. ▶

Explorer's Activity Guide

Use Explorer's Activity Guide hands-on activity on page 104 to explore magnets and evaluate children's understanding of the lesson concept.

Teacher's Assessment Package

A **scoring rubric** to assess student performance is provided on page 53 of the Teacher's Assessment Package.

Activity Results

The magnet will pick up the larger nail, paper clip, metal washer, paper fastener, and jar lid from the packaged materials. The magnet will not pick up the cork, balloon, wood block, plastic spoon, copper strip, shell, smaller nail (which is aluminum), plastic foam piece, or button.

Extend the Activity

Children can use magnets as metal detectors. Invite them to try their own magnets on a metal pot, a juice can, a bicycle rim, appliances at home, a nickel, and other metals. Encourage them to list the objects they tried and the results. Ask children to write a short summary of the activity.

Lesson 4

Lesson Objective
Children learn about some of the uses for magnets.

Introduce

Invite Learning
Provide children with two corks with steel thumbtacks already pushed into them. Prop a large, shallow plastic dish between books, leaving space under the dish for children's hands. Fill the dish with water. Allow children to race their cork "boats" by moving a magnet beneath the dish.

Make Connections
To **assess prior knowledge,** have children describe several toys and objects that contain magnets. Record children's descriptions to use as a **baseline assessment.**

Teach

Observe and Listen
● Let children form small groups to discuss the uses of the magnets shown in the text pictures. Have them explain how magnets might be helpful to them.
● Encourage children to take turns telling the rest of their group what each magnet shown does.

How do you use magnets?

You probably use magnets in many ways. Some magnets can hold up important messages. Other magnets keep the doors of the refrigerator tightly closed. Magnets also keep the cabinet doors closed.

You can find magnets in many objects. Find objects in the picture that have magnets.

Checkpoint

Draw one way you use magnets.

magnet

magnets on bottom

C 28

Science Idea Exchange

Science Background
Some countries, including Japan and Germany, have developed trains that depend on magnetism for the push and pull needed to make the train move. These trains do not have wheels; the electromagnet on the bottom of the train helps the train float above the magnet on the track.

Achieving English Proficiency
Invite children to play a game of buried treasure by using magnets to find magnetic objects buried under sand. After children find the treasure, ask them to describe the object and to tell what they did to find it.

Science and Language Arts
Suggest children write a rebus (a story that uses pictures or symbols to replace syllables or words), about using magnets to find a treasure. For example: "We used a [magnet] to search for a [nickel] that was buried in [sand]."

magnets

magnets

magnets

magnets inside

AKO—

C 29

Have children name other uses for magnets. You may wish to spark their thoughts by mentioning that magnets can pick up metal objects at the bottom of lakes and rivers.

Close

Check for Understanding

● As a follow-up to the **baseline assessment,** ask children if they would like to add to their list of objects that contain magnets. Discuss any additions with the class.

● **Answers to Checkpoint** Children's drawings should include a magnet that is used to pull or push something.

Extend the Lesson

Demonstrate the value of a magnetic compass in finding direction. Allow each child to hold the compass and point to where it shows north. Ask: *Now that you know which direction north is, which direction is south?* Have a child show the class which way south is by pointing in that direction. Ask: *Which direction is east and which is west?* For each direction, ask a child to point in that direction.

Connecting Lessons

In the next lesson, children will learn that a magnetic pull can pass through some materials. ▶

Explorer's Activity Guide

Use Explorer's Activity Guide page 105 with this lesson to help children answer the text question, "How do you use magnets?" with a hands-on activity.

Save the Earth

Ask children to keep a tally of the number of cans their family empties in a week. Tell children to include soft drink cans from vending machines as well as pet food cans. Remind children that the steel and aluminum in these cans are valuable and can be recycled. Ask them to explain how magnets can be used to sort the cans for recycling.

Visual Literacy

To enhance the **visual literacy** connection, use the interactive overhead transparency that correlates with the above two pages. The transparency will help your students understand the key concepts presented on these pages.

Lesson 5

Lesson Objective
Children discover that the pull of a magnet can pass through some materials.

Introduce

Invite Learning
Invite children to place a paper clip on a table top and hold a magnet above the clip so that the paper clip "jumps" up to meet the magnet.

Make Connections
To **assess prior knowledge**, ask children to predict what would happen if a sheet of paper were put between the magnet and the clip in Invite Learning. Save their predictions to use as a **baseline assessment**.

Teach

Activity
Children demonstrate that the pull of a magnet can move through paper, cardboard, plastic, wood, and cloth.
Skills: Recognizing cause and effect, identifying variables

Materials (per group)
Module Kit Items: plastic wrap; cotton cloth; bar magnet; paper clip; wood block
School Supplied Items: sheet of paper (*drawing or copier paper*); piece of cardboard

---

What can a magnet pull through?

How does a magnet hold up a note on a refrigerator? The sides of a refrigerator are metal. The magnet can pull through the note paper. Can a magnet pull through other things?

You will need:

 magnet

 paper clip

 paper

 cardboard

 plastic

 wood

 cloth

Find out about it.

1 Have your partner hold out a sheet of paper.

2 Hold a magnet on top of the paper. Hold a paper clip under the paper below the magnet.

3 Let go of the paper clip. What happens to it?

4 Do the same thing with cardboard, plastic, wood, and cloth. What happens?

C 30

Science Idea Exchange

Science Background
The pull of a magnet is the result of a magnetic field that surrounds the magnet. The force field can pass through many materials including air, water, and paper. The field is strongest at the poles; the field weakens as the distance from the magnet increases.

Collaborative Learning: Small Groups
Assign specific children to gather and clean up materials. All children in the Let's Explore group should take turns testing whether the magnet can pull through different materials. Also, all children in the group should be involved in recording data and sharing results.

Explore Further
Show a magnetic drawing box, such as those sold in stores, to the class. Invite a child to move the special pencil across the screen. Invite children to explain how they know that the pull of the magnetic pencil passes through the screen.

Write about it.

Make a chart like this. Write what you learned.

	Can a magnet pull through these things?				
	paper	cardboard	plastic	wood	cloth
yes					
no					

Checkpoint

1. What can a magnet pull through?

2. Take Action! Find out if a magnet can pull through water.

C 31

Helpful Hints
- Provide materials as close to the same thickness as possible.
- Children may have more success holding the clips in the palm of their hand.

Raise Questions
Help children clarify their thinking by asking: *How do you know the magnet is pulling the paper clip?* (The clip stays attached to the paper only where the magnet is above the clip.) *When the paper clip fell, was it because the magnet stopped working?* (no) *How do you know?* (The magnet still picks up clips.)

Close

Check for Understanding
- As a follow-up to the **baseline assessment,** have children check the predictions they made against their findings.
- **Answers to Checkpoint** 1. Answers may vary. A strong magnet should be able to pull through all the materials listed in the activity. 2. **Take Action!** Designs may vary. Children could put a paper clip at the bottom of a bowl of water and bring a magnet close to the clip to see if it moves.

Connecting Lessons
In the next lesson, children will learn that some magnets are stronger than others. ▶

Explorer's Activity Guide
Use Explorer's Activity Guide hands-on activity on page 106 to explore magnets and evaluate children's understanding of the lesson concept.

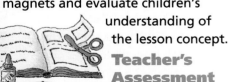

Teacher's Assessment Package
A **scoring rubric** to assess student performance is provided on page 53 of the Teacher's Assessment Package.

Activity Results
The bar magnet pulls through paper, cardboard, plastic, and cloth, but cannot pull through the wood block.

Alternate Activity
Invite children to put a paper clip inside a plastic cup. Suggest that they try to move the paper clip up the side of the cup, using the magnet outside the cup. Repeat using a container made of a different material, such as a paper box or a metal pan. Encourage children to write down their conclusions.

Lesson 6

Lesson Objective
Children learn that some magnets are stronger than others.

Introduce

Invite Learning
Put a variety of magnets—bar magnet, horseshoe magnet, round refrigerator magnet, and flat, flexible magnet—on a table. Invite children to observe the magnets closely. Allow them to **compare** their size, shape, and weight.

Make Connections
To **assess prior knowledge,** ask children to predict which magnet is strongest and which is weakest. Save children's predictions to use as a **baseline assessment.**

Teach

Activity
Children use paper clips to determine which of three magnets is strongest and which is weakest. **Skills:** Identifying variables, inferring

Materials (per group)
Module Kit Items: 3 magnets *(bar, disc, horseshoe)*; 10 paper clips
School Supplied Items: none

Helpful Hints
- Make sure paper clips are connected end-to-end instead of clustered.

Are all magnets strong?

Pretend you bring home two drawings you made in school. You hang one drawing on the refrigerator with a magnet. It stays up. Then you try to hang the other drawing. This time the drawing and the magnet fall to the floor! Could one magnet be stronger than the other? Do the activity to find out.

C 32

Science Idea Exchange

Science Anecdote
When divers test parts of oil rigs 300 m (1000 ft) under water, they use strong magnets to hold cables used for the test. These magnets work under water as well as they do on land.

Science Themes
By discussing the different strengths of the forces of magnets, children develop an understanding of the theme of systems and interactions.

Science and Language Arts
Invite children to make up a story in which the hero uses a strong magnet. Children may want to illustrate their story and tell it to the class.

Find the strongest magnet.

You will need: 3 magnets  paper clips

1. Hold a magnet in your hand. Pick up a paper clip with the magnet.
2. Pick up another paper clip at the end of the first one.
3. Pick up more paper clips to make a chain. Pick up as many paper clips as you can.
4. Do the same thing with 2 other magnets.
5. Count the number of paper clips each magnet can hold.

Checkpoint
Draw a picture showing which magnet is strongest and which is weakest. Write down how you know.

C 33

- *See Equipment Kit Teacher's Guide for additional hints.*

Act as a Consultant
Help children recognize that a magnet's size does not always indicate its strength.

Close

Check for Understanding
- As a follow-up to the **baseline assessment,** have children compare their predictions with their results. Ask them to explain differences between the predictions and the results.
- **Answers to Checkpoint** Pictures should show three magnets, one with more paper clips on the chain than the others. The strongest magnet picks up the longest chain.

Extend the Lesson
Have children put a magnet on one side of a piece of cardboard and a paper clip on the other. Add more cardboard pieces until the magnet will no longer pick up the clip. Ask: *How does this activity measure how strong the magnet is?* (The more pieces of card-board added while the magnet still picks up the clip, the stronger the magnet is.)

Connecting Lessons
In the next lesson, children will learn that batteries can be used to make magnets. ▶

Explorer's Activity Guide
Use Explorer's Activity Guide hands-on activity on page 107 to help children answer the question, "Are all magnets strong?"

Teacher's Assessment Package
A **scoring rubric** to assess student performance is provided on page 54 of the Teacher's Assessment Package.

Activity Results
The strongest magnet will pick up the greatest number of paper clips. Generally, the disc magnet is strongest and the horseshoe magnet is weakest. Children should be able to compare the number of paper clips and infer that the number was an indication of the magnet's strength.

Collaborative Learning: Small Groups
Assign specific children to gather and clean up materials. All children in the Activity group should have an opportunity to test the strength of magnets, draw their observations, and share results.

Lesson 7

Lesson Objective
Children learn that batteries can be used to make electromagnets.

Introduce

Invite Learning
Ask children to name uses for batteries (flashlights, toys, cameras).

Make Connections
To **assess prior knowledge,** ask: *How can you make a magnet with batteries?* Record responses for a **baseline assessment.**

Teach

Activity
Children construct an electromagnet using a battery and a nail. **Skills:** Observing, recognizing cause and effect

Materials (per group)
Module Kit Items: D-cell battery; insulated wire *(about 60 cm);* nail; 2 paper clips; rubber band
School Supplied Items: none
Safety Kit Items: cover goggles *(1/child)*

Helpful Hints
• Wrap the wire around the nail at least 20 times; the wire should cover most of the nail.
• Be sure to strip the ends of the insulated wire for contact with the battery terminals.

How can you make a magnet?

How do you use batteries? You might use batteries to make a flashlight or radio work. Many toys run on batteries. Do you know that you can use a battery to make a magnet? Electricity from a battery can travel through a wire around a nail. Then the nail becomes a magnet.

C 34

 ## Science Idea Exchange

Science Background
In 1819, Danish physicist Hans Oersted discovered that if electricity flows through a wire, a magnetic field is created. If the wire is wrapped around a magnetic material such as iron, the magnetic effect is increased. The magnetic field exists only if electricity flows through the wire.

Collaborative Learning: Cooperative Learning
Assign specific children to gather and clean up materials. All children in the Activity group should have an opportunity to pick up objects with the electromagnet and share observations. Also, each child in the Activity group can be assigned a specific role:
• one who tries to pick up a paper clip with the nail;
• one who wraps the wire around the nail and puts the rubber band around the battery;
• one who attaches the wire to the battery;
• one who tries to pick up a paper clip with the electromagnet.

Make a magnet.

You will need: cover goggles wire nail battery paper clip  rubber band

1. Try to pick up the paper clip with the nail. Is the nail a magnet?
2. Wrap the wire around the nail 20 times.
3. Put the rubber band around the battery.
4. Put the ends of the wire on the battery.
5. Try to pick up the paper clip with the nail. What happens? Is the nail a magnet now?

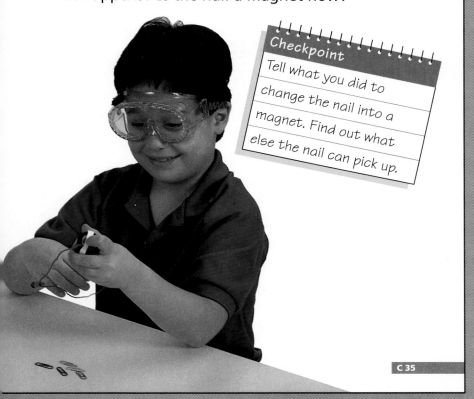

Checkpoint
Tell what you did to change the nail into a magnet. Find out what else the nail can pick up.

Helpful Hints (cont'd.)

- Tightly wrap a thick rubber band around the ends of the battery. Have children connect wires to the battery by inserting wire ends under the rubber band.

Safety Tip

Caution children not to leave the wires attached to the battery; the wires will quickly heat up.

Close

Check for Understanding

- As a follow-up to the **baseline assessment,** ask children to explain how they can use a battery to make a magnet. Compare their responses with those they gave in Make Connections.
- **Answers to Checkpoint** Children should explain that wrapping a wire around a nail and connecting it to a battery changed the nail into a magnet. Children should try to pick up other magnetic metal objects with the nail.

Connecting Lessons

In the next lesson, children will learn that increasing the number of wire coils around a nail makes an electromagnet stronger. ▶

Explorer's Activity Guide

Use Explorer's Activity Guide hands-on activity on page 108 to help children answer the question, "How can you make a magnet?"

Teacher's Assessment Package

A **scoring rubric** to assess student performance is provided on page 54 of the Teacher's Assessment Package.

Activity Results

The nail by itself is not a magnet. When the wire is wrapped around the nail and both ends of the wire are attached to the battery, the nail acts like a magnet. Children should discover that the nail will pick up a number of paper clips.

Visual Literacy

Invite children to take pictures of the steps they followed to make a nail into a magnet. Have them write captions for the pictures and number them in order. Children can put their pictures on the bulletin board.

Lesson 8

Lesson Objective
Children learn that an electromagnet can be made stronger by increasing the number of wire coils around the nail. **Skills:** Organizing information, solving problems

Introduce

Invite Learning
Invite children to think of fun or useful things they could do with a strong magnet. As a class, brainstorm to produce a list.

Make Connections
To **assess prior knowledge,** invite children to think about ways they could make a magnet stronger. Record their responses to use later as a **baseline assessment.**

Teach

Observe and Listen
- Have children form small groups and describe the three drawings of the nails to each other.
- Suggest children work in their groups to answer the questions in the text. Have them work together to complete a chart like the one in the text.

How can you make a stronger magnet?

Suppose you wrap more wire around a nail. Would the nail become a stronger magnet? How can you tell which nail is the strongest magnet?

1. Look at the drawings of the nails. The wire is wrapped around nail A five times. How many times is the wire wrapped around nail B? How many times is the wire wrapped around nail C?

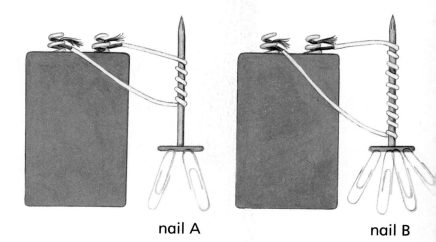

nail A   nail B

C 36

Science Idea Exchange

Science Background
Iron and nickel contain groups of magnetized atoms called magnetic domains. If the domains point in several directions, the material is not a magnet. A current produces a magnetic field. If the field is strong enough, the domains in the iron or nickel line up, and the metal becomes a magnet.

Science and Language Arts
Suggest children write a story about three ordinary nails that were changed into magnets. Tell children to mention what changed the nails, how long the change lasted, how people could tell the nails had changed, and whether different materials were attracted to the nails.

Math/Science Connection
Help children use the information their charts to make a bar graph. T provide further practice in using charts and graphs, have children predict how many paper clips a nai could pick up if the wire were wrapped around the nail 15 times (about six clips). Have them add th to their graph.

2. Draw a chart like this one.

	nail A	nail B	nail C
wire wrapped	5 times	10 times	8 times
paper clips			

3. Write down how many paper clips each nail picked up. Which nail picks up the most paper clips? Which nail has the wire wrapped around it the most times?

Checkpoint

1. Which magnet is the strongest?
2. Does wrapping more wire make a stronger magnet? How do you know?

nail C

Act as a Consultant
Help children identify what is different in each of the three pictures. Guide them to recognize that the number of coils and the number of paper clips is different in each picture.

Close

Check for Understanding
● As a follow-up to the **baseline assessment,** review with children their responses from Make Connections. Ask them what, if any, changes they would like to make in their responses. Encourage children to give reasons for any changes they make.
● **Answers to Checkpoint**   1. The nail with the most wire coils (nail B) is the strongest magnet. 2. Yes, the nail with the most wire coils picked up the most paper clips. The nail with the fewest wire coils picked up the fewest paper clips.

Connecting Lessons
In the next lesson, children will use what they have learned about magnets to write an advertisement for them. ▶

Explorer's Activity Guide
Use Explorer's Activity Guide page 109 to help children solve the question of how to make a magnet stronger. You can also use this hands-on activity page to evaluate how well children understand the concept of this lesson.

Extend the Lesson
Present children with some alternatives to increasing the number of turns in the coil. For example, they may increase the number of batteries used or the wire's thickness. Suggest they draw a picture to show how they would test the alternatives to see which, if any, make a stronger magnet.

Your Ideas

_____

_____

_____

_____

_____

Lesson 9

Lesson Objective
Children write an advertisement to show the concepts they learned in this chapter.

Introduce

Invite Learning
Review the **baseline assessment** activities you used in this chapter. Choose one or more to do again that you think will help children understand the chapter concepts.

Teach

Performance Assessment Activity
Children write an advertisement for magnets. **Skills:** Describing, restating or explaining ideas

Materials (per group)
Module Kit Items: none
School Supplied Items: paper *(1 sheet/child)*; pencil; crayons

Helpful Hint
You might want to have each child write an advertisement for magnets.

Observe and Listen
Encourage children to think of new ways to use magnets in their homes or at school. Guide them to the realization that magnets can be fun to use in toys and are also fun to experiment with.

What did you learn?

What do you know about magnets? You know that magnets have poles. They can pick up some metal things. Magnets can pull through things. You also know that some magnets are stronger than others. Now pretend that you sell magnets. Write an advertisement for magnets.

You will need:  paper   pencil   crayons

Write an ad for magnets.
1. Draw pictures for your ad.
2. You can show how a magnet can help clean your room. You can show how to make a game using magnets.
3. List ways a magnet can be useful.
4. Share your ad with your class.

C 38

 ## Science Idea Exchange

Teacher's Assessment Package
Use the pages from the Teacher's Assessment Package at this time to promote **performance assessment** opportunities for your children.

Science Background
The uses of electromagnets include large industrial electromagnets used to sort scrap metal at junkyards. At the other extreme, small electromagnets are part of the ear piece in telephones. A current passes through an electromagnet in the ear piece, causing it to vibrate and create the sound we hear.

Activity Results
The ads should show an understanding of the characteristics of magnets: the push and pull, magnets' poles, the effect of magnets on certain metals, the different strengths of magnets, the construction of electromagnets, and the variety of uses for magnets.

Share what you learned.

1. How do the magnets in your ad help people?
2. Which way would you use magnets?

Act as a Consultant
Bring several simple advertisements to class. Help children model their magnet advertisements on the ads.

Close
Check for Understanding
- Ask children how magnets can be used to make moving things easier for people. (Magnets can pick up certain metal things. Magnets can work through different materials.)
- **Answers to Share what you learned** Ads should show that magnets have different strengths, can help make pulling and moving some things easier for people, and can pull on some metal objects through different kinds of materials.

Ask Open-ended Questions
To prepare children for the next chapter, review the module literature selection *Ferryboat* by Betsy and Giulio Maestro (Crowell, 1986) with children. Ask: *Where in the story do you think magnets are being used? Do you think magnets can help make things easier to move? What other objects do people use to make it easier to move things?*

Connecting Chapters
In the next chapter, children will discover that simple machines can make it easier to move things. ▶

Explorer's Activity Guide
Use Explorer's Activity Guide page 110 as a hands-on activity to evaluate how well children understand the concepts covered in this chapter.

Alternate Activity
Ask children to create a class story book entitled, "The Story of Magnets." Allow them to work in pairs, each pair writing and illustrating eight chapters, one for each lesson. Invite the pairs to share each chapter with the class by reading it and describing the pictures.

Collaborative Learning: Small Groups
Assign specific children to gather and clean up materials. All members of the Chapter Review group should be involved in writing and illustrating the advertisement and in sharing the ad with the class.

Chapter 3 Planning Guide
Moving and Machines

Lessons / *Skills*

Lesson 1
Discover Activity: **What is the easiest way to move a box?**
pp. C40–C41
(observing, identifying and suggesting alternatives)

Lesson 2
What is a machine? pp. C42–C43
(comparing, describing)

Lesson 3
How can a ramp help move things? pp. C44–C45
(observing, recognizing cause and effect)

Lesson 4
How can a lever help move things? pp. C46–C47
(experimenting)

Lesson 5
Let's Explore: **How do ball bearings help move things?**
pp. C48–C49
(recording, making physical models)

Lesson 6
How are body parts like a machine? pp. C50–C51
(comparing, observing, classifying)

Lesson 7
How do you move? pp. C52–C53
(observing)

Lesson 8
Let's Explore: **How do muscles work?** pp. C54–C55
(observing, making physical models)

Lesson 9
Let's Solve It!: **How many bones do body parts have?**
pp. C56–C57
(organizing information, solving problems)

Lesson 10
Chapter Review: **What did you learn?** pp. C58–C59
(recording, organizing information)

Materials (per group)

Lesson 1 Activity: *What is the easiest way to move a box?*
Module Kit Items: wax paper *(about 1 m)*; 4 marbles
School Supplied Items: 3 rubber balls *(same size)*; 2 baseball bats *(or pencils)*; 2 or 3 books; cardboard box *(or shoe box)*; skateboard *(or toy trucks)*

Lesson 3 Activity: *Use a ramp.*
Module Kit Items: piece of string *(about 1 m)*; large rubber band; board
School Supplied Items: book; small chair
Safety Kit Items: cover goggles *(1/child)*
Advance Prep: Cut string into 1-meter lengths ahead of time. You might want to tie the string and rubber band to the book before the activity.

Lesson 4 Activity: *Use a lever.*
Module Kit Items: masking tape; wooden ruler
School Supplied Items: book; 3 pencils
Advance Prep: Make the fulcrum for each group by taping the pencils together so that they form a small pyramid.

Lesson 5 Activity: *How do ball bearings help move things?*
Module Kit Items: piece of string *(about 1 m)*; jar lid; 10 marbles; large rubber band
School Supplied Items: large book
Safety Kit Items: cover goggles *(1/child)*
Advance Prep: Cut string into 1-m lengths ahead of time.

Lesson 8 Activity: *How do muscles work?*
Module Kit Items: balloon; brass fastener
School Supplied Items: 2 pieces cardboard
Safety Kit Items: cover goggles *(1/child)*
Advance Prep: Make two bones for each group from a 20-cm x 50-cm cardboard strip. Cut a slit on one bone at the end opposite where the brass fastener will attach. Cut a slit in the center of the other bone.

Lesson 10 Activity: *Make a book.*
Module Kit Items: none
School Supplied Items: crayons; construction paper *(1 sheet/child)*; drawing paper *(2 sheets/child)*; pencils *(1/child)*
Advance Prep: You might want to help children generate ideas by bringing to class pictures of machines and people doing various activities.

Assessment Options

	Content	Performance	Portfolio
Teacher's Assessment Package			
Chapter Test, pp. 61–62	✓		✓
Group Interview Assessment, p. 63	✓	✓	✓
Performance Strategies, p. 64	✓	✓	✓
Explorer's Activity Guide			
Activity worksheets, pp. 111–122		✓	✓
Chapter Review, pp. 123–124	✓		✓
Interactive Transparency Package			
Transparency 12 and BLM	✓	✓	✓
Teacher's Guide, pp. 28–29	✓	✓	
Hands-on activity for second-language learners	✓	✓	✓
Science Literature Library			
Machines at Work		✓	✓
Interactive Videodisc Software **Teacher's Guide,** pp. 62–70			
Computer-based Activity	✓	✓	
Journal Presentations	✓	✓	✓
Videodisc Classroom Guide, pp. 25–32, or **Video Reader**			
Hands-on activity	✓	✓	✓
ExploraCenter Teacher's Guide, pp. 8, 10, 11, 19, 21, 23, 33, 34, 35			
ExploraCenter			
Science activity cards 3, 5, 6, 14, 16, 18, 28, 29, 30	✓	✓	✓
ScottForesman Online Service			
Online field trips	✓	✓	✓
	✓	✓	✓

Chapter Overview

Children begin this chapter by finding the easiest way to move a box. Then they experiment with a ramp, a lever, and ball bearings to see how these machines help move things. They learn about their muscles, bones, and joints and how these help the body move.

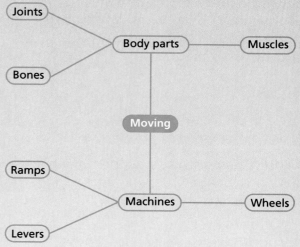

Lesson Objective
Children use prior knowledge to explore ways to make moving an object easier.

Introduce

Invite Learning
Show the videodisc segment for this chapter. Bar codes and a description of this segment are given below on page C41.

Make Connections
To **assess prior knowledge**, point to a heavy object and ask children how they could move it. Children may think they can move only things lighter than they are. Record their responses as a **baseline assessment.**

Teach

Discover Activity

Children demonstrate ways of moving a heavy box. **Skills:** Observing, identifying and suggesting alternatives

Materials (per group)
Module Kit Items: wax paper *(about 1 m)*; 4 marbles
School Supplied Items: 3 rubber balls *(same size)*; 2 baseball bats *(or pencils)*; 2 or 3 books; cardboard box *(or shoe box)*; skateboard *(or toy trucks)*

Chapter 3
Moving and Machines

Suppose you want to move the teddy bear. The picture shows a hard way to move it. Can you think of an easier way to move the bear?

You move things every day. Just look around you. Find things that you can move. What could help you make something easier to move?

C 40

Science Idea Exchange

Collaborative Learning: Small Groups
Assign specific children to gather and clean up materials. All children in the Discover Activity group should try ways to move the box and be involved in answering questions and sharing results.

Family/School Partnership: Family Support
Encourage families to be active partners in learning by suggesting that they and their children:
- observe wheels, ramps, and levers at home and in their neighborhood,
- access the *Young America* electronic field trip presented by ScottForesman and Delphi Internet.

Science and Literature
The chapter literature selection, *Machines at Work* by Byron Barton (Crowell, 1987), may be used to help children recognize that complex machines are combinations of simple machines. Have children review the selection after each lesson and identify the simple machines pictured.

What is the easiest way to move a box?

1 Drag the mystery box across the floor.

2 How hard did you work to drag that box?

3 Find things that can help you move the mystery box. Now how hard do you work?

4 **Tell about it.** Tell about things that helped you move the box.

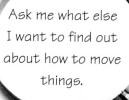

Ask me what else I want to find out about how to move things.

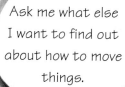

C 41

Helpful Hints
- Toy trucks or cars could be substituted for the skateboard.
- Shoe skates will not work.
- *See Equipment Kit Teacher's Guide for additional hints.*

What to Expect
Children will probably say that it is easier to drag the mystery box when it is placed on something round.

Close

Check for Understanding
- As a follow-up to the **baseline assessment,** ask children if they would like to change or add to their responses.
- **Answers to Tell about it** Children should tell how they used wax paper, wheels, balls, bats, rollers, and any other objects to help them move the box.

What Else Do You Want to Find Out?
Using a **constructivist** approach, ask: *What did you do to make moving the box easier? What other questions do you have about how to make moving things easier? How can we find the answers to your questions?* Refer to the questions throughout the chapter.

Connecting Lessons
In the next lesson, children will discover that machines make moving objects easier. ▶

Explorer's Activity Guide
The **Discover Activity recording sheet** on page 111 of the Explorer's Activity Guide can be used by children to record their activity results.

Visual Literacy

Discover the Wonder Videodisc, Grade 2, Module C, presents a series of still images showing simple and complex machines across time periods and cultures. Use these images to increase children's awareness and appreciation of the antiquity of certain simple machines and their development through history.

Bar Codes

Chapter 14: Stills

Step

Interactive Software

Lesson 2

Lesson Objective
Children discover that machines make work easier and learn about some types of machines.

Introduce

Key Terms
machine
wheel

Invite Learning
Display tools such as a screwdriver, can opener, and nutcracker. Invite children to explain how each of these objects is used. Ask: *What do these items have in common?* (They all help you do things, or help make work easier.)

Make Connections
To **assess prior knowledge,** have children look again at the objects from Invite Learning. Ask: *Which of the items are machines?* Ask other questions, such as: *How would you get a screw into wood without a screwdriver?* Record children's responses to use as a **baseline assessment.**

Teach

Observe and Listen
Encourage pairs of children to look at the photographs on pages C42 and C43 and identify the machines they see. Ask them to describe to each other what each machine does.

What is a machine?

Close your eyes and think of a machine. Maybe you think of something big like a truck. Maybe you think of something small like a wagon. Anything that makes work easier is a **machine.** Bicycles and baby strollers are machines. Hammers are machines too. What other machines can you think of?

C 42

Science Idea Exchange

Science Background
Scientifically, a simple machine is a tool consisting of one or two parts that (1) multiplies the force, (2) changes the direction of the force, or (3) changes the speed at which the force acts. There are two general groups of simple machines—levers, which includes pulleys and wheel and axles, and inclined planes, which includes wedges and screws. These simple machines combine to make compound and complex machines.

The pupil text uses a more general definition of "machine," does not limit the discussion to simple machines, and includes objects such as wheels and ball bearings. These objects, while not machines in the scientific definition, make work easier because they reduce friction between moving parts.

Science and Language Arts
Invite children to write an acrostic about machines. Have children write the word "machine" vertically along the left margin of their paper. Then have them use the letter at the beginning of each line to begin the first word of that line. Encourage children to share their acrostics with the class.

Remember how you moved the box in the last lesson. Maybe you used a machine! The girl in the picture put a skateboard under a box. The wheels can help move the box. A **wheel** is a kind of machine. How can you find out more about machines? You can try using them!

Checkpoint
Draw someone using a machine to make moving a heavy box easier.

Invite children to make their own definition for "machine." Record the definition on chart paper. Allow children to change their definition as they progress through the chapter.

Close

Check for Understanding
- As a follow-up to the **baseline assessment**, have children look again at the objects from Invite Learning. Ask: *Which of these objects are machines?* Encourage children to give reasons for their answers. If necessary, refer them to their definition for "machine."
- **Answers to Checkpoint** Illustrations may include machines such as wheels, rollers, levers, forklifts, cranes, and so on.

Ask Open-ended Questions
To guide children into the next three lessons, ask them to think about the many different machines they use each day. Ask: *How do you think your life would be different if there were no machines?* (Possible answers: I would have to walk to school. It would take longer to do things.)

Connecting Lessons
In the next lesson, children will learn that a ramp can make work easier. ▶

Explorer's Activity Guide
Use Explorer's Activity Guide page 113 with this lesson to help children answer the text question, "What is a machine?" with a hands-on activity.

Math/Science Connection
Display several toys, or pictures of toys, and have children count the number of wheels on each. For example, how many wheels are there on 2 tricycles? on 1 bicycle and 1 toy car? on 2 roller skates and 1 skateboard?

Visual Literacy
Have children use a camera to take pictures of machines in their home, playground, and neighborhood. Display the pictures on a bulletin board. As children learn more about machines, have them label any machines they know.

Lesson 3

Lesson Objective
Children find out that a ramp can be used to make work easier.

Introduce

Key Term
ramp

Invite Learning
Ask children to think about how they could use a board to move a large ball to the top of a stack of books without picking up the ball.

Make Connections
To **assess prior knowledge,** ask children to demonstrate their solution to the challenge in Invite Learning. If possible, videotape their trials and use the video as a **baseline assessment.**

Teach

Activity
Children demonstrate how a ramp reduces the amount of force needed to lift an object. **Skills:** Observing, recognizing cause and effect

Materials (per group)
Module Kit Items: piece of string *(about 1 m);* large rubber band; board
School Supplied Items: book; small chair
Safety Kit Items: cover goggles *(1/child)*

How can a ramp help move things?

Pretend you are pushing a friend in a wheelchair. You come to the school. How will you get the heavy wheelchair to the school door? You see a **ramp.** The ramp can make your work easier.

A ramp is a kind of machine. A ramp helps you move things to a higher or lower place using less force. How can you use a ramp?

C 44

 Science Idea Exchange

Science Background
A ramp is an inclined plane. Wedges and screws are actually modified inclined planes. A wedge, such as a sewing needle, a knife, or an ax, is two inclined planes put back to back. A screw is an inclined plane wrapped around a shaft. The edges of the plane form the threads on the screw.

Science and Language Arts
Suggest that children observe places around their school and neighborhood where, if they were in a wheelchair, they would and would not be able to go. Have them identify places where ramps would be helpful. Have children write a letter to a friend explaining why a ramp would be helpful in one place they observed.

Collaborative Learning: Small Groups
Assign specific children to gather and clean up materials. All children in the Activity group should set up materials, move the book with and without a ramp, draw their observations, and share results.

Use a ramp.

You will need: cover goggles  rubber band book string chair  ramp

1. Tie the string around the book. Tie the rubber band to the string.
2. Put the book on the floor next to the chair.
3. Pull on the rubber band to raise the book as high as the chair seat.
4. Lean a ramp against the chair. Put the book at the bottom of the ramp.
5. Hold the rubber band. Pull the book up the ramp as high as the chair seat. How does the ramp help you move the book?

Checkpoint
Draw the easiest way to move the book. Tell how you know.

Safety Tips
- Children should use cover goggles when pulling with the rubber band.
- Children should not pull the rubber band toward their face.

Helpful Hints
- Be sure to have children rest the ramp against a child-size chair. If the ramp slips, anchor it with clay.
- *See Equipment Kit Teacher's Guide for additional hints.*

Raise Questions
Invite children to think about how a ramp is used in the literature selection *Ferryboat* by Betsy and Giulio Maestro (Crowell, 1986). Ask: *Why does the ferryboat need a ramp?* (so the cars can get on and off the boat)

Close

Check for Understanding
- As a follow-up to the **baseline assessment**, review with children their videotape from Make Connections. Ask if their ideas have changed.
- **Answers to Checkpoint** Drawings should show the book being pulled up the ramp. The rubber band stretches less, showing that the ramp makes moving the book easier.

Connecting Lessons
In the next lesson, children will learn that a lever can make work easier. ▶

Explorer's Activity Guide
Use Explorer's Activity Guide hands-on activity on page 114 to help children answer the question, "How can a ramp help move things?"

Teacher's Assessment Package
A **scoring rubric** to assess student performance is provided on page 59 of the Teacher's Assessment Package.

Activity Results
The rubber band will stretch the most when the book is lifted straight up. The rubber band will stretch the least when the book is pulled up the ramp.

Extend the Lesson
Ask children to predict what would happen to the length of the rubber band if the book were pulled up ramps of different steepness. Have children test the predictions by repeating the experiment with increased and decreased ramp steepness.

Lesson 4

Introduce

Key Term
lever

Invite Learning
Put books or rocks in a lunchbox to make it heavy. Invite children, one by one, to lift one edge of the lunchbox off a table or desk. Tell them to think about the heaviness of the lunchbox.

Make Connections
To **assess prior knowledge**, tell children to use a wooden ruler and an eraser to again lift one edge of the lunchbox. Watch for the use of the ruler as a lever and the eraser as the fulcrum—the point on which the lever turns. Record children's methods in a chart and save it as a **baseline assessment**.

Teach

Activity
Children demonstrate how a lever reduces the amount of force needed to lift an object. **Skill:** Experimenting

Materials (per group)
Module Kit Items: masking tape; wooden ruler
School Supplied Items: book; 3 pencils

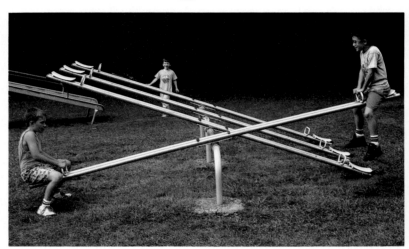

How can a lever help move things?

The children in the picture are playing on a seesaw. They can lift each other into the air. A seesaw is another kind of machine. It is called a **lever**. A lever helps you move things using less force. You can push down on one end of a lever to lift something on the other end.

C 46

Science Idea Exchange

Science Anecdote
Children are likely to be familiar with several examples of levers. Tell them they use or see levers regularly, such as seesaws and pull-tops on soft drink cans.

Science and Social Studies
Finding ways to move water from a river to a field of crops has concerned farmers from the earliest civilizations. Over 3500 years ago, Egyptian hydrologists (water experts) designed the shaduf, a lever used to lift water buckets from a river to an irrigation ditch that brought the water to farmers' fields.

Explore Further
Challenge children to design a new machine to do a certain job. They should draw and label a picture of their machine, or use materials such as boxes and paper tubes to construct their machine. Encourage children to explain how their machines work and what they do.

Use a lever.

You will need: book   3 pencils
wooden ruler   masking tape

1. Put the pencils under the ruler.
2. Put the book on one end of the ruler.
3. Push down the other end of the ruler. How hard do you push to move the book?
4. Move the pencils closer to the book. Push down again.
5. Move the pencils farther away from the book. Push down again. How hard did you push down this time?

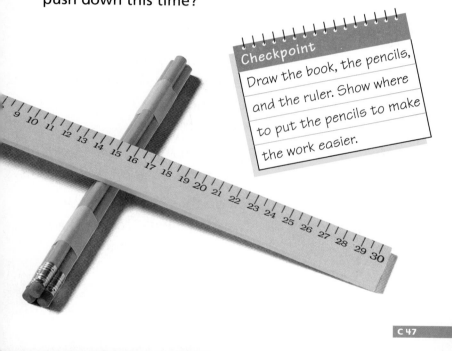

Checkpoint
Draw the book, the pencils, and the ruler. Show where to put the pencils to make the work easier.

C 47

Lesson 5

Lesson Objective
Children learn that ball bearings help make objects easier to move.

Introduce

Invite Learning
Invite children to compare moving a book resting on several pencils to moving one resting on blocks.

Make Connections
To assess **prior knowledge,** have children explain why the book was easier to move when it was placed on objects that roll. Record children's responses as a **baseline assessment.**

Teach

Activity
Children demonstrate how ball bearings make objects easier to move. **Skills:** Recording, making physical models

Materials (per group)
Module Kit Items: piece of string *(about 1 m);* jar lid; 10 marbles; large rubber band
School Supplied Item: large book
Safety Kit Items: cover goggles *(1/child)*

Safety Tip
Remind children to keep the jar lid away from the table's edge so that marbles do not fall on the floor.

C 48

Let's Explore

How do ball bearings help move things?

Ball bearings are smooth round balls that can help move things. You can find out how ball bearings work.

Find out about it.

1 Tie the string around the book. Tie the string to the rubber band.

2 Place the book on the jar lid.

3 Pull on the rubber band until the book starts moving. Notice how much the rubber band stretches.

4 Put the marbles under the jar lid. Put the book on the lid.

5 Pull on the rubber band until the book moves. Notice how much the rubber band stretches.

You will need:

 cover goggles

 large book

 10 to 15 marbles

 jar lid with rim

 string

 large rubber band

Science Idea Exchange

Science Background
Ball bearings reduce friction, making objects easier to move. Bearings are an important part of most industrial activity and production. They are used inside generators and turbines and in tools needed to make other tools.

Science and Language Arts
Invite children to write an acrostic for "ball bearings." You might start with the following example.

Big or small
Always round
Let you move things easily
Let you move yourself

Encourage students to complete the acrostic.

Achieving English Proficiency
Encourage children to make a catalog of machines. Have them draw or find pictures of machines in magazines for their catalog. Have them find and label the machines that they can recognize in each picture and write a short description of their uses.

Write about it.

Make a chart like this. Draw how the rubber band looks when the book moves.

book	how the rubber band looks
without marbles	
with marbles	

Checkpoint

1. Did the marbles help move the book? How do you know?

2. Take Action! Draw an imaginary toy that has ball bearings.

C 49

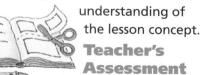

Lesson 6

Lesson Objective
Children learn that some parts of their bodies work like machines.

Introduce

Invite Learning
Ask children to demonstrate or pantomime some physical activities, such as running, throwing, catching, kicking, and swimming.

Make Connections
To **assess prior knowledge**, have children identify, on a body outline poster, the body parts that make moving things easier. Ask children to identify any body parts that they think might act like machines. Keep the labeled poster as a **baseline assessment** that you can use for a follow-up in Check for Understanding.

Teach

Observe and Listen
Divide the class into groups of three or four. Allow the members of a group to take turns pantomiming an action or movement. Other group members should identify the movement and the body parts involved. They can then describe how the body parts help make moving something easier.

How are body parts like a machine?

Mmm! The milk tastes so good. You lift the glass for another sip. Your arm is working like a machine. Your arm is a lever when you bend it to lift the glass.

C 50

Science Idea Exchange

Science Anecdote
Covered by muscle, tissue, and skin, the human skeleton is a hidden wealth of machines. Jaws and forearms are examples of levers. A tooth is a wedge (two ramps that are back-to-back).

Science and Health
Invite children to write a story about how their bodies act like machines. Have them **describe** how they use their hands, legs, feet, and jaws. Suggest that some children write from a perspective of taking care of their "machines."

Multicultural Connection
In the 8th and 9th centuries, superstition hampered the practice of medicine in Europe. However, Muslim physicians throughout Spain, North Africa, and the Middle East developed cures based on a patient's symptoms and the effect of treatment. Besides treating illnesses, these licensed physicians performed delicate surgery.

Other parts of your body can work like machines too. What happens when you throw a ball into the air? Your whole arm moves around in your shoulder. The upper end of your arm bone moves like a ball bearing.

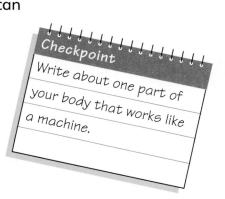

Checkpoint

Write about one part of your body that works like a machine.

Ask for Evidence

Remind children that the definition of a machine is something that makes work easier. Ask: *Are teeth machines?* (yes) *Why?* (because they make breaking up food easier) Ask: *Are arms machines?* (yes) *Why?* (because they make lifting things easier)

Act as a Consultant

Help children recognize that a tooth is like two ramps placed back-to-back forming a triangular shape—a wedge. Challenge children to demonstrate how a wedge separates material, like a boat separating water or a tooth separating food.

Close

Check for Understanding

- As a follow-up to the **baseline assessment**, ask children if they would change or add anything to the body outline poster.
- **Answers to Checkpoint** Children will probably describe how the arm acts as a lever and the upper end of the arm bones moves like a ball bearing. They might mention how other body parts make work easier for people.

Connecting Lessons

In the next lesson, children will learn how muscles that are attached to bones move their bodies. ▶

Explorer's Activity Guide

Use Explorer's Activity Guide page 117 with this lesson to help children answer the text question, "How are body parts like a machine?" with a hands-on activity.

Visual Literacy

Have children take pictures of people using their bodies in sports games, doing chores, at their jobs, and while eating. Post the pictures and have the class identify the activity and the body part that is acting like a machine.

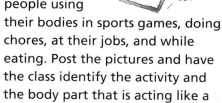

Your Ideas

_____

_____

_____

_____

_____

Lesson 7

Lesson Objective
Children learn that their bones and muscles work together to move their bodies in different ways.

Introduce

Key Terms
muscle
bone
joint

Invite Learning
Invite children to play a game of "Simon Says" involving bending at a joint. Have "Simon" request a variety of exercises such as arm bends, lifting a knee to the chest, and bending at the waist.

Make Connections
To **assess prior knowledge,** ask children to select one of the movements they just made in "Simon Says" and explain what happens inside their body to make that movement. Tape-record their responses as a **baseline assessment.**

Teach

Observe and Listen
- Divide the class into small groups and assign part of the body for each group to investigate, such as head and arms.
- Encourage group members to describe the movement of the body part to one another.

How do you move?

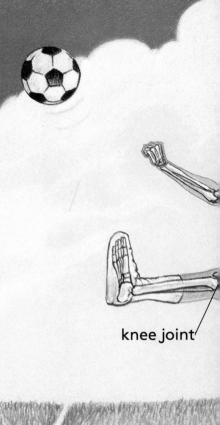

Muscles and **bones** help you move. Bones move when muscles pull on them.

Find the place where the leg bones come together at the knee. A place where bones come together is a **joint.** Joints help your body bend, turn, and twist.

Now find the muscles near the joint. These muscles work with the bones to help move the girl's leg.

knee joint

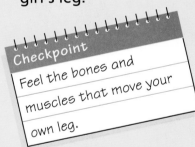

Checkpoint
Feel the bones and muscles that move your own leg.

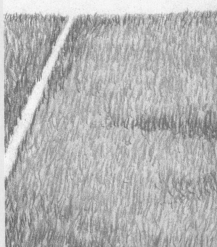

C 52

 ## Science Idea Exchange

Science Background
Muscles work together to move bones. For example, when raising your arm, one group of muscles contracts to pull your arm upward. When lowering your arm, another group of muscles contracts, pulling your arm downward.

Special Education
Show children X rays, or photographs of X rays, of joints and bones. Invite children to identify the joints and bones in each X ray and point to the comparable part of their body.

Your Ideas

Bones

Muscles

C 53

C 53

Act as a Consultant

Guide children in making a simple model that shows muscles move bones by taping both ends of a piece of tape to both ends of a pencil. Allow the middle of the tape to bulge up slightly. Children can then pull up on the tape toward one end and see how the pencil moves. Ask what body part is like the pencil (a bone) and what body part is like the tape (a muscle).

Encourage Student Definitions

Ask children how they would describe what a joint is to a younger child.

Close

Check for Understanding

● As a follow-up to the **baseline assessment,** play back children's tape-recorded response. Then ask children again to explain a body movement. Look for a greater understanding of muscles and bones working together.

● **Answers to Checkpoint** Children should be able to locate muscles and bones of the thigh, calf, abdomen, and back that participate in moving the leg. Muscles identified will be different depending on whether the leg is moved forward or backward.

Connecting Lessons

In the next lesson, children will learn more about how muscles work. ▶

Explorer's Activity Guide

Use Explorer's Activity Guide page 119 with this lesson to help children answer the text question, "How do you move?" with a hands-on activity.

Science Themes

By discussing how bones and muscles work together to move their bodies, children develop an understanding of the theme of **systems and interactions.**

Visual Literacy

To enhance the **visual literacy** connection, use the interactive overhead transparency that correlates with the above two pages. The transparency will help your students understand the key concepts presented on these pages.

Lesson 8

Lesson Objective
Children learn how bones and muscles work together.

Introduce

Invite Learning
Pair children and have one observe the partner's biceps muscle as he or she slowly moves the forearm up and down. Then have the same child bend the arm slowly while holding a book. Children can take turns making this movement, comparing how the muscle looks.

Make Connections
To **assess prior knowledge,** ask children to explain how they think bones and muscles work together. Record their responses as a **baseline assessment.**

Teach

Activity
Children construct a model of the human arm and illustrate how the muscles and bones of the arm work together. **Skills:** Observing, making physical models

Materials (per group)
Module Kit Items: balloon; brass fastener
School Supplied Items: 2 pieces cardboard *(20 cm x 50 cm)*
Safety Kit Items: cover goggles *(1/child)*

How do muscles work?

How do bones and muscles work together? You can do this activity to find out how they work.

Find out about it.

You will need:

 cover goggles

 2 cardboard bones

 long balloon

 paper fastener

1 Get cardboard models of bones from your teacher.

2 Put the bones together with the paper fastener.

3 Blow air into the balloon. Tie a knot in each end of the balloon.

4 Slide the knots of the balloon muscle into the slits in the cardboard bones.

5 Move the bones. How does the muscle look?

C 54

 ## Science Idea Exchange

Science Background
The human body has three kinds of muscles. Skeletal muscles (in the arms, legs, and chest) hold the bones of the skeleton in place and make the body move. Smooth muscles (in the stomach walls) control the various body processes. The cardiac muscle is found only in the heart.

Collaborative Learning: Small Groups
Assign specific children to gather and clean up materials. All children in the Let's Explore group should assemble the model arm, move the bones and muscles, record data, and share results.

Your Ideas
_____
_____
_____
_____
_____

Write about it. ✏️

Make a chart like this one. Write what you found out.

bones	How does the muscle look?
bones open wide	
bones close together	

Checkpoint
1. How does the muscle change when the bones move?
2. Take Action! Make your model show how to throw a ball underhand.

C 55

Helpful Hints
- Make two cardboard bones for each group. On one bone, cut a slit opposite the fastener. Cut a slit in the center of the other bone.
- Punch a hole at one end of each bone for the fastener.
- *See Equipment Kit Teacher's Guide for additional hints.*

Raise Questions
Ask: *How is this model like your arm?* (The muscle gets thicker when bones pull together and thinner when they move apart.) *How is it different?* (In the arm, the muscle pulls on the bone.)

Close

Check for Understanding
- As a follow-up to the **baseline assessment,** have children **describe** what happens to the muscle, bones, and joint in the activity.
- **Answers to Checkpoint** 1. As the bones move toward one another, the muscle gets thicker and shorter. As the bones move apart, the muscle gets longer and thinner. 2. **Take Action!** Children should straighten and then bend the model to show the motion of throwing a ball.

Connecting Lessons
In the next lesson, children will learn the number of bones in different parts of the body. ▶

Explorer's Activity Guide
Use Explorer's Activity Guide hands-on activity on page 121 to explore muscles and evaluate children's understanding of the lesson concept.

Teacher's Assessment Package
A **scoring rubric** to assess student performance is provided on page 60 of the Teacher's Assessment Package.

Activity Results
Children's charts should show that the balloon muscle is long and thin when the bones are far apart, and short and thick when the bones are close together.

Explore Further
Challenge children to find examples of muscle pairs. Have children raise one leg with the knee bent and feel their muscles on the top and under the thigh. The top muscle will be contracted, and the bottom muscle will be relaxed.

Lesson 9

Lesson Objective
Children learn about the number of bones in different parts of the body.
Skills: Organizing information, solving problems

Introduce
Invite Learning
Invite children to draw what they think a human skeleton looks like. Suggest that they do their drawing without looking at a book or other references.

Make Connections
To **assess prior knowledge**, have children predict which part of their body contains the most bones. Ask children to estimate how many bones are in their hand, head, and foot. Record their estimates as a **baseline assessment.**

Teach
Observe and Listen
- Have children form small groups and invite each group to study the skeleton picture.
- Allow groups to discuss proposed answers and reach an agreement before filling in the chart.

How many bones do body parts have?

Think about the bones in your body. Some body parts have more bones than other body parts. You can find out how many bones some body parts have.

1. Look at the picture. The hand has 27 bones. How many bones are in your foot?
2. Copy the chart below.
3. Write how many bones are in different parts of your body.

part of body	number of bones
head	22
arm	
hand	
leg	
foot	
spine	

 ## Science Idea Exchange

Science Background
The center of a bone contains a soft substance called bone marrow. Bone marrow produces new blood cells. Bone marrow from a healthy person may be transplanted into another person to treat some diseases of the blood.

Math/Science Connection
Suggest that children find out the total number of bones in the body by adding up the numbers of bones in each part of the body. Encourage children to find out whether cats, dogs, or fish have more or fewer bones than people do. Have children order the animals showing increasing number of bones.

Science and Health
Have children work in small groups. Let each child take a turn moving one of his or her joints. Let the other children in the group identify whether that joint moves like a hinge on a door (elbows, knees, knuckles) or moves around in a circle (shoulders, hips, head).

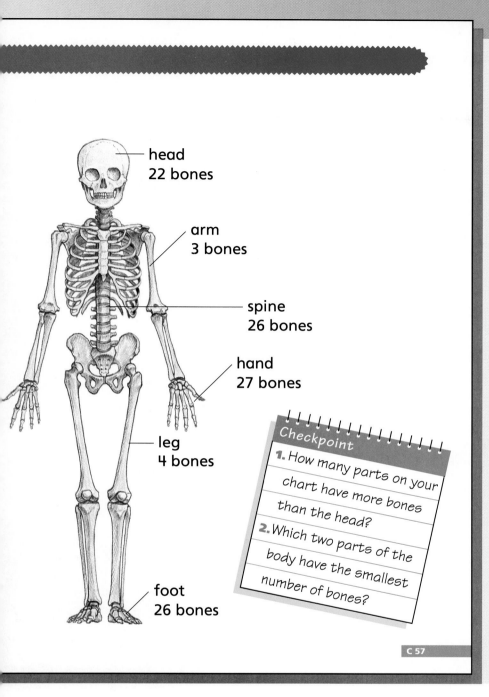

head
22 bones

arm
3 bones

spine
26 bones

hand
27 bones

leg
4 bones

foot
26 bones

Checkpoint

1. How many parts on your chart have more bones than the head?

2. Which two parts of the body have the smallest number of bones?

Ask: *Why do you think the hands and feet have so many bones?* (Both need to be able to make many movements.)

Close

Check for Understanding

- As a follow-up to the **baseline assessment,** review with children the estimates they gave in Make Connections. Ask children if they would like to change any of their answers.
- **Answers to Checkpoint** 1. Three body parts on the chart have more bones than the head. 2. The arm and leg have the smallest number of bones.

Connecting Lessons

In the next lesson, children will make a book to review the concepts of this chapter. ▶

Explorer's Activity Guide

Use Explorer's Activity Guide page 122 to help children solve the question of how many bones body parts have. You can also use this hands-on activity page to evaluate how well children understand the concept of this lesson.

Achieving English Proficiency

Show children pictures of body parts such as head, arms, hands, legs, and feet. Then play a game of "Simon Says," directing children to indicate specific body parts as they are named.

Science and Music

Teach children the song "Dry Bones." Invite them to point to each bone as it is named in the song.

Lesson 10

Lesson Objective
Children make a book to show the concepts they learned in this chapter.

Introduce

Invite Learning
Review the **baseline assessment** activities you used in this chapter. Choose one or more to do again that you think will help children understand the chapter concepts.

Teach

Performance Assessment Activity
Children make a book about machines.
Skills: Recording, organizing information

Materials (per group)
Module Kit Items: none
School Supplied Items: crayons; construction paper (*1 sheet/child*); drawing paper (*2 sheets/child*); pencils (*1/child*)

Helpful Hints
- You may wish to spark children's ideas by bringing to class a selection of pictures showing machines and people doing various activities.
- You could staple the pages of children's books inside the covers.

What did you learn?

You learned about some machines that help move things. You know about ramps and levers and ball bearings. You learned that some parts of your body act like machines! Now you can make your own book about machines.

Make a book.

You will need: 2 sheets of paper   pencil crayons construction paper

1. Draw a picture that shows you moving something with a machine.
2. Write the name of the machine at the top of the picture.
3. Draw a picture that shows you using a body part like a machine.
4. Write a sentence that tells how the body part is like a machine.
5. Make a cover for your book. Put the pages inside the cover.

Science Idea Exchange

Teacher's Assessment Package
Use the pages from the Teacher's Assessment Package at this time to promote **performance assessment** opportunities for your children.

Save the Earth
Point out that all machines use energy, whether supplied by your body, the sun, a fuel such as gasoline, or some other source. Explain that using energy supplied by fuels efficiently at home will help lead to a cleaner environment because less fuel will be used to run the machines. Have children **list** machines they use that they could use less often or do without.

Alternate Activity
Invite children to make up a pantomime about a machine that makes moving an object easier. Encourage them to explain the kind of machine they are illustrating. Have them demonstrate body movements involved in moving an object and explain how muscles and bones make the movements possible.

Share what you learned.

1. How do the machines in your book help you?
2. What machines would you use to move books from one room to another?

C 59

People at Work

Nature of Work
Bicycle factory workers know about the many parts of a bicycle. They also know that the same part can be made lighter, heavier, thicker, or thinner and how these parts may be put together to make different kinds of bicycles.

Places of Work
There are bicycle factories across the United States. Factories that make special kinds of bikes, such as racing bikes, may be small or medium sized. However, most bicycle factories are large and employ hundreds of workers who do different jobs.

Training
Many bicycle designers have degrees in physics or engineering. Some bicycle racers learn enough about how a bicycle works and what they need to win that they design their own bicycles. Many assembly-line workers have completed training courses, while other workers receive on-the-job training after completing high school.

Preparation
Children interested in bicycle design might join a bicycle racing club or a club that sponsors other kinds of bicycle competitions.

People at Work

A visit to a bicycle factory

A bicycle factory is a busy place. You hear noisy machines. You see many workers. You might wonder what these workers do.

It takes many **factory workers** to make a bicycle. Each worker needs to know how to use special machines. Some workers make bicycle parts. Some workers spray the bicycles with paint. Other workers put the bicycle parts together. One day you might see the bicycles in a store!

C 60

 ## Science Idea Exchange

Examine the Career
Ask children what bicycle factory workers need to know to do their job (how a bicycle works, how to work the machines in the factory, how to put a bicycle together).

Explore Further
Children interested in learning more about occupations in bicycle manufacturing can put together a scrapbook of articles and pictures that relate to bikes and bike manufacturing. You might wish to organize a visit to a local manufacturing plant or bike shop.

How does a bicycle work?

5 The brakes make the bicycle stop. Some bicycles have levers that work the brakes.

1 The frame of the bicycle holds other parts of the bicycle together.

2 The pedals move the chain.

3 The chain moves the back wheel.

4 The ball bearings help the wheels move around.

Checkpoint

How does a bicycle make it easier for you to get from one place to another?

C 61

Science Background
You may wish to share some of the following information about bicycles and bicycle factories with children:
- The first bicycle was constructed in 1839 by Scottish inventor Kirkpatrick Macmillan.
- The first bicycle manufacturing process was begun in 1867 by Frenchman Pierre Michaux.
- Bicycles were first manufactured in the United States in 1878 by a man named A. A. Pope.
- It may take a month to make a single bicycle frame.
- Some frames are assembled by hand; others, such as those made in Taiwan, are assembled by robots.
- The bicycle factory makes the frame and may make or purchase the other parts such as gears, pedals, brakes, and seat. Although the frames are assembled at the factory, the remaining bicycle parts are usually put on at the retailer or bicycle shop.

Discussion
Discuss how the parts of a bicycle work together to move the bike. Children can explain the push-and-pull forces involved.

Answers to Checkpoint
Answers may vary but should include the idea that, using the same amount of force, you can go farther on a bicycle than you can on foot. Students might point out the crank and pedals and the wheels as machines that make riding the bicycle easier than walking.

Collaborative Learning: Small Groups
Have groups of three children work together on an "assembly line" to make a collage scene showing a bicycle race. One child might draw the elements (sky, land, bicycles); another might color the elements; a third might cut out and glue the elements.

Module Review

Show What You Know

- Use the first text paragraph to begin assessing what children know about motion. Children can brainstorm a list of items to include in the playground. Record their ideas on the chalkboard.
- Some children may have limited exposure to playgrounds that have a variety of rides and equipment. Help them consider the possible diversity as they use the concepts they have learned—and their imaginations—in developing ideas.

Plan Your Playground

Have children list their steps verbally or in writing before beginning their projects. Ask how they will share their projects. Some children may decide to write, while others prefer oral presentations.

Assessment Projects

- **Make a chart** Children may need help in developing their charts. Suggest that they use the column headings "Ride," "Change," and "What Happens." In the first column, children should name a piece of playground equipment (for example, a swing). In the second column, they should explain how they would change the equipment (for example, big push). In the third column, they should describe the expected result (goes higher).

Module Review

Show what you know.

Think about things you see in a playground. Some things can move up and down. Some things can move around. Now think about how you could plan a new playground. Use what you know about force, magnets, and machines to help you.

Plan your playground.

1. Choose a project to do.
2. What will you do first?
3. What will your project look like when it is finished?
4. Decide how to share your project.

Make a chart.

Imagine making rides in a playground go faster or slower. Imagine making rides go higher or lower. Make a chart of playground rides. Show ways you can change how the rides move.

ride   change   what happens

C 62

Science Idea Exchange

Develop a Project

Children may choose to do one of the projects in the book, or they may be able to think of another playground project they would like to do.

Explorer's Activity Guide

For a **Home/School Connection,** use Explorer's Activity Guide pages 125–126. This letter home describes the concepts children have learned in this module and also provides a hands-on activity that the family can do together.

Using Multiple Intelligences (See page T5.)

The projects presented on these pages provide the opportunity for children to show their understanding of concepts using their strongest individual problem-solving abilities, or intelligences. The chart at right shows which of the seven intelligences are developed within each project and which chapter concepts each project assesses.

Invent a ride.

Use what you know about forces, magnets, and machines to invent a playground ride. Build a model that works. Tell what makes your ride move.

Draw a picture.

Draw a picture of a playground. Show children pushing and pulling things. Tell how your body works as a machine when you play.

Share what you know.
1. Share your project.
2. How do the other projects tell about moving things?
3. What do you like best about your project?

C 63

● **Invent a ride** Some children may prefer to work in pairs to build the model. Models should use some of the principles of machines and magnets. Have children explain how their playground equipment works.
● **Draw a picture** Encourage children to show as many different kinds of equipment and motion—children pushing, pulling, climbing, swinging, and so on—as they can.

Share What You Know
1. Encourage children to share their projects in a format that is comfortable for them: large group, small group, or one-on-one.
2. Assess children's understanding of the concepts presented in the other projects. Elicit specific observations whenever possible, either in groups or individually.
3. Discuss with children how they made their project plans. See if they can name one specific thing they liked best about doing it. Also, ask them what they would do differently if they were to do their projects again.

Performance Assessment
The module assessment projects can be used as performance assessment activities.

Playground

Project	Intelligence	Chapters Covered
Chart	logical/mathematical visual/spatial	1, 2, 3
Invention	visual/spatial logical/mathematical verbal/linguistic body/kinesthetic	1, 2, 3
Drawing	visual/spatial verbal/linguistic	1, 2, 3

Family/School Partnership: Progress Report
Share with families their child's progress in the following areas:
● makes and records observations
● compares and contrasts objects
● classifies in more than one way
● experiments to solve problems
● asks questions and communicates information

*Module C
Making Things Move* C 63

Module C
Math/Science Connection

Measure How Far You Can Jump

Have children jump up and down in place. Ask them what happens to their leg bones as they jump. Can children predict how far they could jump from where they're standing? Suppose they had a running start? How far could they jump this time?

PROBLEM

Invite children to find out how much farther they can jump with a running start. To solve this problem, they'll measure the distances they jump from a standing position and from a running start.

Materials (per group)

masking tape, tape measure or meter stick, pencils or crayons, graph paper *(1-cm square)*

SOLVE THE PROBLEM

- Mark a starting line with masking tape. Let groups of children take turns standing behind the line and then jumping as far as they can. Mark the place where each child lands. Allow children several practice jumps, recording only the best jump. Have children help each other measure and record the distances they jump. Children can measure to the nearest centimeter.

- Allow children to repeat the activity using a running start. Mark where each child lands. Have children help one another measure and record the distances they jump.

Share the Solutions

Invite groups of children to share their results. Then help children record the information on a class bar graph or table. Encourage children to compare the distances jumped from a standing start with the distances jumped from a running start. Then discuss the following questions:

- How far did you jump from a standing start?
- How far did you jump from a running start?
- How much farther did you jump from a running start?
- Why do you think you can jump farther from a running start?

Observe how well students:

✓ use and read a tape measure or meter stick,

✓ measure in units the distances jumped, and

✓ compare the lengths of the distances jumped.

Matthew

Distance in Centimeters

standing   running

EXTEND THE PROBLEM

- Encourage children to make number sentences about the distances they jumped. (Example: subtraction sentences such as the following: 150 cm - 80 cm = 70 cm)

- Children may use different units of measure, such as the length of a shoe, the span of a hand, a length of yarn, or a ruler they design themselves to measure distances jumped.

- You might ask children to estimate which objects in the classroom are shorter than, the same length, or longer than a distance they jumped. Then have children measure the objects and compare those measurements with the length of the distance jumped.

Your Ideas

The Earth and Sky

Module D Planning Guide
The Earth and Sky

Themes: *Systems and Interactions, Energy, Modeling*

In this module, children learn how the sun's energy interacts with and benefits living things on the earth. Children also develop physical models to show the effects of solar energy, constellations, and landforms.

Activity Opportunities		Assessment Opportunities (CONTENT • PORTFOLIO • PERFORMANCE)	
Pupil's Edition	**Teacher's Edition/Ancillaries**	**Pupil's Edition**	**Teacher's Edition/Ancillaries**
Discover Activity p. D5 Activity p. D9 Activity p. D11 Let's Explore pp. D12–D13 Activity p. D17 Let's Solve It! pp. D20–D21 Chapter Review pp. D22–D23	Explorer's Activity Guide pp. 127–140 ExploraCenter Teacher's Guide pp. 16, 25, 26, 31 Videodisc Classroom Guide pp. 33–40 Interactive Transparency Guide pp. 30–31 Interactive Videodisc Software Teacher's Guide pp. 71–79	Checkpoint pp. D6, D9, D11, D13, D15, D17, D19, D21 Chapter Review Performance Assessment Activity pp. D22–D23	Teacher's Edition • Check for Understanding pp. D5, D7, D9, D11, D13, D15, D17, D19, D21, D23 Teacher's Assessment Package • Activity Rubrics pp. 69–70 • Chapter Test pp. 71–72 Explorer's Activity Guide • Chapter Review p. 140
Discover Activity p. D25 Let's Explore pp. D30–D31 Activity p. D33 Activity p. D35 Let's Solve It! pp. D38–D39 Chapter Review pp. D40–D41	Explorer's Activity Guide pp. 141–152 ExploraCenter Teacher's Guide pp. 27, 31 Videodisc Classroom Guide pp. 33–40 Interactive Transparency Guide pp. 32–33 Interactive Videodisc Software Teacher's Guide pp. 71–79	Checkpoint pp. D27–D28, D31, D33, D35, D37, D39 Chapter Review Performance Assessment Activity pp. D40–D41	Teacher's Edition • Check for Understanding pp. D25, D27, D29, D31, D33, D35, D37, D39, D41 Teacher's Assessment Package • Activity Rubrics p. 75 • Chapter Test pp. 77–78 Explorer's Activity Guide • Chapter Review p. 152
Discover Activity p. D43 Activity p. D45 Let's Explore pp. D46–D47 Activity p. D49 Activity p. D53 Let's Solve It! pp. D56–D57 Chapter Review pp. D58–D59	Explorer's Activity Guide pp. 153–162 ExploraCenter Teacher's Guide pp. 16, 20, 24, 25, 26, 31 Videodisc Classroom Guide pp. 33–40 Interactive Transparency Guide pp. 34–35 Interactive Videodisc Software Teacher's Guide pp. 71–79	Checkpoint pp. D45, D47, D49–D50, D53, D55, D57 Chapter Review Performance Assessment Activity pp. D58–D59	Teacher's Edition • Check for Understanding pp. D43, D45, D47, D49, D51, D53, D55, D57, D59 Teacher's Assessment Package • Activity Rubrics pp. 81–82 • Chapter Test pp. 83–84 Explorer's Activity Guide • Chapter Review p. 162
	Explorer's Activity Guide • Family letter pp. 163–164 **Teacher's Edition** • Math/Science Connection pp. D63a–D63b	**Module Review** pp. D62–D63	**Teacher's Assessment Package** • Performance Assessment Test pp. 87–88

Module D Event
Earth and Space Voyage

Planning

An Earth and Space Voyage can be an engaging performance assessment for this module. Families and other children in the school may be invited to tour the exhibit on a given day.

Every child should participate in planning and guiding the voyage. To prepare ahead, you can collect visuals and written materials produced during the activities in the module.

Getting Started
Understanding how the sun, moon, earth, and stars are related is an important aspect of this module. Children should extend the diaries they write in the second lesson of Chapter 2 to include visits to the moon and sun. They should also pretend to be visitors from outer space and describe their visit to the earth. Encourage children to write or draw their ideas in their diary. Their ideas could be used to plan the voyage.

Activity Options

Technology Connection
Obtain magazine pictures taken on various NASA moon missions. Have children use the NASA pictures and their own drawings or models to show how people traveled to the moon and what they found there. Encourage children to show how visitors to the moon dressed, lived, and traveled across the surface of the moon. Children should include pictures of the objects people left behind on the moon and describe what those objects were for. The crater models children make in Chapter 2 can form part of this exhibit.

Multicultural Connection
Use an astronomy book to help children find out what constellations are seen in the Southern Hemisphere. Have children make foil patterns of some of these constellations to include in a display. Share with children folktales about the southern constellations, such as those found in *Myths and Legends of Incas* by Danièle Küss (Cavendish, 1991). Children may enjoy telling these South American or African folktales about the constellations to visitors.

Art Connection
The posters created at the end of Chapter 3 would make an attractive art display. Chalk drawings on black paper could connect the earth and space displays along the route of the voyage.

The activities on these pages provide the opportunity for students to use their strongest individual problem-solving abilities, or intelligences. The chart shows which of the seven intelligences are developed within each activity option. In addition, all students can develop interpersonal intelligence as they participate in the Module Event, Earth and Space Voyage.

Activity	Intelligences
Technology Connection	visual/spatial
Multicultural Connection	interpersonal; verbal/linguistic
Art Connection	visual/spatial
Language Arts Connection	verbal/linguistic

Language Arts Connection

Children will enjoy grouping their charts and graphs of plant growth from Chapter 1, solar cooking times from Chapter 1, and moon phases from Chapter 2 into an exhibit showing the importance of record keeping in science. Present the charts and graphs like a slide show. Children should work together to write a script explaining the information shown in each chart or graph. Encourage children to take turns narrating the slide show for visitors. Volunteers can answer questions.

Let Parents Try It

Exhibits can be made interactive by inviting parents and guardians to "measure the sun," as in Chapter 1, or to make moon craters. Also, provide soil samples and a hand lens and invite visitors to guess where in the community the samples came from.

The Big Event

Set up various areas to display the exhibits that you and the children have decided to include in the voyage. As visitors arrive, have children take turns meeting them at the door and acting as their "pilot" for the voyage. At one stop, between the sun and earth, children using a globe and a flashlight can show how day and night occur. At the next stop, they can show the size of the sun compared with the earth. Other stops should include a display about stars and constellations and a display about the moon, showing its composition and phases. Displays about the earth should show the various parts of the earth and the importance of the sun in producing heat and light.

Many activities in the module can be used or expanded upon for exhibit ideas. Allow children to take turns piloting visitors on the voyage, monitoring and explaining the exhibits, or answering questions.

Module D
Across the Curriculum

Science Background

The Sun

Although the sun is 150 million kilometers away, light from the sun takes only eight minutes to reach the earth. The temperature at the sun's surface is approximately 6,000° Celcius. Like all stars, the sun contains mostly hydrogen. Helium makes up about ten percent of the sun.

The sun's center has a temperature of about 15,000,000° Celsius. At this temperature, hydrogen atoms are separated into protons and electrons. Protons move so fast that they crash into each other and sometimes stick together. This combining of particles is called fusion. During fusion, mass is lost. A little mass changes into a lot of energy. Tiny amounts of this energy reach us as sunlight.

Stars

Stars are large balls of hot gases, thousands to millions of miles in diameter. They emit large amounts of radiant energy from nuclear reactions within them. Stars are different from planets because they give off their own light, while planets reflect light from the sun. Most stars appear only as small points of light because of their great distance from the earth. The brightest stars, as well as many star constellations, have been given names by various cultures over the years. Some of those names, such as Polaris, are used today. Some stars, called variable stars, have changing brightnesses and are identified by letter rather than by name.

A physicist, Max Planck, determined a way of estimating the temperature of stars. A "cool" star gives off mostly red light. A "hot" star emits blue light. Using a measurement of the ratio of blue to red light coming from a star, scientists can determine its temperature.

Science Across Cultures

Observing the Sky

People have long been fascinated with the sky—sometimes in connection with religious beliefs but also to address some practical concerns. Ancient people used observations of the sky to predict weather and seasonal changes, thereby helping them decide when to plant and harvest crops. The most easily observed astronomical feature was the moon and its phases. The position of the sun and the changing patterns of the stars throughout the year were also apparent to early astronomers; the movement of the planets was less easily observed.

The moon was the basis of the first Egyptian calendar. Egypt's high priests declared that the first day that they could see the crescent moon was to be the first day of the month. This led to a lunar calendar with months of 29 or 30 days. While the lunar calendar satisfied the high priests, it did not help predict weather or seasonal changes. Astronomers in Mesopotamia, Greece, Rome, India, and China adjusted their lunar calendars by adding a leap month when observations of the crops made it necessary.

The ancient Greeks accepted Plato's concept of the perfection of circular motion. They believed that objects in space were attached to connected concentric spheres that moved in a complex pattern of circles. Ptolemy (c. 100–165) combined these ideas into a theory of astronomical motion with the earth as the center of the universe. In 1543 Copernicus published a description of the heliocentric, or sun-centered, model of the universe. Because Copernicus's model contradicted religious teaching, his ideas were rejected and condemned for many years. While Copernicus's idea held true for the "universe" of his day, the modern model extends far beyond the solar system.

Cross-curricular Activities

The activities in this module provide many opportunities to make connections between science and other areas of the elementary curriculum.

In addition, the wide variety of cross-curricular activities helps make learning both interesting and fun!

Music
Teacher's Edition, pages D19, D54

Literature
Teacher's Edition, pages D1g, D4, D24, D42

Health
Teacher's Edition, page D20

Technology
Videodisc

Interactive Videodisc Software Activity

ScottForesman Online Service

Language Arts
Teacher's Edition, pages D1g, D8, D10, D14, D18, D28, D32, D34, D36, D39, D44, D50, D54

The Earth and Sky

Multicultural Connections
Teacher's Edition, pages D6, D12, D28, D30, D36, D38, D48

Interactive Videodisc Software Activity

Social Studies
Teacher's Edition, pages D18, D23, D34

Art
Teacher's Edition, pages D1g, D26

Math
Pupil's Edition, pages D20–D21, D38–D39, D56–D57

Teacher's Edition, pages D6, D20, D37, D38, D56, D63a–D63b

Also see Discover the Wonder ExploraCenter

Family/School Partnership
Teacher's Edition, pages D4, D24, D42, D63

Explorer's Activity Guide, pages 163–164

Module D
Links to Literature

Introducing the Literature Library Selection

The literature library selection for this module is *Begin at the Beginning* by Amy Schwartz (Harper & Row, 1983). In this selection, a young girl named Sara is picked by her teacher to paint a wonderful picture for the school art show. Sara thinks at first that she will paint the whole universe, but she does not know where to begin. After many false starts, she listens to her mother's wise remarks and begins with something familiar.

In addition to the module literature selection, each chapter has a companion book.

- *Nine O'Clock Lullaby* by Marilyn Singer (HarperCollins, 1991) shows what is happening around the world while Mama reads a story at 9 P.M. in Brooklyn. While it is day in one part of the world, it is night in another.
- In *The Big Dipper* by Franklyn M. Branley (Harper Trophy, 1991), a girl tells about the Big Dipper, the North Star, and other constellations.
- *My Little Island* by Frank Lessac (J. B. Lippincott, 1984) is about a boy and his friend who visit a little Caribbean island where

he was born. The story celebrates the sights and sounds of life on the earth.

Activity Corner

Cross-Curricular Activities

Language Arts
- **Retelling a Story** Review important vocabulary from the story. Then have children retell the story using the words.

Language Arts
- **Making a New Ending** Have children suggest what might have happened in the story if Sara hadn't listened to her mother or if Sara had tried to paint the whole universe.

Art
- **Drawing a Picture** Have children draw a picture of their favorite place on the earth. Encourage them to describe the place to the class. You might want to display children's drawings in the classroom.

Beginning with the Bulletin Board

Making Connections

Have children construct a bulletin-board display by collecting pictures related to the earth and space, an activity inspired by the literature library selection *Begin at the Beginning* by Amy Schwartz.

You will need:

 magazine pictures

 construction paper

 drawing paper

 safety scissors

 pushpins

 envelopes

 self-sealing plastic bags

 tape

 index cards

Preparing the Bulletin Board

Divide the bulletin board into three sections as shown. The bottom section represents the earth. Use construction paper or drawing paper to create two scenes in the top sections, one with a night

time sky and the other with a daytime sky.

Attach two envelopes to the bottom of the bulletin board. In the first envelope, place magazine pictures of scenes related to the earth and space. You may include pictures of the sun, the moon, and stars. Also include pictures of landforms such as hills, lakes, and mountains. Include items such as plants, rocks, or other objects found on the earth. In the second envelope, place index-card labels such as *Sun, Moon, Stars, Earth,* and *Space.*

Bulletin Board Activity

Have children select one label from the second envelope. Help them attach the label to the appropriate part of the bulletin board. Children should select one picture from the other envelope that would appear in the same section of the picture. Have children tell why they chose to attach the item in that section.

Extend the Activity

Children may also make packets by placing small amounts of material such as sand, clay, dirt, or salt in plastic bags and sealing them. Have children place their packets an envelope. Then have children choose and place labels, choose packets, and place them correctly on the bulletin board.

The Earth and Sky

Close your eyes and imagine the sky. You might think of the sun, or the moon, or the stars. Look where you are standing. What can you learn about the earth?

Chapter 1

The Sun

When you think about the sun, you might think of a big yellow ball. But what is the sun really like? Page **D 4**

D 2

Chapter 2

The Moon and Stars

The moon and stars light up the night sky. What makes the moon and stars shine so brightly? Page **D 24**

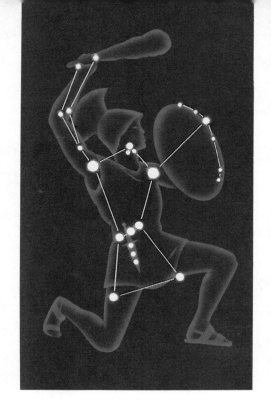

Chapter 3

Looking at the Earth

The earth looks different in different places. But no matter where on the earth you are, you can see land or water. Page **D 42**

Chapter 1 Planning Guide
The Sun

Lessons / *Skills*	Materials (per group)

Lesson 1
Discover Activity: **How are day and night different?** pp. D4–D5
(observing, describing)

Lesson 1 Activity: *How are day and night different?*
Module Kit Items: flashlight with batteries; masking tape; golf ball
School Supplied Items: none

Lesson 2
How does day turn into night? pp. D6–D7
(comparing, describing)

Lesson 3
How big is the sun? pp. D8–D9
(measuring, drawing conclusions)

Lesson 3 Activity: *Show why the sun looks small.*
Module Kit Item: metric ruler
School Supplied Item: paper plate

Lesson 4
What is the sun? pp. D10–D11
(observing, comparing)

Lesson 4 Activity: *Show that sunlight warms the earth.*
Module Kit Items: 2 small aluminum pans
School Supplied Items: 2 ice cubes; clock or watch

Lesson 5
Let's Explore: **How does sunlight help plants grow?**
pp. D12–D13
(observing, drawing conclusions)

Lesson 5 Activity: *How does sunlight help plants grow?*
Module Kit Items: none
School Supplied Items: 2 identical plants; water in watering can
Advance Prep: You may want to grow your own plants to use for this activity. Grass grows quickly and works well. You can grow grass in paper cups in about a week.

Lesson 6
How does the sun help animals? pp. D14–D15
(describing, explaining ideas)

Lesson 7
How can you use sunlight? pp. D16–D17
(making physical models)

Lesson 7 Activity: *Make a solar oven.*
Module Kit Items: aluminum foil; tape; 1 sheet of plastic wrap
School Supplied Items: small potato; cardboard box *(shoe box or larger)*

Lesson 8
How do coal and oil come from sunlight? pp. D18–D19
(observing)

Lesson 9
Let's Solve It!: **How fast can you cook food in a solar oven?**
pp. D20–D21
(organizing information, solving problems)

Lesson 10
Chapter Review: **What did you learn?** pp. D22–D23
(listing, summarizing, explaining ideas)

Lesson 10 Activity: *Make a cartoon strip.*
Module Kit Items: none
School Supplied Items: markers; crayons; drawing paper *(4 sheets/child)*; transparent tape

Assessment Options	Content	Performance	Portfolio
Teacher's Assessment Package			
Chapter Test, pp. 71–72	✓		✓
Group Interview Assessment, p. 73	✓	✓	✓
Performance Strategies, p. 74	✓	✓	✓
Explorer's Activity Guide			
Activity worksheets, pp. 127–139		✓	✓
Chapter Review, p. 140	✓		✓
Interactive Transparency Package			
Transparency 13 and BLM	✓	✓	✓
Teacher's Guide, pp. 30–31	✓	✓	
Activity for second-language learners	✓	✓	✓
Science Literature Library			
Nine O'Clock Lullaby		✓	✓
Interactive Videodisc Software Teacher's Guide, pp. 71–79			
Computer-based Activity	✓	✓	
Journal Presentations	✓	✓	✓
Videodisc Classroom Guide, pp. 33–40, **or Video Reader**			
Hands-on activity	✓	✓	✓
ExploraCenter Teacher's Guide, pp. 16, 25, 26, 31			
ExploraCenter			
Science activity cards 11, 20, 21, 26	✓	✓	✓
ScottForesman Online Service			
Online field trips	✓	✓	✓

Chapter Overview

In this chapter, children learn that the sun gives us light and warmth and that most living things need the sun. They learn that the sun helps make fuels and provides solar energy. They also make a solar oven and chart its cooking time.

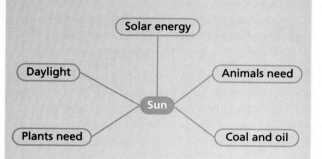

Lesson Objective
Children use prior knowledge to explain how day and night occur.

Introduce

Invite Learning
Show the videodisc or videotape segment for this chapter. Bar codes and a description of this segment are given below on page D5.

Make Connections
To **assess prior knowledge**, have children draw a picture of where the sun is during the day. Then ask them to explain where it is at night. Save their responses as a **baseline assessment** that you can use for a follow-up in Check for Understanding. Children might think the sun actually moves across the sky instead of just appearing to move as the earth turns.

Teach

Discover Activity

Children use a ball and a flashlight to show what causes day and night.
Skills: Observing, describing

Materials (per group)
Module Kit Items: flashlight with batteries; masking tape; golf ball
School Supplied Items: none

Chapter 1

The Sun

Think about day and night. How are they different? Why is it light during the day? Why is it dark at night?

You know that the sky looks different during the day and at night. You see the sun in the sky during the day. Can you see the sun at night?

D 4

Science Idea Exchange

Family/School Partnership: Family Support
Encourage families to be active partners in learning by suggesting that they and their children:
● tell how day and night look,
● describe how they feel in the sunlight and in the shade, and
● observe where plants grow.

Collaborative Learning: Cooperative Learning
All children in the Discover Activity group should share results. Also, each child in the group can be assigned a specific role:
● one to mark the ball with tape;
● one to hold the flashlight;
● one to move the ball to make it day and night at the tape;
● one to draw the position of the tape during the day and night.

Science and Literature
Use the literature selection *Nine O'Clock Lullaby* by Marilyn Singer (HarperCollins, 1991) to help reinforce the concept that it is day in one part of the world, while night in another. Then help children use a flashlight and a globe to demonstrate how day and night occur as the earth turns.

How are day and night different?

1. Pretend a flashlight is the sun. Pretend a ball is the earth.
2. Mark a spot on the ball with a piece of tape.
3. Hold the flashlight still.
4. Move the ball so it is day at the piece of tape.
5. Move the ball so it is night at the piece of tape.
6. **Tell about it.** Tell how you moved the ball to make night and day.

Ask me what else I want to find out about the sun.

D 5

Safety Tip
Warn children not to look at the sun or shine the flashlights in people's eyes.

Helpful Hint
Children could use the brand name on the ball for a reference spot instead of marking the ball with tape.

What to Expect
Children should see that it gets dark at night because the earth has turned and the sun is shining on the other side.

Close

Check for Understanding
- As a follow-up to the **baseline assessment,** ask children to explain again where the sun is during the day and at night. Compare their responses with those from Make Connections. Look for an increased understanding.
- **Answers to Tell about it**   To make day, the ball was moved so the light would shine on the tape. To make night, the ball was moved so the light would not shine on the tape.

What Else Do You Want to Find Out?
Write children's questions on chart paper to revisit as they progress through the chapter.

Connecting Lessons
In the next lesson, children will find out how day turns into night. ▶

Explorer's Activity Guide
The **Discover Activity recording sheet** on page 129 of the Explorer's Activity Guide can be used by children to record their activity results.

Visual Literacy
Discover the Wonder Videotape or *Videodisc,* Grade 2, Module D, presents a video segment investigating the world of space and space exploration. Use this video to enhance children's understanding of the celestial bodies they observe from the earth.

Bar Codes

Chapter 16: Video, English

Chapter 16: Video, Spanish

Play

Interactive Software

Lesson Objective

Children learn how the sun and the earth are positioned in space and how the turning of the earth causes day and night.

Introduce

Invite Learning

Shine a large-beam flashlight on a globe. Encourage children to turn the globe and talk about how the earth is lit.

Make Connections

To **assess prior knowledge,** ask children to explain what causes day and night in terms of the flashlight and globe they used in Invite Learning. Save their explanations as a **baseline assessment** that you can use for a follow-up in Check for Understanding.

Teach

Observe and Listen

Have children work in pairs to **compare** the pictures in the text. Listen as they explain to each other what is happening in each picture.

Raise Questions

● Close your eyes. Ask a child to shine a flashlight on your face. Ask: *Is it day or night on my face? Where is the sun?*

How does day turn into night?

Day and night happen because the earth turns. Then the sun lights different parts of the earth.

Look at the top pictures. Find San Francisco on the part of the earth where the sun is shining. The city has day. Look at the bottom pictures. The earth has turned. The sun is not shining on San Francisco. Is it day or night there?

Checkpoint

Write a story about how day and night happen.

D 6

 # Science Idea Exchange

Science Background

Explain to students that because the earth rotates, the sun seems to move across the sky during the day. It appears low in the east at sunrise, seems to travel in an arc to its highest point at midday, and sets in the west at nightfall. In the continental United States, the sun never reaches a point directly overhead.

Math/Science Connection

Help small groups of children make clocks by writing numbers around the edge of a paper plate and attaching construction-paper hands to the center of the plate with a paper fastener. Challenge children to set their clocks to show the times (to the hour) of sunrise, noon, and sunset.

Multicultural Connection

Share with children that througho history people of many cultures have developed beliefs to explain why the sun appears to move acro the sky. In ancient Egypt, for example, people believed the sun was a god named Ra (rä) who slowly sailed across the sky every day in his boat.

Sun

Earth

X

San Francisco

Sun

Earth

X

San Francisco

D 7

- Slowly turn around so your back is to the light. Repeat the questions. Then ask: *If people are awake on the sunlit side of the earth, what are people doing on the dark side?* (sleeping)

Ask for Evidence
Show children the flashlight and globe. Slowly turn the globe. Then stop when your location is in the "sunlight" and ask: *Suppose the earth didn't turn. Would we still change from day to night every day?* (No, if the earth never moved, there would always be sunlight on only one side of the earth.)

Close

Check for Understanding
- As a follow-up to the **baseline assessment,** ask children to demonstrate what causes day and night. They may role-play being the rotating earth while you role-play being the sun. Look for an increased understanding of how the turning of the earth causes day and night.
- **Answers to Checkpoint** Children's stories should reflect the fact that day and night are caused by the turning of the earth.

Connecting Lessons
In the next lesson, children will find out how big the sun is. ▶

Explorer's Activity Guide
Use Explorer's Activity Guide page 131 with this lesson to help children answer the text question, "How does day turn into night?" with a hands-on activity.

Science Themes
By exploring the positions of the sun and the earth in relation to each other, children develop their understanding of the theme of **modeling.**

Visual Literacy
To enhance the **visual literacy** connection, use the interactive overhead transparency that correlates with the above two pages. The transparency will help your students understand the key concepts presented on these pages.

Lesson 3

Lesson Objective
Children learn about the sizes of the sun and the earth.

Introduce

Invite Learning
Use the literature selection *Begin at the Beginning* by Amy Schwartz (Harper & Row, 1983) to discuss how to draw huge objects such as the earth and sun. Invite children to think of something big and draw it on the chalkboard. Ask: *Do the things you drew always look big to you?*

Make Connections
To **assess prior knowledge,** ask children to make clay models of the sun and the earth. Save their models as a **baseline assessment** that you can use in Check for Understanding. Children may think that the sun is a small ball or disk rather than the huge sphere it is.

Teach

Activity
Children demonstrate how distance can make the sun look small. **Skills:** Measuring, drawing conclusions

Materials (per group)
Module Kit Item: metric ruler
School Supplied Item: paper plate

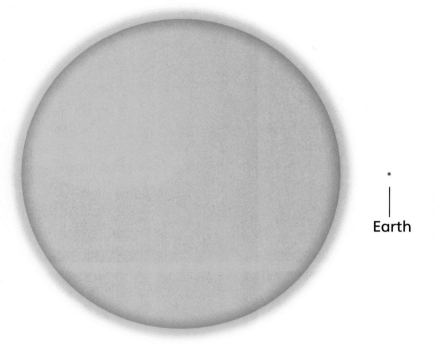

How big is the sun?

Earth

Sun

How big do you think the sun is? Is it larger or smaller than the earth? Look at the drawing to find out.

You can see that the sun is much larger than the earth. Let's find out why the sun might look small in the sky.

D 8

Science Idea Exchange

Science Anecdote
Sometimes the sun appears larger at sunrise or sunset because of the earth's atmosphere. Dust and water vapor in the atmosphere scatter some of the sun's light, making it appear larger. When we see the sun near the horizon, more dust and vapor are scattering the light.

Collaborative Learning: Small Groups
Assign specific children to gather and clean up materials. All children in the Activity group should take turns holding the plate and using the ruler to measure how big the plate looks.

Science and Language Arts
Encourage children to make up poems about the sun and the earth. Allow volunteers to share their poems with the class.

Show why the sun looks small.

You will need: metric ruler 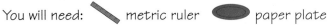 paper plate

1. Hold up the plate. Have your partner measure across the plate.
2. Move back six steps. Your partner should not move.
3. Have your partner measure how big the plate looks again. Do this by holding the ruler in front of the plate.
4. What happens to the size of the plate?

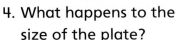

Checkpoint
Tell how you made the plate look smaller.

D 9

Helpful Hints

- You can use any size paper plate.
- Children can cut out paper circles instead of using plates.
- Show how to measure the plate when it is near you by placing the ruler directly on it. Then demonstrate how to measure the plate when it is farther away by holding the ruler in the air, as shown.
- Remind children with rulers to hold still; only children with plates should move.

Ask for Evidence

Ask: *What tells you that the sun is much bigger than it looks?* (Big things look smaller when they are far away.)

Act as a Consultant

Challenge children to **list** other big things that look smaller when far away (buildings, trees, cars, airplanes).

Close

Check for Understanding

- As a follow-up to the **baseline assessment,** ask children to refashion their clay models of the sun and the earth. Look for increased understanding of the relative sizes of the two bodies.
- **Answers to Checkpoint** By moving the plate farther away, it appeared smaller.

Connecting Lessons

In the next lesson, children will find out what the sun is made of and how it affects the earth. ▶

Explorer's Activity Guide

Use Explorer's Activity Guide hands-on activity on page 132 to help children answer the question, "How big is the sun?"

Teacher's Assessment Package

A **scoring rubric** to assess student performance is provided on page 69 of the Teacher's Assessment Package.

Activity Results

Children should relate the smaller image of the plate when it moves farther away to the small image of the sun. They should understand that if the earth and sun were closer, the sun would look much larger.

Science Themes

By observing the changing scale of the sun model as they change the viewing distance, children develop their understanding of the themes of **scale and structure** and **modeling.**

Lesson 4

Introduce

Invite Learning
Invite children to draw objects that give off heat and light. Expect pictures of the sun, lamps, and fire.

Make Connections
To **assess prior knowledge,** have children make a list of things they think the sun is made of and a list of things the sun does for the earth. Save their lists as a **baseline assessment** that you can use for a follow-up in Check for Understanding.

Teach

Activity
Children compare the rate at which two ice cubes melt when one is placed in sunlight and the other is placed in shade. **Skills:** Observing, comparing

Materials (per group)
Module Kit Items: 2 small aluminum pans
School Supplied Items: 2 ice cubes; clock or watch

What is the sun?

You learned that the sun is big. Now let's find out some other things about the sun. The sun is our closest star. You can see that it is shaped like a ball. The sun is made of very hot gases.

What do you think the sun does for the earth? The sun gives the earth light. Sunlight makes daytime on the earth. Sunlight warms the earth too.

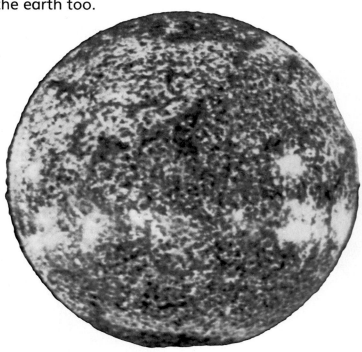

D 10

Science Idea Exchange

Science Background
When light energy from the sun is absorbed by an object, the light energy is converted to thermal energy. The darker the object, the less light it reflects and the more it absorbs, so the hotter it gets. Share with children that dark-colored objects get hotter in the sunlight than light-colored objects.

Science and Language Arts
Write "sun" on the chalkboard. Ask: *What words do you know that begin with sun?* Write children's examples on the chalkboard ("sunrise," "Sunday," "sunburn"). You might provide prompts for familiar words they do not name. Explain that these words show how much the sun affects us.

Gifted and Talented
Challenge children to **record** outside temperatures from a thermometer at home over the weekend. Invite them to write down four readings each day—at breakfast, lunch, dinner, and bedtime—and to bring the readings to school. Ask children to explain why the temperatures usually go up during the day and down at night.

Show that sunlight warms the earth.

You will need: 2 plates timer

 2 ice cubes

1. Put an ice cube on each plate.
2. Put one plate in a place that gets sunlight. Put the other plate in a place that gets no sunlight.
3. Time how long each ice cube takes to melt.

Checkpoint

Draw a picture of an ice cube in a place where it melts fast.

D 11

Helpful Hints

- Ice cubes from a tray might take over an hour to completely melt. To decrease this time, you could break the ice cubes into smaller pieces. However, the pieces used should be the same size.
- Suggest that each group either write the time or draw the clock to record start and finish times for each cube.
- *See Equipment Kit Teacher's Guide for additional hints.*

Act as a Consultant

Encourage children to **predict** which cube will melt faster and how long it will take.

Close

Check for Understanding

- As a follow-up to the **baseline assessment,** ask children to draw a picture of the sun shining on the earth. Ask them to label what the sun is made of. Then ask them to list on their drawings things the sun does for the earth.
- **Answers to Checkpoint** Children should draw a picture of an ice cube in the sunlight.

Connecting Lessons

In the next lesson, children will find out how sunlight helps plants grow. ▶

Explorer's Activity Guide

Use Explorer's Activity Guide hands-on activity on page 133 to help children answer the question, "What is the sun?"

Teacher's Assessment Package

A **scoring rubric** to assess student performance is provided on page 69 of the Teacher's Assessment Package.

Activity Results

The ice cube placed in sunlight will melt faster than the ice cube not in sunlight.

Collaborative Learning: Small Groups

Assign specific children to gather and clean up materials. All children in the Activity group should help put the ice cubes in position, check the time, and share results.

Lesson 5

Introduce

Invite Learning
Invite children to pretend they are plants that are growing. They might start in a crouched position and reach upward and outward.

Make Connections
To **assess prior knowledge,** have children make a picture of things that plants need to grow. Save their pictures as a **baseline assessment** that you can use again in Check for Understanding.

Teach

Activity
Children place one plant in sunlight and one in darkness to demonstrate how sunlight helps green plants grow.
Skills: Observing, drawing conclusions

Materials (per group)
Module Kit Items: none
School Supplied Items: 2 identical plants; water in watering can

Safety Tip
Children should wash their hands after handling plants.

Let's Explore

How does sunlight help plants grow?

Think about a park. What plants might grow there? Is the sun important to plants? You can find out if plants need sunlight to grow.

You will need:

2 plants

water

Find out about it.

1 Put one plant in a sunny place.

2 Put the other plant in a dark place.

3 Water each plant.

4 Look at both plants each day.

D 12

Science Idea Exchange

Science Background
Green plants make sugars from water and carbon dioxide, a reaction called photosynthesis that requires light energy (sunlight or artificial light). Removing light energy stops photosynthesis, and plants die.

Science Themes
By discovering that plants need sunlight to grow, children begin to develop their understanding of the theme of **energy.**

Multicultural Connections
Rice, corn, and wheat are plants grown for food on every continent except Antarctica. Invite children from various cultural backgrounds to describe for the class a favorite food made from one of these plants.

Write about it.

Make a chart like this one. Write down what you see each day.

days	plant in sunny place	plant in dark place
day 1		
day 2		
day 3		
day 4		
day 5		

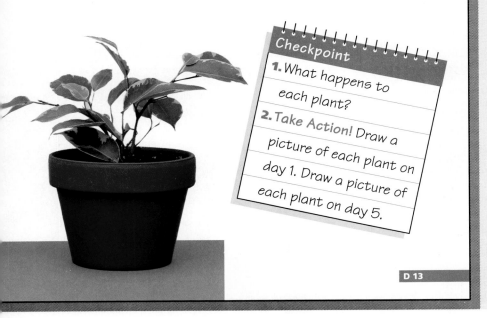

Checkpoint

1. What happens to each plant?

2. Take Action! Draw a picture of each plant on day 1. Draw a picture of each plant on day 5.

D 13

Act as a Consultant
Invite children to look out the window, or take children for a walk outdoors. Have them **compare** the numbers and kinds of plants that grow in sunny places with those that grow in shady places. Explain that different plants need different amounts of sunlight.

Close
Check for Understanding
- As a follow-up to the **baseline assessment,** ask children to make another picture of what plants need to grow. Compare their pictures with the originals. Look for an understanding that plants need sunlight.
- **Answers to Checkpoint** 1. Plants in sunlight grow, and those in the dark die. 2. **Take Action!** Pictures should show a difference in the height and the condition of each plant.

Connecting Lessons
In the next lesson, children find out that animals need the sun. ▶

Explorer's Activity Guide
Use Explorer's Activity Guide hands-on activity on page 134 to explore sunlight and evaluate children's understanding of the lesson concept.

Teacher's Assessment Package
A **scoring rubric** to assess student performance is provided on page 70 of the Teacher's Assessment Package.

Activity Results

Collaborative Learning: Small Groups
Assign specific children to gather and clean up materials. All children in the Let's Explore group should help place the plants in position, water the plants, record data, and share results.

Lesson Objective
Children learn that animals need the sun.

Introduce

Invite Learning
Invite each child to pick an animal and act like it. Ask children to tell how they think the animal would feel if the sun went away.

Make Connections
To **assess prior knowledge**, ask children to tell why they think animals need the sun. Write children's responses on a chart and use it as a **baseline assessment**.

Teach

Observe and Listen
Divide the class into small groups. Ask children to explain to each other how the sun helps each animal. Listen for the understanding that the sun is the source of warmth and food for animals.

Act as a Consultant
Have children discuss how the sun helps animals that eat plants get food and how it helps animals that eat other animals get food. Use examples such as the rabbit and the fox to illustrate the concept: Plants need the sun in order to grow; rabbits need to eat plants; foxes need to eat animals like rabbits.

How does the sun help animals?

You already learned how the sun is important to plants. But how does the sun help animals?

Animals need food to stay alive. Where do animals get food? Some animals use plants for food. Some animals eat other living things that use plants for food. The plants need sunlight to grow.

D 14

 ## Science Idea Exchange

Science Background
Plants are called producers because they use light energy from the sun to make sugars during photosynthesis. Animals cannot carry out photosynthesis. They eat plants and are called consumers. Plants are necessary for animal life, and energy from the sun is necessary for all life on the earth.

Science and Language Arts
Invite children to write a list of reasons the sun is important to them. Ask children to share two or three items from their lists.

Science Themes
By learning in Lesson 5 that plants need the sun and in this lesson that animals need the sun, children are exploring the theme of **systems and interactions**.

The sun is important to animals in another way too. Can you guess how? You already know that sunlight warms the earth. Sunlight also helps animals stay warm.

Checkpoint
Paint a picture showing how the sun is important to animals.

Raise Questions

Ask: *You probably drink cow's milk. Where would you get cow's milk if the sun didn't shine anymore and there wasn't any grass for cows to eat?* (You couldn't get milk because cows couldn't survive.)

Close

Check for Understanding

- As a follow-up to the **baseline assessment,** refer children to their chart listing reasons animals need the sun. Invite children to add to the chart.
- **Answers to Checkpoint** Children's paintings should show at least one of these ideas: sunlight helps animals stay warm, sunlight helps plants grow, and animals need to eat plants to stay alive.

Extend the Lesson

Have children apply what they've learned to humans. Ask them to look around their classroom, outside, and within their homes for ways that people need the sun. Then ask them to make posters showing how the sun is important for people.

Connecting Lessons

In the next lesson, children will find out that solar energy from the sun can help people. ▶

Explorer's Activity Guide

Use Explorer's Activity Guide pages 135–136 with this lesson to help children answer the text

question, "How does the sun help animals?" with a hands-on activity.

Explore Further

Suggest to children that they set up a bird feeder in the school yard, where they can **observe** birds eating. Have them examine bird food and then point out to them that birds are animals that eat plant seeds that are produced by plants that grew in sunlight.

Your Ideas

_____

_____

_____

_____

Lesson Objective
Children learn that the sun is the source of solar energy.

Introduce

Key Term
solar energy

Invite Learning
If it is a warm sunny day, invite children to stand in the sunlight with their faces toward the sun, eyes closed. Then have them move from the sun to the shade.

Make Connections
To **assess prior knowledge**, ask: *How do you feel when you stand in the sun and in the shade? Why is it different?*

Teach

Encourage Student Definitions
Write the term "solar energy" on chart paper and ask what it means. Write the definitions children suggest for a **baseline assessment.**

Activity
Children make a simple solar oven and cook a potato in it. **Skill:** Making physical models

Materials (per group)
Module Kit Items: aluminum foil; tape; 1 sheet plastic wrap
School Supplied Items: small potato; cardboard box *(shoe box or larger)*

How can you use sunlight?

Pretend you are playing in the sun. Does your skin feel warm? Think of other things that might feel warm in the sun.

Did you know that the sun can cook food? When you use the sun to cook, you use **solar energy**. Solar energy is energy that comes from the sun. You can try using the sun to cook some food.

D 16

Science Idea Exchange

Science Background
The inside of a solar oven absorbs solar energy, which is converted to thermal energy. The lid keeps the thermal energy from escaping. As energy is converted, the oven heats up enough to cook food. Similarly, people warm their homes with solar energy using windows that face the sun.

Science Themes
By using solar energy to cook a potato, children develop their understanding of the themes of **energy** and **modeling.**

Collaborative Learning: Small Groups
Assign specific children to gather and clean up materials. All children in the Activity goup should participate in building the solar oven and cooking the potato and then record data and share results.

Make a solar oven.

You will need: foil cardboard box

 tape small potato  plastic wrap

1. Tape the foil to the inside of the box. Be sure the foil is shiny side up.
2. Put the potato in the box.
3. Cover the box with plastic wrap.
4. Put the box in the sun.
5. Cook the potato.

Checkpoint

Draw a magazine ad for a solar oven. Tell how it can cook food.

D 17

Safety Tips

- Invite children to help wash the potatoes. Explain that food must be clean to keep us healthy.
- Steam inside a cooking potato can cause it to explode. Explain this fact as you stick potatoes with a clean fork so steam can escape.

Helpful Hints

- Place ovens in direct sunlight all day.
- Solar ovens, like the one in the photograph, can be purchased, but a homemade one works equally well.
- *See Equipment Kit Teacher's Guide for additional hints.*

Close

Check for Understanding

- As a follow-up to the **baseline assessment,** ask children to use the term "solar energy" to explain how their potato cooked.
- **Answers to Checkpoint** Children should use descriptive words, slogans, and pictures in their advertisements for the solar oven.

Connecting Lessons

In the next lesson, children will discover how coal and oil come from sunlight. ▶

Explorer's Activity Guide

Use Explorer's Activity Guide hands-on activity on page 137 to help children answer the question, "How can you use sunlight?"

Teacher's Assessment Package

A **scoring rubric** to assess student performance is provided on page 70 of the Teacher's Assessment Package.

Activity Results

It will probably take a couple of hours for the potato's outer layer to cook. The whole potato may take all day to cook to where it is soft enough for most people's taste. But by smelling it and feeling its outer softness, children will be able to tell the potato is cooking and that they have made an instrument that uses the sun's energy to cook food.

Extend the Lesson

Suggest that children think of times when there is too much solar energy. Ask: *What happens if you leave a chocolate bar in the sunlight?* (It melts.) *What happens if you wear a heavy sweater and sit in the sunlight during summer?* (You get too hot.)

Lesson Objective
Children learn that coal and oil are stored forms of solar energy.

Introduce

Key Term
fuel

Invite Learning
Invite children to examine a piece of coal and tell what it is and what it might be used for. Then display a can of oil and again ask children to tell what it is and what it might be used for. Record and save children's responses on chart paper.

Make Connections
To **assess prior knowledge,** place a leaf near the piece of coal and ask: *What does a leaf have to do with coal?*

Teach

Encourage Student Definitions
As a **baseline assessment,** ask children to define the term "fuel." Write responses on the same chart paper you used for Invite Learning. Add to responses as children progress through the lesson.

How do coal and oil come from sunlight?

You used solar energy from the sun. People also use **fuels** such as coal and oil for energy. People can burn these fuels to get heat they can use. The sun helped make coal and oil.

D 18

 # Science Idea Exchange

Science Background
Millions of years ago, swamps covered many land areas. Volcanic ash, sand, and mud buried dead plants and compressed them into coal. In shallow seas, marine organisms formed oil and natural gas. These slow processes continue today. People use fossil fuels to release the stored solar energy.

Science and Language Arts
Challenge children to write a rebus story about how coal and oil are formed. Encourage children to use pictures in place of the words for "sun," "plants," "animals," "coal," and "oil."

Science and Social Studies
Ask children how they think coal and oil are taken out of the earth. Explain that coal is dug in mines and transported by trucks, trains, and ships. To get oil and natural gas, deep wells are dug into the ground. Oil and gas are pumped through buried pipes. Show pictures of mines, drills, and tankers.

Long ago the earth looked like this picture. The sun helped these plants grow. Animals used the plants as food. When the plants and animals died, sand and soil covered them. Over many years the plants and animals changed into oil and coal.

Checkpoint
Do a radio commercial for coal or oil. Tell how the fuels formed. Tell how they can help people.

Observe and Listen
Invite children to discuss the picture in small groups. Listen for an understanding that the sun helped plants grow and animals survive, and that when the plants and animals died, they slowly turned into coal and oil.

Raise Questions
Ask: *What did all of these plants need to grow?* (sunlight) *When these plants and animals died, what happened to them?* (They slowly changed into coal and oil.)

Ask for Evidence
Have children draw a picture showing that coal has energy stored within it.

Close
Check for Understanding
- As a follow-up to the **baseline assessment,** ask children to define "fuel" again. See if their definitions include coal and oil and the concept that fuel has stored solar energy.
- **Answers to Checkpoint** Children's radio commercials should tell how sunlight helped plants grow, how coal formed when plants died, and various ways that people use fuel.

Connecting Lessons
In the next lesson, children discover how long it takes to cook various foods in a solar oven. ▶

Explorer's Activity Guide
Use Explorer's Activity Guide page 138 with this lesson to help children answer the text question, "How do coal and oil come from sunlight?" with a hands-on activity.

Save the Earth
Explain that some power plants make electricity by burning coal or oil. This process causes air pollution and uses up these fuels. People can help reduce pollution and save fuel by using less electricity. Help children develop a class list of how people can use less electricity (turn off lights and TV when not needed).

Science and Music
Invite children to sing the first stanza of "The Farmer in the Dell." Work with them to write words for the song so it tells about coal or oil. The song could be about sunlight growing plants, animals eating plants, or coal or oil forming underground. Sing the finished song together.

Lesson 9

Lesson Objective

Children learn that different foods need to be cooked for different lengths of time. **Skills:** Organizing information, solving problems

Introduce

Invite Learning
Make available fruit, vegetables, bread, cans of soup, and the solar ovens from Lesson 7. Ask children to show how they would cook each food.

Make Connections
To **assess prior knowledge,** ask children to predict how long it would take to cook fruit, vegetables, bread, and soup in a solar oven. Record their predictions on a chart. Save the chart as a **baseline assessment** that you can use in Check for Understanding.

Teach

Observe and Listen
Have children work in small groups to **compare** the amount of time it takes to cook foods in a solar oven, based on the chart.

How fast can you cook food in a solar oven?

Remember how you cooked food in a solar oven? You found out how long a potato takes to cook. Do you think all foods take the same time to cook? Let's find out.

cooking time		
1 to 2 hours	3 to 4 hours	5 to 8 hours
fruit	vegetables	soup
egg	bread	stew
fish	most meat	

1. Look at the chart. Bread and vegetables take 3 to 4 hours to cook. Name the foods that take the most time to cook.

Science Idea Exchange

Science Background
Cooking times shown in the chart vary widely because solar cooking has many variables: the oven's shape and size; proper positioning in the sunlight; weather; how far from the equator you are, time of year, and time of day (all affect sunlight intensity); and how large and moist each food item is.

Math/Science Connection
Ask children to imagine that they can build a solar oven that will cook everything twice as fast. Ask: *What will this do to the cooking times on your chart?* (cut times in half) *How fast will your new cooker cook an egg?* (half an hour to an hour)

Science and Health
On three separate pieces of paper, have children draw pictures of thre foods that could be part of a healthful meal. Place the pictures i a paper bag. Invite children to take turns choosing three pictures from the bag. Have them tell if the food they chose make up a healthful meal. Small groups of children use their pictures to make a book abou healthful meals.

2. Draw a chart like this one.

foods	cooking time		
	1–2 hours	3–4 hours	5–8 hours
egg	▓▓▓▓▓		
most meat		▓▓▓▓	
fish			
vegetables			
stew			
bread			
fruit			
soup			

3. The chart shows how long it takes to cook an egg and most meat. Color your chart to show how long the other foods take to cook.

Checkpoint

1. Does fish or bread take longer to cook?

2. What foods would be best to cook if you were in a hurry?

Act as a Consultant
Offer assistance to groups, as needed, in interpreting the chart.

Raise Questions
Ask: *What do the filled-in rectangles on your chart show?* (amount of time needed for cooking) *What does the chart tell you about soup?* (Soup needs 5 to 8 hours to cook in a solar oven.) *What do you see that is often different for each food?* (The cooking time sometimes differs.)

Ask for Evidence
Have children point out which foods take the shortest and which foods take the longest amount of time to cook.

Close

Check for Understanding
- As a follow-up to the **baseline assessment,** ask children to revise the predictions they made for cooking times in Make Connections.
- **Answers to Checkpoint** 1. Bread takes longer. 2. egg, fish, fruit

Connecting Lessons
In the next lesson, children will draw a cartoon strip to show what they have learned. ▶

Explorer's Activity Guide
Use Explorer's Activity Guide page 139 to help children solve the question of how long it takes different foods to cook in a solar oven. You can also use this hands-on activity page to evaluate how well children understand the concept of this lesson.

Achieving English Proficiency
Making a chart is a visual and numerical language that helps communicate concepts. Encourage children to continually verbalize as they draw and interpret their charts.

Your Ideas
_____
_____
_____
_____

Lesson 10

Lesson Objective
Children make a cartoon strip to show the concepts they learned in this chapter.

Introduce

Invite Learning
Review the **baseline assessment** activities you used in this chapter. Choose one or more to do again that you think will help children understand the chapter concepts.

Teach

Performance Assessment Activity
Children make a cartoon strip to show what they have learned about the sun.
Skills: Listing, summarizing, explaining ideas

Materials (per group)
Module Kit Items: none
School Supplied Items: markers; pencil; crayons; drawing paper *(4 sheets/child);* transparent tape

Helpful Hints
- Help each child tape together four sheets of letter-size (8 1/2 in. x 11 in.) paper.
- Before they draw their cartoon panels, encourage children to **list** ways in which the sun is important.

What did you learn?

You know that the sun gives light and warmth to the earth. You also know that all living things need the sun. Now draw a cartoon strip to show the things you learned.

You will need: pencil crayons paper tape markers

D 22

 ## Science Idea Exchange

Teacher's Assessment Package

Use the pages from the Teacher's Assessment Package at this time to promote **performance assessment** opportunities for your children.

Gifted and Talented
Different regions of the United States receive different amounts of solar energy. Invite children to check the newspaper's weather page on a daily basis for a week. Children should chart the daily high and low temperatures over this period in a city of their choosing. Then have children discuss variations in temperatures among the cities they choose.

Collaborative Learning: Small Groups
Assign specific children to gather and clean up materials. All children in the Chapter Review group should plan the cartoon strip, prepare the paper, draw the cartoons, and share results.

Make a cartoon strip.

1. Think about why the sun is important.
2. Tape pieces of paper together to make a long strip.
3. Draw lines across the strip to make squares.
4. Write the name of your cartoon strip in the first square.
5. Draw pictures in the other squares. Show different ways the sun is important.
6. Share your cartoon strip with a classmate.

Share what you learned.

1. What is your favorite part of your cartoon strip? Tell why.
2. What fun things can you do because of the sun?

D 23

Act as a Consultant

Suggest to children that they look back through the chapter to help them list ways the sun is important.

Raise Questions

Using a **constructivist** approach, refer children to the questions they had in What Else Do You Want to Find Out? in Lesson 1. Ask which questions they can now answer. Invite children to suggest ways to find answers to the questions that remain.

Close

Check for Understanding

- Ask: *If the sun didn't shine anymore, what are the most important things we would lose?* (light, warmth, plants, animals)
- **Answers to Share what you learned**
  1. Accept any answer. Make sure children justify their answer. 2. Possible responses include play outside, swim, enjoy summer vacation, and participate in sports.

Connecting Chapters

In the next chapter, children will learn about how stars are grouped, reflected moonlight, and the moon's phases. ▶

Explorer's Activity Guide

Use Explorer's Activity Guide page 140 as a hands-on activity to evaluate how well children understand the concepts covered in this chapter.

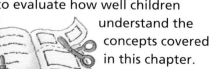

Activity Results

Children's cartoon strips should show ways the sun is important, such as providing light and warmth, helping plants and animals grow, and producing solar energy.

Science and Social Studies

Using a flashlight and globe, demonstrate how solar energy falls unevenly on the earth. Call attention to the limited solar energy at the poles. Encourage discussion of why the poles are icy and have so few plants, animals, and people.

Chapter 2 Planning Guide
The Moon and Stars

Lessons / *Skills*

Lesson 1
Discover Activity: **What does the night sky look like?**
pp. D24–D25
(visualizing, recognizing time relationships)

Lesson 2
How are other stars like the sun? pp. D26–D27
(comparing, describing)

Lesson 3
How are stars grouped? pp. D28–D29
(observing)

Lesson 4
Let's Explore: **What star group can you make?** pp. D30–D31
(observing, recognizing patterns, making physical models)

Lesson 5
What else is in the night sky? pp. D32–D33
(observing, making physical models, drawing conclusions)

Lesson 6
What does the moon look like? pp. D34–D35
(observing, recognizing cause and effect, comparing)

Lesson 7
What shapes does the moon have? pp. D36–D37
(observing, sequencing)

Lesson 8
Let's Solve It!: **How does the shape of the moon change?**
pp. D38–D39
(organizing information, solving problems)

Lesson 9
Chapter Review: **What did you learn?** pp. D40–D41
(comprehending meaning, describing)

Materials (per group)

Lesson 1 Activity: *What does the night sky look like?*
Module Kit Items: black construction paper *(1 sheet/child);* white chalk
School Supplied Items: none

Lesson 4 Activity: *What star group can you make?*
Module Kit Items: flashlight with batteries; black construction paper
School Supplied Item: pencil
Safety Kit Items: cover goggles *(1/child)*

Lesson 5 Activity: *Light up the moon.*
Module Kit Items: flashlight with batteries; inflatable globe; golf ball *(or use any other small ball)*
School Supplied Items: none

Lesson 6 Activity: *Make craters.*
Module Kit Items: sand *(about 1 cup);* golf ball; marble; large foil pan
School Supplied Items: none

Lesson 9 Activity: *Play a memory game.*
Module Kit Items: 10 index cards
School Supplied Item: pencil

Module D
The Earth and Sky

Assessment Options	Content	Performance	Portfolio
Teacher's Assessment Package			
Chapter Test, pp. 77–78	✓		✓
Group Interview Assessment, p. 79	✓	✓	✓
Performance Strategies, p. 80	✓	✓	✓
Explorer's Activity Guide			
Activity worksheets, pp. 141–151		✓	✓
Chapter Review, p. 152	✓		✓
Interactive Transparency Package			
Transparency 14 and BLM	✓	✓	✓
Teacher's Guide, pp. 32–33	✓	✓	
Activity for second-language learners	✓	✓	✓
Science Literature Library			
The Big Dipper		✓	✓
Interactive Videodisc Software Teacher's Guide, pp. 71–79			
Computer-based Activity	✓	✓	
Journal Presentations	✓	✓	✓
Videodisc Classroom Guide, pp. 33–40, or **Video Reader**			
Hands-on activity	✓	✓	✓
ExploraCenter Teacher's Guide, pp. 27, 31			
ExploraCenter			
Science activity cards 22, 26	✓	✓	✓
ScottForesman Online Service			
Online field trips	✓	✓	✓

Chapter Overview

In this chapter, children learn about the stars—what they are made of and how they are grouped into constellations. They also learn about the moon—what it looks like and where its light comes from. Children discover what causes the phases of the moon and then chart the phases for one month.

Craters — Moon — Phases

The Night Sky

Hot gases — Stars — Constellations

Lesson 1

Lesson Objective
Children use prior knowledge to show how a night sky looks.

Introduce

Invite Learning
Show the videodisc segment for this chapter. Bar codes and a description of this segment are given below on page D25.

Make Connections
To **assess prior knowledge,** ask children to list words that describe the things they see in the night sky. Record their answers on chart paper as a **baseline assessment** to use in Check for Understanding.

Teach

Discover Activity

Children draw a picture of the night sky.
Skills: Visualizing, recognizing time relationships

Materials (per group)
Module Kit Items: black construction paper *(1 sheet/child);* white chalk
School Supplied Items: none

Helpful Hints
- You can use construction paper of any dark color.

Chapter 2

The Moon and Stars

"Star light, star bright. First star I see tonight." Maybe you will say this when you look up at the sky tonight!

What things do you see in the night sky? What do you know about these things? What do you wonder about?

D 24

Science Idea Exchange

Managing Groups
Assign specific children to gather and clean up materials. Each child in the Discover Activity group should draw the night sky and write a sentence about it.

Family/School Partnership: Family Support
Encourage families to be active partners in learning by suggesting that they and their children:
- observe the night sky,
- describe the night sky, and
- observe how the shape of the moon changes.

Science and Literature
Share with children the literature selection *The Big Dipper* by Franklyn M. Branley (Harper Trophy, 1991). Suggest that on a clear evening, children look for the Big Dipper. Encourage children to draw what they see and describe where they were when they saw this group of stars.

What does the night sky look like?

1. Draw a picture of things you might see in the sky at night.
2. Write a sentence that tells about the night sky.
3. **Tell about it.** Tell about the things you drew in the night sky.

Ask me what else I want to find out about the night sky.

D 25

Helpful Hints (cont'd.)

- You may wish to save children's pictures for use in the Science and Art activity in Lesson 2.
- *See Equipment Kit Teacher's Guide for additional hints.*

What to Expect

Children's pictures may include the moon, moon phases, stars, and planets.

Close

Check for Understanding

- As a follow-up to the **baseline assessment,** invite children to share their pictures with the class. Ask them if they wish to revise their answers from Make Connections.
- **Answers to Tell about it** Children are likely to tell how the stars and moon look.

What Else Do You Want to Find Out?

Stimulate children's interest in the night sky with a **constructivist** approach by asking: *What do you already know about the night sky? What else would you like to learn? How can we find the answers to your questions?* Record children's questions on chart paper.

Connecting Lessons

In the next lesson, children will learn how the sun and stars are alike. ▶

Explorer's Activity Guide
The **Discover Activity recording sheet** on page 141 of the Explorer's Activity Guide can be used by children to record their activity results.

Visual Literacy
Discover the Wonder Videodisc, Grade 2, Module D, provides a series of stills to challenge children's imagination. Use these images to encourage children's creative expression as they explore and discover more about the nature of space.

Bar Codes

Chapter 18: Stills

Step

Interactive Software

Lesson 2

Lesson Objective
Children compare the sun with other stars in the sky.

Introduce

Invite Learning
Most children know the song "Twinkle, Twinkle, Little Star." Write the words on the chalkboard and invite children to sing along. Point to the words of the second line to emphasize "How I wonder what you are!"

Make Connections
To **assess prior knowledge,** encourage children to reply to the song by telling what they think the sun and other stars are. Have them tell what they know about stars. Children may think that the sun is not a star, even though it is. Record their answers on chart paper to use as a **baseline assessment.**

Teach

Observe and Listen
Encourage children to work in pairs. Have each child look at the illustration. Invite them to tell their partner what they see. Have children take turns describing the sun and the stars to their partner.

How are other stars like the sun?

Did you draw stars in your picture of the night sky? Sometimes you can see many stars on a clear night.

Remember that the sun is a **star.** Like the sun, all stars are made up of hot gases. Stars shine because the gases glow. You can see the light from the glowing, hot gases.

D 26

 ## Science Idea Exchange

Science Anecdote
Explain to children that astronomers use telescopes because many stars cannot be seen without one. Some telescopes are so huge they take up a whole building. Others, such as the Hubble Telescope, have been launched into space to get a better view of stars and other objects in space.

Science and Art
Provide children with glue and shiny materials such as sequins, glitter, or aluminum foil. Invite children to use the materials to embellish their pictures of the night sky that they made in the Discover Activity in Lesson 1.

Save the Earth
The sun's rays help plants and animals live, but they can also be dangerous. The ozone layer has always protected life on the earth. Now, because of chemicals in products made of polystyrene and some kinds of aerosol cans, the ozone layer is thinning in certain places. Ask children to name products they could avoid using to help preserve the ozone layer.

You know that the sun looks smaller than it really is. It looks small because it is far away. Other stars look small because they are far away too. These stars look smaller than the sun. They are even farther away from the earth than the sun is. Many of these stars are really much bigger than the sun.

Checkpoint

List ways the sun and other stars are alike.

D 27

Invite children to write a class definition for the words "sun" and "star." Record their definitions on chart paper.

Ask Open-ended Questions

Ask: *Do you think people will ever land spaceships on the sun or another star? Why or why not?* (Children may realize that the sun and other stars are too hot for a spaceship to land on.)

Close

Check for Understanding

- As a follow-up to the **baseline assessment,** review with children their earlier descriptions. Suggest they compare these descriptions with the class definitions of "sun" and "star."
- **Answers to Checkpoint** Lists should include that the sun and other stars are made up of hot gases, they shine because the hot gases glow, and they seem small because they are far away.

Extend the Lesson

Suggest children imagine that they are space travelers. Ask them to describe what they see as their spaceship approaches stars.

Connecting Lessons

In the next lesson, children will learn that people group stars into constellations. ▶

Explorer's Activity Guide

Use Explorer's Activity Guide page 142 with this lesson to help children answer the text question,  "How are other stars like the sun?" with a hands-on activity.

Visual Literacy

A photograph can show that close objects often look larger than distant ones. Take a picture of one child posed at the front of the frame and another child, of the same height, at the back. Invite children to **compare** the heights of the two children.

Science Themes

By comparing the sun with others stars in the sky, children begin to develop their understanding of the themes of **energy** and **modeling.**

Lesson 3

Introduce

Invite Learning

Ask four volunteers to hold flashlights so they form the corners of a square. Darken the room and invite children to show how imaginary lines could connect the four lights to form a square.

Make Connections

To **assess prior knowledge,** display a poster or pictures of a starry night sky. Ask children what they see when they look at the stars. Record their observations as a **baseline assessment.**

Teach

Observe and Listen

- Invite children to work in pairs. Have them take turns describing their pictures to each other.
- Provide children with copies of the same star patterns shown on these pages, but without the connecting lines. Suggest children connect the stars to form new pictures different from those in the book.
- Encourage children to discuss different images that they see among the stars with their partners.

How are stars grouped?

Long ago, people imagined that lines connected the stars. The lines and stars looked like pictures in the sky. People made up stories about the pictures.

Count the stars that make up the hunter's belt. Find the stars that make pictures of the lion and the bear. Now look at the last box. Use your finger to connect some stars to make a picture.

Checkpoint
Draw stars. Connect them to make a picture. Tell a story about the picture.

D 28

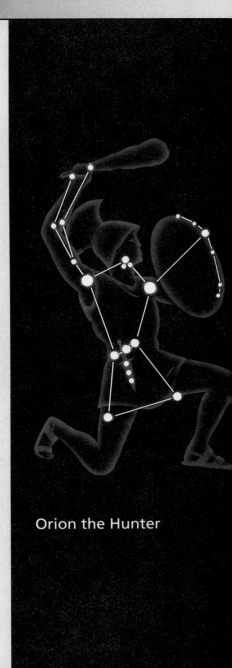

Orion the Hunter

 Science Idea Exchange

Science Background

The constellations serve as a map of the sky. For hundreds of years, they have helped astronomers and navigators find particular stars or other landmarks. For example, the two stars forming the outer border of the Big Dipper, a group of stars in the Great Bear constellation, always point to the North Star.

Science and Language Arts

Encourage children to make up stories to explain a group of stars. Suggest they make up their own story about the Great Bear or the Big Dipper. Remind them to explain how and why these stars were placed in the sky.

Multicultural Connection

Different cultures have different legends about the constellations and other star groups. The group of stars known as the Big Dipper in this country is called a plow in England. These same stars are seen as representing seven wise men by Hindus in India. The ancient Viking cultures of Scandinavia saw a wagon in this pattern; the ancien Chinese saw a chariot.

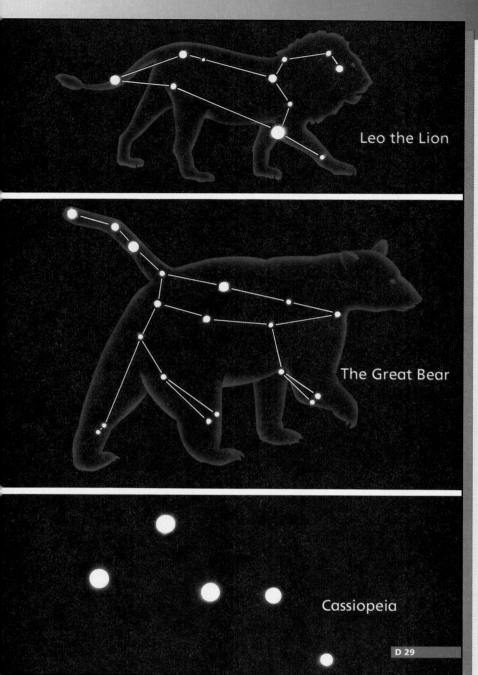

Leo the Lion

The Great Bear

Cassiopeia

Ask for Evidence

Repeat the activity from Invite Learning. Encourage children to be creative as they think of other imaginary lines to connect the lights.

Act as a Consultant

Find stories of constellations in star guides and encyclopedias to share.

- The *Great Bear* was once a beautiful young woman named Callisto. When Hera, queen of the gods, became jealous of Callisto, Zeus changed her into a bear to keep her safe.
- *Taurus the Bull* was Zeus. He disguised himself as a white bull to attract the attention of Europa, a princess.

Close

Check for Understanding

- As a follow-up to the **baseline assessment,** invite children to add names of star groups to their descriptions.
- **Answers to Checkpoint** Pictures should show stars with lines connecting them. Children should be able to tell a story about the image they drew.

Connecting Lessons

In the next lesson, children will create their own constellations. ▶

Explorer's Activity Guide

Use Explorer's Activity Guide page 143 with this lesson to help children answer the text question, "How are stars grouped?" with a hands-on activity.

Visual Literacy

To enhance the **visual literacy** connection, use the interactive overhead transparency that correlates with the above two pages. The transparency will help your students understand the key concepts presented on these pages.

Your Ideas

_____

_____

_____

_____

_____

Lesson 4

Lesson Objective
Children learn that a constellation is a group of stars that forms a picture in the sky.

Introduce

Key Term
constellation

Invite Learning
Cut thirty 2.5-cm (1-in.) circles from yellow or white paper and attach tape to them. Invite children to work in groups to make a constellation by attaching the circles to the chalkboard.

Make Connections
To **assess prior knowledge**, ask: *Do you see a picture in each group of stars? What do you think we call such a picture?*

Teach

Activity
Children use a flashlight and construction paper to make a constellation.
Skills: Observing, recognizing patterns, making physical models

Materials (per group)
Module Kit Items: flashlight with batteries; black construction paper
School Supplied Item: pencil
Safety Kit Items: cover goggles *(1/child)*

What star group can you make?

A group of stars that forms a picture in the sky is a **constellation.** Some constellations have shapes that look like animals or people. You can make your own constellation.

Find out about it.

You will need:
- cover goggles
- black construction paper
- pencil
- flashlight

1 Poke holes through the paper with a pencil. Do not tear the paper.

2 Make the room dark. Hold the paper up facing the wall.

3 Shine a flashlight so the light comes through the holes. What picture do you see on the wall?

Science Idea Exchange

Collaborative Learning: Cooperative Learning
Assign specific children to gather and clean up materials. All children in the Let's Explore group should decide where to put holes for the stars and share results. Also, each child in the group can be assigned a specific role:

- one who pokes the holes in the paper and holds the paper near the wall;
- one who shines the flashlight on the paper;
- one who draws the stars that can be seen on the wall;
- one who connects the stars to make a constellation.

Multicultural Connection
In West Africa, history is often handed down through generations by griots, or storytellers. Invite children to be griots as they make their constellation part of the class's history. Encourage children to sit in a circle. As each constellation is projected onto the wall of the darkened classroom, the pairs of children who made it can tell its story.

Write about it. ✏️

Make a chart like this one. Draw stars.
Connect the stars to make a constellation.

my stars	my constellation

Checkpoint

1. How many stars are in your constellation?

2. Take Action! Pretend you are a teacher. Tell your class about your constellation.

Helpful Hints
- Aluminum foil could be used instead of construction paper.
- *See Equipment Kit Teacher's Guide for additional hints.*

Act as a Consultant
Help children recognize that the holes they make can be different sizes. Explain that stars are different sizes and that they look larger the closer they are to the earth.

Close

Check for Understanding
- Ask: *Which of the pictures you made is a constellation?* (They all are.) *What is a constellation?* (a group of stars that forms a picture)
- **Answers to Checkpoint** 1. The number of stars will vary. 2. **Take Action!** Children's stories should be related to the constellation they made.

Ask Open-ended Questions
In the literature selection *Begin at the Beginning* by Amy Schwartz (Harper Trophy, 1983), Sara started her painting just as the sky was darkening. To guide children into the next lesson, ask: *What could Sara paint in the night sky?*

Connecting Lessons
In the next lesson, children will learn about another object in the night sky—the moon. ▶

Explorer's Activity Guide
Use Explorer's Activity Guide hands-on activity on page 145 to explore stars and evaluate children's understanding of the lesson concept.

Teacher's Assessment Package
A **scoring rubric** to assess student performance is provided on page 75 of the Teacher's Assessment Package.

Activity Results
When the children hold the flashlight behind the construction paper, some light will shine through the holes in the paper and onto the wall or ceiling, giving the appearance of stars shining in the night sky. Encourage children to predict and then determine the best distance to stand from the wall to project a clear picture.

Visual Literacy
Let small groups of children take turns using an instant camera on a scavenger hunt for patterns. Encourage children to find "constellations" in the patterns. You might wish to photocopy the pictures at various sizes for the whole class.

Lesson 5

Lesson Objective
Children learn that sunlight shining on the moon makes the moon shine.

Introduce

Key Term
moon

Invite Learning
Bring a piece of reflective tape to class. Turn off the lights and ask why the tape does not shine. Invite a volunteer to shine a flashlight on the tape. Tell children that the tape is reflecting the light of the flashlight.

Make Connections
To **assess prior knowledge,** ask: *Where does the moon's light come from?* Save responses as a **baseline assessment.**

Teach

Activity
Children use models of the earth, sun, and moon to demonstrate that moonlight is actually reflected sunlight.
Skills: *Observing, making physical models, drawing conclusions*

Materials (per group)
Module Kit Items: flashlight with batteries; inflatable globe; golf ball (*or use any other small ball*)
School Supplied Items: none

What else is in the night sky?

You can see many stars in the night sky. What else can you see? You often can see the **moon** shine in the night sky.

The moon is the brightest thing in the night sky. But the moon is not a star. Where does the moon's light come from?

Moonlight comes from the sun. Sunlight shining on the moon makes the moon shine. You can show how the sun makes the moon shine.

D 32

Science Idea Exchange

Science Anecdote
The moon is not as bright as the sun because fusion in the sun gives off tremendous amounts of light energy. The moon does not produce such energy. It only reflects light. Also, most rocks and dust on the moon's surface are dark gray and reflect only about 10% of the sun's light.

Science and Language Arts
The moon often inspires folklore. For example, the full moon is supposed to be the best time to plant crops that grow above the soil. Encourage children to ask parents and others about moon folklore and share their stories with the class.

Special Education
Make the concept of reflection more concrete by asking a volunteer to toss a soft rubber ball against a wall. Point out that the ball comes from the pitcher and bounces off at an angle. Light acts the same way. When the sun's light reaches the moon (like the ball bumped into the wall), it bounces off. This bouncing of light in different directions is reflection.

Light up the moon.

You will need: small ball   flashlight   globe

1. Make the room dark.
2. Pretend the ball is the moon. Pretend the flashlight is the sun.
3. Hold the ball in one hand. Hold the globe in the other hand.
4. Have your partner shine the flashlight on the ball and globe.

Checkpoint
Tell what makes the moon shine.

D 33

Helpful Hints
- Have children shine the flashlight first in a straight line with the globe and the ball, then not in line with them.
- *See Equipment Kit Teacher's Guide for additional hints.*

Act as a Consultant
Help children recognize that if the globe were between the flashlight and the ball, people on the dark side of the globe would see no moon.

Ask for Evidence
Ask children to show how they know the ball is not making its own light. Have them describe how the ball would look if the flashlight were turned off.

Close

Check for Understanding
- As a follow-up to the **baseline assessment,** ask children to draw a diagram to show how the sun makes the moon shine. Invite children to **compare** these diagrams with their responses from Make Connections.
- **Answers to Checkpoint** The moon shines because it reflects light from the sun.

Connecting Lessons
In the next lesson, children will get a close-up view of the moon's surface. ▶

Explorer's Activity Guide
Use Explorer's Activity Guide hands-on activity on page 146 to help children answer the question, "What else is in the night sky?"

Teacher's Assessment Package
A **scoring rubric** to assess student performance is provided on page 75 of the Teacher's Assessment Package.

Activity Results
Children should see that the moon receives light just like the globe does from the flashlight. The child holding the ball and globe will have the dark sides facing him or her, while the lit sides face the partner with the flashlight.

Collaborative Learning: Small Groups
Assign specific children to gather and clean up materials. All children in the Activity group should take turns holding the balls and shining the flashlight and should record data and share results.

Lesson 6

Lesson Objective
Children learn how the surface of the moon looks and that craters are features of the moon's surface.

Introduce

Key Term
crater

Invite Learning
Invite children to shine a flashlight across bumpy surfaces, or surfaces with objects on them (a computer keyboard, stacks of unevenly piled books). Encourage children to observe the shadows that result.

Make Connections
To **assess prior knowledge,** show children a photograph of the moon in which shadows can be seen. Ask children to explain what they think causes the shadows and the bright spots on the moon. Record their answers as a **baseline assessment.**

Teach

Activity
Children demonstrate how craters are formed. **Skills:** Observing, recognizing cause and effect, comparing

Materials (per group)
Module Kit Items: sand *(about 1 cup);* golf ball; marble; large foil pan
School Supplied Items: none

What does the moon look like?

What would you find if you could visit the moon? The moon has no water, air, or living things. It does have rocks, soil, and mountains. The moon also has many holes called **craters.**

Long ago, rocks from space crashed into the moon. The rocks made craters. Some craters are small. Other craters are very big. You can find out why craters are different sizes.

D 34

Science Idea Exchange

Science Background
Until the early 1600s, people thought the surface of the moon was smooth. In 1609 Galileo Galilei developed a telescope strong enough to show the features on the moon's surface. Galileo was the first person to see that the moon's surface had both mountains and craters.

Science and Language Arts
Encourage children to think about what it might be like to spend a vacation on the moon. What sights would they see? What clothes would they wear? Invite children to write a letter describing their trip to a friend at home on the earth.

Science and Social Studies
Someday people may live on the moon. If so, people will have to live in enclosed areas where air, food, and water are available. Have children discuss and describe the possible changes in their lifestyles if they lived in a futuristic moon colony.

Make craters.

You will need: pan of sand marble golf ball

1. Hold the marble as high as your waist.
   Drop it into the sand.
2. Pick up the marble. Observe how big the
   hole in the sand is.
3. Hold the golf ball as high as your waist.
   Drop it into a different part of the sand.
4. Pick up the ball. Observe how big the
   hole in the sand is.

Checkpoint

Tell what makes the bigger crater. What makes craters different sizes?

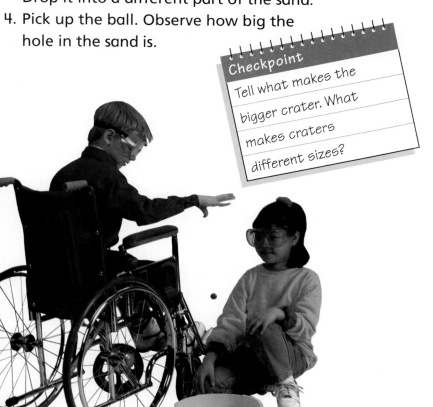

D 35

Helpful Hints

- Pour sand to a depth of at least 4 cm
  (1 1/2 in.) into each pan and smooth the
  sand before children begin the activity.
- Make sure children drop the marble
  and golf ball from the same height.
- *See Equipment Kit Teacher's Guide for
  additional hints.*

Ask for Evidence

Ask children how they can identify
which marks were left by the golf ball
and which were left by the marble. (The
golf ball craters are wider and deeper
and have little indentations.)

Close

Check for Understanding

- As a follow-up to the **baseline
  assessment,** review with children the
  explanations they gave in Make
  Connections. Ask children if they would
  like to change their explanations. Have
  them give reasons for any changes they
  make.
- **Answers to Checkpoint** The golf ball
  makes the bigger crater. Children
  should realize that the size of the
  object determines the size of a crater.

Connecting Lessons

In the next lesson, children will learn
why the moon seems to change
shape. ▶

Explorer's Activity Guide

Use Explorer's Activity Guide hands-
on activity on page 147 to help
children answer the question,

 "What does the
moon look like?"

Teacher's Assessment Package

A **scoring rubric** to assess student
performance is provided on page 75
of the Teacher's Assessment Package.

Activity Results

After the activity, the sand's
surface will have circular indentations of different diameters
and depths made by the marble
and the golf ball. Some sand will
be scattered around the indentations; some sand will be piled
up beside them.

Collaborative Learning: Small Groups

Assign specific children to gather
and clean up materials. All
children in the Activity group
should take turns dropping the
balls and should observe the
craters, record data, and share
results.

Lesson 7

Lesson Objective
Children learn that the movement of the moon around the earth causes the phases of the moon.

Introduce

Key Term
phases

Invite Learning
Invite children to come to the chalkboard and draw pictures of the moon. Ask volunteers if they have seen any shapes in addition to completely round.

Make Connections
To **assess prior knowledge,** ask children to explain why the moon seems to be shaped differently at different times. Some children may think that the shape of the moon physically changes. Record their answers as a **baseline assessment.**

Teach

Observe and Listen
- Divide children into teams of three or four. Suggest they take turns explaining the phases of the moon.
- Encourage children to include information in their descriptions about the moon's light, such as where the light comes from, and why the moon is not always full.

What shapes does the moon have?

Some nights the moon looks like a whole circle in the sky. Other nights the moon looks like part of a circle. But the moon is always the same shape. One side of the moon is always lit. Why does the shape of the moon seem to change?

The moon moves around the earth. You only see the part of the moon that has light shining on it. Sometimes you see all of the lighted side. Sometimes you see part of the lighted side. So you see different shapes of the moon.

D 36

Science Idea Exchange

Science Anecdote
On July 20, 1969, two *Apollo 11* astronauts, Neil Armstrong and Edwin (Buzz) Aldrin, became the first people to walk on the moon. They took pictures, collected rocks and soil, installed a laser-beam reflector, and set up seismic and solar wind experiments.

Science and Language Arts
Before the theory explaining the phases of the moon was discovered, stories were invented to explain them. Invite children to work in small groups to make up a story about the moon's phases and put on a play telling the story.

Multicultural Connection
On September 12, 1992, Dr. Mae Jemison became the first African-American woman to travel in space. While on the shuttle *Endeavor,* Dr. Jemison conducted experiments on how tadpoles mature in weightlessness. Before joining NASA, she served as a doctor with the Peace Corps in Sierra Leone and Liberia, countries in Africa.

The shapes of the moon are called **phases**. The pictures show four phases of the moon. Point to the phases you have seen.

Checkpoint

Draw pictures of two phases of the moon. Use crayons to color your pictures.

Have groups of four to six children sit in a circle on the floor. Place a ball in the center of the circle. Lay a flashlight on the floor and shine it on the ball. Have children draw what the ball looks like to them from their position in the circle. Have them tape their pictures on a wall in the order in which they were seated in their group and discuss the differences in the pictures. Help children write a class definition of the word "phases." Ask a volunteer to label the series of pictures "Phases of the Moon."

Close

Check for Understanding

- As a follow-up to the **baseline assessment,** review with children their answers from Make Connections. Have them give reasons for any changes they wish to make. Look for the explanation that the moon's phases result from the moon moving around the earth.
- **Answers to Checkpoint** Children's drawings should include any two phases of the moon: full moon, half moon, crescent moons of differing widths, or a new moon.

Connecting Lessons

In the next lesson, children will chart the phases of the moon. ▶

Explorer's Activity Guide
Use Explorer's Activity Guide pages 149–150 with this lesson to help children answer the text question,

"What shapes does the moon have?" with a hands-on activity.

Science Themes
By discussing the recurring cycle of lunar phases, children begin to develop their understanding of the themes of systems and interactions and patterns of change.

Math/Science Connection
Provide groups of children with the following shapes of the moon made from construction paper: waxing crescent, first quarter, waxing gibbous, full moon, waning gibbous, last quarter, waning crescent. Challenge children to place the shapes of the moon in the correct order.

Lesson 8

Lesson Objective

Children learn that the moon goes through all of its phases in about a month. **Skills:** Organizing information, solving problems

Introduce

Invite Learning

Post a large calendar on the chalkboard or make an overhead transparency of the current month. Pose questions about the calendar. Be sure phases of the moon are recorded.

Make Connections

To **assess prior knowledge,** ask whether children know how often the full moon appears each month. Record their answers as a **baseline assessment.**

Teach

Observe and Listen

• Have children work in pairs to interpret the information on the calendar in the book. Encourage them to pick a date and ask one another what phase of the moon they would see on that date.

How does the shape of the moon change?

Each day the moon seems to change shape. It moves all the way around the earth in about a month. The moon goes through all its phases in about a month.

1. Look at the calendar. It shows what the moon looked like on each day of a month. On June 15 you could see a full moon. What could you see on June 8?

D 38

 ## Science Idea Exchange

Science Background

The ancient Egyptians were likely the first civilization to use a solar calendar. Today much of the world uses the Gregorian calendar, named after Pope Gregory XIII, who introduced it in 1582. There are 365 days in the Gregorian calendar year, with one extra day in leap years.

Math/Science Connection

Provide more practice with calendars. Distribute blank calendar pages and encourage children to keep track of achievements, homework assignments, or special events. Encourage children to add their own ideas. They might wish to make a special family calendar showing birthdates of family members.

Multicultural Connection

Tell children that throughout history, different societies have shared similar customs. Many cultures measured time by the moon. The Old English language gave us the words "month" and "Monday." The Chinese calendar is also based on the moon—each month begins at the new moon and contains 29 or 30 days.

2. Make a chart like this one.

3. Use the calendar to fill in the chart. Write down the dates you would see each of the phases of the moon.

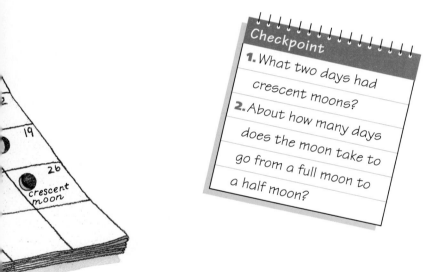

phase of moon		date
full moon	○	
half moon	◑	
crescent moon	◗	

Checkpoint

1. What two days had crescent moons?

2. About how many days does the moon take to go from a full moon to a half moon?

Observe and Listen (cont'd.)

- Suggest that children change partners. Encourage them to choose a phase of the moon and ask one another when they would see that phase.

Act as a Consultant

Guide children to the realization that they can match the picture of the moon in the chart with the pictures of the moon on the calendar. Help them match the pictures to learn the date for a given phase of the moon.

Close

Check for Understanding

- As a follow-up to the **baseline assessment,** children's charts should indicate that the full moon appears on June 15, the half moon on June 7 and June 23, and the crescent shown in the chart on June 4 and June 27.

- **Answers to Checkpoint** 1. June 4 and June 27 had crescent moons like the one shown in the chart. Accept other dates that show the shape of a crescent. 2. It takes about seven days for the moon to change from a full moon to a half moon.

Connecting Lessons

In the next lesson, children will demonstrate mastery of the chapter concepts by playing a memory game. ▶

Explorer's Activity Guide

Use Explorer's Activity Guide page 151 to help children solve the question of how the moon changes shape. You can also use the hands-on activity page to evaluate how well children understand the concept of the lesson.

Science and Language Arts

Encourage children to keep a diary or journal for at least a week. Suggest that they make an entry for each day, writing brief notes about important events of their day or recording their thoughts. Encourage them to include a small drawing of the phase of the moon for each date.

Your Ideas

_____

_____

_____

_____

Lesson 9

Lesson Objective
Children play a memory game to show the concepts they learned in this chapter.

Introduce

Invite Learning
Review the **baseline assessment** activities you used in this chapter. Choose one or more to do again that you think will help children understand the chapter concepts.

Teach

Performance Assessment Activity
Children write words they have learned on note cards and play a memory game with a partner. **Skills:** Describing, comprehending meaning

Materials (per group)
Module Kit Items: 10 index cards
School Supplied Item: pencil

Helpful Hints
- Remind children that as they turn cards faceup and facedown the cards should be in the same location.
- You might want to encourage children to use crayons or markers to decorate the cards.
- *See Equipment Kit Teacher's Guide for additional hints.*

What did you learn?

Now you know some things about the night sky. You know what the words *constellation* and *phase* mean. Play a game to show what else you learned.

You will need: ☐ 10 note cards pencil

Play a memory game.
1. Think of five words that tell about the night sky. Write each word on two cards.
2. Mix up your cards.
3. Place the cards facedown on the table. Decide who will play first.
4. Turn over two cards. Read the words. Then use each word in a sentence.
5. If the words match, keep the cards. Turn the cards down if the words do not match.
6. Take turns until all the cards are matched.
7. Play the game again. Use the cards your partner made.

D 40

 ## Science Idea Exchange

Teacher's Assessment Package
Use the pages from the Teacher's Assessment Package at this time to promote **performance assessment** opportunities for your children.

Science Background
For centuries, people believed that the sun, moon, and stars moved around a stationary earth. Aristarchus, an early Greek astronomer, and later Nicolaus Copernicus thought otherwise. In the 1500s, Copernicus illustrated how he thought the earth, other planets, and stars moved around the sun. His work is the foundation of modern astronomy.

Collaborative Learning: Small Groups
Assign specific children to gather and clean up materials. All children in the Chapter Review group should work together to write words on cards, place them on the table, and use the words in the matching game.

Observe and Listen
Walk among the children to offer encouragement and listen to their sentences. When you hear a child using a difficult word correctly, you might suggest that the child repeat the sentence for the class.

Act as a Consultant
Help children verify pronunciations. Clarify concepts as necessary, reminding children of activities they performed or providing new examples.

Close

Check for Understanding
- Challenge children to write a story using the words on their cards. Encourage them to share their stories with the class.
- Answers to Share what you learned
  1. Answers will vary. Children may say that the hardest words were the names of constellations. 2. The class may be divided on whether or not they would like to travel to the moon. Reasons will vary.

Connecting Chapters
In the next chapter, children will learn about the surface and atmosphere of the earth. ▶

Share what you learned.
1. Which word was hardest to use in a sentence?
2. Would you like to travel to the moon some day? Why or why not?

Explorer's Activity Guide
Use Explorer's Activity Guide page 152 as a hands-on activity to evaluate how well children understand the concepts covered in this chapter.

Activity Results
As children play the memory game, they will cooperate to decide if the sentences make sense in light of what they have learned in the chapter.

Achieving English Proficiency
Print words from children's memory game cards on slips of paper and fold. Invite children to take turns choosing a slip of paper and giving clues to help the class guess the word. The clue giver may pantomime the word or draw pictures but may not talk.

Chapter 3 Planning Guide
Looking at the Earth

Lessons / *Skills*

Lesson 1
Discover Activity: **What parts of the earth can you find?**
pp. D42–D43
(classifying, inferring)

Lesson 2
What makes up the earth? pp. D44–D45
(observing, classifying, comparing)

Lesson 3
Let's Explore: **What is soil like?** pp. D46–D47
(observing, recording, inferring)

Lesson 4
What are different kinds of land? pp. D48–D49
(classifying, making physical models)

Lesson 5
Where is water on the earth? pp. D50–D51
(observing, describing)

Lesson 6
How are salt water and fresh water different? pp. D52–D53
(observing, classifying, identifying variables)

Lesson 7
What is around the earth? pp. D54–D55
(observing, describing)

Lesson 8
Let's Solve It!: **Does the sun heat things the same way?**
pp. D56–D57
(organizing information, solving problems)

Lesson 9
Chapter Review: **What did you learn?** pp. D58–D59
(organizing information, summarizing)

Materials (per group)

Lesson 1 Activity: *What parts of the earth can you find?*
Module Kit Items: 4 plastic bags; masking tape
School Supplied Items: marker; schoolyard soil
Advance Prep: If you can't conduct this activity outdoors, you may want to prepare samples of soil, rocks, water, sand, and clay for children to examine.

Lesson 2 Activity: *Sort the rocks.*
Module Kit Items: none
School Supplied Items: 12 assorted rocks
Advance Prep: If you do not have enough rocks from the Activity on page D43, suggest children bring some in from home or engage in a rock hunt on the school grounds.

Lesson 3 Activity: *What is soil like?*
Module Kit Items: 4 toothpicks; vacant lot soil *(about 1/2 cup)*; hand lens; plastic spoon
School Supplied Items: white paper; 2 sheets paper towel; container of water *(about 1/2 cup)*
Safety Kit Items: cover goggles *(1/child)*

Lesson 4 Activity: *Make a model of land.*
Module Kit Items: pebbles/gravel *(about 1/2 cup)*; sand *(about 1/2 cup)*; aluminum foil; 2 sticks modeling clay *(1 green, 1 brown)*
School Supplied Items: rocks *(about 1/2 cup)*; paper plate *(or cardboard)*

Lesson 6 Activity: *Find out about salt water and fresh water.*
Module Kit Items: salt *(about 4 spoonfuls)*; 2 pieces bar soap; masking tape; 2 cups; spoon
School Supplied Items: marker; container of water *(about 1 1/2 cups)*

Lesson 9 Activity: *Make a poster.*
Module Kit Items: none
School Supplied Items: marker or crayon; posterboard *(1 sheet/child)*; magazines; glue; scissors *(1/child)*
Advance Prep: Find magazines with outdoor scenes in them and provide enough for each group to have two magazines.

Assessment Options	Content	Performance	Portfolio
Teacher's Assessment Package			
Chapter Test, pp. 83–84	✓		✓
Group Interview Assessment, p. 85	✓	✓	
Performance Strategies, p. 86	✓	✓	✓
Explorer's Activity Guide			
Activity worksheets, pp. 153–161		✓	✓
Chapter Review, p. 162	✓		✓
Interactive Transparency Package			
Transparency 15 and BLM	✓	✓	✓
Teacher's Guide, pp. 34–35	✓	✓	
Hands-on activity for second-language learners	✓	✓	✓
Science Literature Library			
My Little Island		✓	✓
Interactive Videodisc Software			
Teacher's Guide, pp. 71–79			
Computer-based Activity	✓	✓	
Journal Presentations	✓	✓	✓
Videodisc Classroom Guide, pp. 33–40, or			
Video Reader			
Hands-on activity	✓	✓	✓
ExploraCenter Teacher's Guide, pp. 16, 20, 24, 25, 26, 31			
ExploraCenter			
Science activity cards 11, 15, 19, 20, 21, 26	✓	✓	✓
ScottForesman Online Service	✓	✓	✓
Online field trips	✓	✓	✓

Chapter Overview

Rocks, soil, water, land, and air—in this chapter, children learn that the earth is made up of all these things. Children experiment to find what soil is made of and to determine how fresh water and salt water are different. Children also determine which is warmed the fastest by sunlight—air, water, or soil.

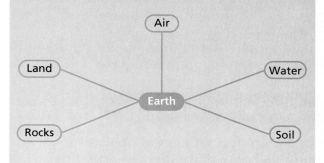

Lesson 1

Lesson Objective
Children make inferences about what materials make up the earth.

Introduce

Invite Learning
Show the videodisc segment for this chapter. Bar codes and a description of this segment are given below on page D43.

Make Connections
To **assess prior knowledge**, ask children to draw a picture or make a model of what they think the earth is made of. Save the drawings and models as a **baseline assessment** that you can use in Check for Understanding.

Teach

Discover Activity

Children collect samples of objects that they think make up the earth.
Skills: Classifying, inferring

Materials (per group)
Module Kit Items: 4 plastic bags; masking tape
School Supplied Items: marker; schoolyard soil

Safety Tip
Caution children not to pick up glass, wire, metal, trash, or any sharp objects.

Chapter 3

Looking at the Earth

You are digging a hole in the ground. You want to find out what makes up the earth. You might dig through sand, soil, or clay. What else can you find when you dig? Let's find out what the earth is made of!

D 42

Science Idea Exchange

Collaborative Learning: Small Groups
Assign specific children to gather and clean up materials. All children in the Discover Activity group should find nonliving things in the ground, sort what they find, and share results.

Family/School Partnership: Family Support
Encourage families to be active partners in learning by suggesting that they and their children:
- observe rocks and soil,
- describe how the land looks where they live, and
- observe a stream, river, lake, or ocean, or pictures of them.

Science and Literature
Read the literature selection *My Little Island* by Frané Lessac (J. B. Lippincott, 1984) to the class, and encourage children to describe how the land on the island appeared from the air as well as on the ground.

Discover Activity

What parts of the earth can you find?

1 Look at the ground near school. Find nonliving things that make up the earth.

2 Put the things in plastic bags.

3 Write the name of each thing on tape. Put the tape on the bag.

4 Share what you found with your classmates.

5 **Tell about it.** Tell what kinds of things everyone found.

Ask me what else I want to find out about the earth.

D 43

Helpful Hints

- If you are unable to conduct this activity outdoors, you may want to prepare samples of soil, rocks, water, sand, and clay for children to examine.
- Keep any rocks to use in the next lesson.
- *See Equipment Kit Teacher's Guide for additional hints.*

What to Expect

Children will collect varied samples. Use prepared samples to illustrate items children don't find.

Close

Check for Understanding

- As a follow-up to the **baseline assessment,** review with children the drawings and models from Make Connections. Ask children if there is anything they would like to change on their drawings and models.
- **Answers to Tell about it** Children should name the nonliving things they found including rocks, sand, and clay.

What Else Do You Want to Find Out?

Using a **constructivist** approach, ask: *What else would you like to know about what makes up the earth? How can we find answers to your questions?*

Connecting Lessons

In the next lesson, children classify rocks that make up the earth. ▶

Explorer's Activity Guide

The **Discover Activity recording sheet** on page 153 of the Explorer's Activity Guide can be used by children to record their activity results.

Visual Literacy

Discover the Wonder Videodisc, Grade 2, Module D, provides video clips and stills offering a rich array of views of the earth. Use these images to stimulate discussions about various features of the earth's surface.

Bar Codes

Chapter 17: Video and Stills

Play

Step

Interactive Software

Lesson 2

Lesson Objective
Children learn that there are differences among the rocks that make up the earth.

Introduce

Invite Learning
Invite children to draw and then describe rocks they have seen.

Make Connections
To **assess prior knowledge**, ask children to list similarities and differences among rock characteristics. Save their lists to use as a **baseline assessment**. You can follow up on this assessment in Check for Understanding.

Teach

Activity
Children observe rocks and classify them by their characteristics. **Skills:** Observing, classifying, comparing

Materials (per group)
Module Kit Items: none
School Supplied Items: 12 assorted rocks

Safety Tips
- Make sure children don't use rocks with sharp edges.
- Direct children to wash their hands thoroughly after this activity.

What makes up the earth?

What did you find that makes up the earth? You might find mostly rocks, soil, and water. Look closely at what you found. Is all the soil alike? Is all the water alike? Are all the rocks alike?

You probably found many different kinds of rocks. Look at all the rocks your class found. How could you sort the rocks?

Science Idea Exchange

Science Background
Rocks are classified as igneous, sedimentary, or metamorphic, according to how they were formed. Conditions such as heat, pressure, chemical reactions, and erosion change one type of rock to another in a continuous process called the rock cycle.

Science and Language Arts
Suggest that children choose their favorite rock and make up a story about it. Ask each child to write, tell, or act out the story for the class. Alternatively, help children write a rhyming poem, limerick, or rebus story about a rock.

Collaborative Learning: Small Groups
Assign specific children to gather and clean up materials. All children in the Activity group should work together to sort rocks and share results.

Sort the rocks.

You will need: rocks

1. Work with a group. Put all the rocks the group found in a pile.
2. Look at the rocks carefully. Look at their size and color.
3. Touch the rocks. Do they all feel the same?
4. Sort the rocks different ways. Group them by how they are alike.

Checkpoint
Tell how you sorted the rocks.

Helpful Hints

- Invite children to group the rocks by size, color, weight, texture (roughness), or any other criteria.
- If you do not have enough rocks from the previous activity, suggest children bring some in from home or engage in a rock hunt.

Act as a Consultant

Encourage groups to think of ways they can sort the rocks. Have children list their ideas on chart paper. Invite groups to discuss, and then demonstrate, their different methods of sorting.

Ask Open-ended Questions

Ask: *Can you think of any other ways rocks might be classified?* (by what they are made of, by how easily they break)

Close

Check for Understanding

- As a follow-up to the **baseline assessment,** ask children to add to their list of the characteristics of rocks. Look for an increased understanding of the varieties of rocks.
- **Answers to Checkpoint** Children should indicate that they classified rocks by size, color, weight, texture, or other criteria.

Connecting Lessons

In the next lesson, children will find out what soil is like. ▶

Explorer's Activity Guide

Use Explorer's Activity Guide hands-on activity on page 154 to help children answer the question,  "What makes up the earth?"

Teacher's Assessment Package

A **scoring rubric** to assess student performance is provided on page 81 of the Teacher's Assessment Package.

Activity Results

Children will have their rocks sorted into groups with distinctive characteristics. They should realize that a variety of rocks are part of what makes up the earth and that these rocks can be classified by their characteristics, such as color and size.

Extend the Lesson

Invite children to examine their rocks with a hand lens. Encourage them to describe what they see and to tell how looking through a hand lens changes what they know about the rock. Try to use samples with small crystals, colors, fossils, minerals, sand grains, or veins.

Lesson 3

Lesson Objective
Children learn that soil contains air and water in addition to rocks, clay, and plant and animal debris.

Introduce

Invite Learning
Invite children to look at a large box of crayons and choose the crayons that are the color of soil. Ask what they think is in soil that gives it these colors.

Make Connections
To **assess prior knowledge,** present children with a variety of soil ingredients—sand, rock bits, decaying bones, clay, water, and air. Ask children to predict which of the items they will find in soil. Record their predictions as a **baseline assessment.**

Teach

Activity
Children examine a sample of soil and determine what is in it.
Skills: Observing, recording, inferring

Materials (per group)
Module Kit Items: 4 toothpicks; vacant lot soil *(about 1/2 cup);* hand lens; plastic spoon
School Supplied Items: white paper; 2 sheets paper towel; container of water *(about 1/2 cup)*
Safety Kit Items: cover goggles *(1/child)*

Let's Explore

What is soil like?

You looked closely at rocks. Now look closely at soil. Soil has bits of rock in it. What else do you think is in soil?

Find out about it.

You will need:

 cover goggles

 soil

 toothpicks

 hand lens

 white paper

 spoon

 paper towels

cup of water

1 Put soil on the white paper.

2 Move the soil with a toothpick.

3 Look at the soil with a hand lens. List the things you find.

4 Drop 2 spoonfuls of soil into the water. Look for bubbles of air.

5 Put a spoonful of soil between 2 paper towels.

6 Press the towels together. Look for wet spots on the towels. Where did the wetness come from?

Science Idea Exchange

Collaborative Learning: Cooperative Learning

Assign specific children to gather and clean up materials. All children in the Let's Explore group should spread out the soil, look at it with a hand lens, observe the soil in water and in paper towels, and share results. Also, each child in the group can be assigned a specific role:

- one who puts the soil on white paper;
- one who lists what is in the soil;
- one who drops soil into water;
- one who puts soil between two paper towels and presses the towels together.

Science Background

Soil is a product of weathering—a group of processes that break down rocks through exposure to air, water, temperature changes, plants, animals, and bacteria. Over time, rock fragments become smaller and smaller and combine with air, water, and organic material to become soil.

Write about it.

Make a chart like this one. Write down or draw the things you found in the soil.

things in soil

Checkpoint

1. What nonliving things did you find in soil?

2. Take Action! Draw a picture that shows how you can sort the things you found.

D 47

Safety Tips
- Direct children to wear cover goggles and use toothpicks with care.
- Remove any dangerous material, such as broken glass or rusty metal.

Helpful Hints
- Use clean soil that contains a mix of: sand, clay, rock, plant and animal debris.
- Keep the soil moist in a plastic bag.
- *See Equipment Kit Teacher's Guide for additional hints.*

Act as a Consultant
Help children use their observations of the bubbles in water and the wet paper towel to infer that soil contains air and water.

Close

Check for Understanding
- As a follow-up to the **baseline assessment,** refer to children's predictions and ask: *Which of the items did you find in soil?* Look for increased knowledge of the components of soil.
- **Answers to Checkpoint** 1. Children should name air, water, rocks, and sand. 2. **Take Action!** Pictures may show that the things found in soil can be sorted by size, color, visibility, and so on.

Connecting Lessons
In the next lesson, children will make a model of what land looks like. ▶

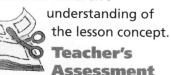

Explorer's Activity Guide
Use Explorer's Activity Guide hands-on activity on page 155 to explore soil and evaluate children's understanding of the lesson concept.

Teacher's Assessment Package
A **scoring rubric** to assess student performance is provided on page 81 of the Teacher's Assessment Package.

Activity Results
Children will observe that soil is a mixture of air, water, rocks, sand, and plant parts.

Your Ideas
_____
_____
_____
_____
_____

Lesson 4

Introduce

Invite Learning
Have children make landforms in the air with their hands: a tall mountain, a small hill, a valley, a flat area.

Make Connections
To **assess prior knowledge,** have children draw pictures of different kinds of land. Children may have the idea that all land is alike. Save their drawings to use as a **baseline assessment.**

Teach

Activity
Children use simple materials to make a model of land. **Skills:** Classifying, making physical models

Materials (per group)
Module Kit Items: pebbles/gravel *(about 1/2 cup);* sand *(about 1/2 cup);* aluminum foil; 2 sticks modeling clay *(1 green, 1 brown)*
School Supplied Items: rocks *(about 1/2 cup);* paper plate *(or cardboard)*

What are different kinds of land?

You might have seen pictures of land in different places. Land in some places is flat. Land in other places has hills. Some places have mountains and valleys. What is the land like where you live?

You can make a model of what the land looks like. You can make a model of your favorite place. You can make a model of the land where you live. Here's how!

D 48

Science Idea Exchange

Science Background
Over time, colliding continents slowly push up mountains; rivers deposit sediments, forming floodplains; fast-flowing streams carve steep valleys; glaciers carve wide U-shaped valleys; wind piles sand into dunes; sea waves form beaches; groundwater dissolves limestone, forming caves.

Collaborative Learning: Cooperative Learning
All children in the Activity group should have an opportunity to work on the model and share results. Also, each child in the group can be assigned a specific role:
- one who models soil and grass;
- one who models hills and mountains;
- one who models other land;
- one who models water.

Multicultural Connection
Around 2700 years ago, cultures such as the Adena and Hopewell began to build large mounds as burial places. Several mounds are animal-shaped, including a serpen in southern Ohio, an eagle in Georgia, and birds, bears, and panthers in the Midwest. Invite children to draw a mound in a shape they would like to build.

Make a model of land.

You will need: aluminum foil cardboard

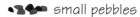 modeling clay sand rocks

 small pebbles

1. Use the things your teacher gives you to make your model.
2. Show soil and grass on your model.
3. Make hills and mountains on your land.
4. Show other kinds of land and water on your model.

Checkpoint

Tell what kind of land you show in your model. What other kinds of land could you show?

D 49

Helpful Hints

- You may wish to have children use salt dough colored with acrylic or watercolor paint.
- *See Equipment Kit Teacher's Guide for additional hints.*

Act as a Consultant

Encourage children to think of land where they live or that they have seen. Making a drawing first might help some children visualize and plan their model.

Ask Open-ended Questions

Using a **constructivist** approach, ask children what kind of land they would like to live on. Ask: *What do you know about different kinds of land? What do you want to know about different kinds of land? How can we find the answers to your questions?*

Close

Check for Understanding

- As a follow-up to the **baseline assessment,** have children revise the drawings they made in Make Connections.
- **Answers to Checkpoint** Other kinds of land might include a mountain, hill, valley, plain or flatland, seashore, or island.

Connecting Lessons

In the next lesson, children will find out where water is on the earth. ▶

Explorer's Activity Guide

Use Explorer's Activity Guide hands-on activity on page 156 to help children answer the question,

"What are different kinds of land?"

Teacher's Assessment Package

A **scoring rubric** to assess student performance is provided on page 82 of the Teacher's Assessment Package.

Activity Results

Children's models may represent many kinds of land, such as mountains, hills, valleys, flat areas or plains, and seacoasts.

Visual Literacy

Take pictures of any large and small land-forms that may be near the school: mountains, hills, beaches, rocky places, plains, and valleys. Invite children to describe each kind of land and write a label for each picture.

Lesson 5

Lesson Objective
Children learn that water is found in different places on the earth.

Introduce

Invite Learning
Slowly turn a globe and invite children to point out where there is water on the earth and where there is land. Ask volunteers to cover the land with their hands. Then have them cover the water with their hands. Ask if there is more water on the earth, or more land (more water).

Make Connections
To **assess prior knowledge,** ask children to list places where water is found on the earth. Save their lists as a **baseline assessment** that you can use for a follow-up in Check for Understanding.

Teach

Observe and Listen
Invite groups of children to draw pictures of places where they have seen water. Encourage them to describe the places they draw. Listen for descriptions including "large," "cold," "wavy," "deep," "shallow," "blue," and "salty." Have each group share its pictures and descriptions with the rest of the class.

Where is water on the earth?

Where do you see water on the earth? You might see water in puddles after the rain. You might see water in pools or ponds. You can see water in these pictures.

Most of the water on the earth is in oceans. Water is also in lakes, rivers, and streams. There are even rivers under the ground.

Checkpoint
Draw the places where you could find water.

ocean

stream

Science Idea Exchange

Science Background
Groundwater is water that sinks below the earth's surface into the ground, gathering in pores (holes) and cracks in rock. Once groundwater reaches a layer of nonporous rock, it stops moving and collects to form a water table. People drill water wells to reach the water table.

Science and Language Arts
Invite children to write a poem or a story about where water is on the earth. Children might pretend they are fish or frogs or plants that live in water. Encourage children to describe where the water is and how it looks, feels, smells, tastes, and sounds. Allow children to share their poem or story with the class.

Save the Earth
Ask children to think about what they use water for (drinking, bathing, brushing teeth). Point out that in some places, there is not enough water for everyone. Challenge children to list ways they can use less water in their daily lives. Encourage them to keep a record of how they conserve water.

river

lake

Act as a Consultant

Show children a map of your state or a map of your local region. Help them use their fingers to follow the shoreline of a lake, pond, or ocean. Guide them as they use their finger to trace the route of a river or stream. Help them recognize that the map does not show all the different places where water is found. For example, it does not show water under the ground or it may not show every small stream, depending on the map's scale.

Close

Check for Understanding

- As a follow-up to the **baseline assessment,** have children match the pictures they make in Checkpoint with the items on their list from Make Connections. Allow children to revise the list they made in Make Connections.
- **Answers to Checkpoint** Children's drawings might include an ocean, a lake, a river, a stream, or a puddle.

Connecting Lessons

In the next lesson, children will find out how salt water and fresh water are different. ▶

Explorer's Activity Guide

Use Explorer's Activity Guide pages 157–158 with this lesson to help children answer the text question, "Where is water on the earth?" with a hands-on activity.

Extend the Lesson

Invite a volunteer to hold a finger against a globe in an ocean area and to "sail" all the way around the globe without leaving the water and without lifting his or her finger from the globe to cross continents. Slowly turn the globe, allowing the volunteer time to sail around the continents. Then allow others to "sail around the world."

Visual Literacy

To enhance the **visual literacy** connection, use the interactive overhead transparency that correlates with the above two pages. The transparency will help your students understand the key concepts presented on these pages.

Lesson Objective

Children learn that salt water and fresh water have different properties.

Introduce

Invite Learning

Show children a glass of fresh water and salt water but do not identify them as such. Ask what they think might be different about the water in each glass.

Make Connections

To **assess prior knowledge,** ask: *Do you think the ocean water is fresh or salty?* Invite children to describe salt water and fresh water. They may think all water is the same and is drinkable. Record their descriptions on chart paper and save them to use as a **baseline assessment.**

Teach

Activity

Children examine samples of fresh water and salt water and find out how they are alike and how they are different. **Skills:** Observing, classifying, identifying variables

Materials (per group)

Module Kit Items: salt *(about 4 spoonfuls);* 2 pieces bar soap; masking tape; 2 cups; spoon

School Supplied Items: marker; container of water *(about 1 1/2 cups)*

How are salt water and fresh water different?

You know that most of the water on earth is in oceans. Do you know that ocean water is salty? You cannot drink the salty water in oceans.

The water you drink every day is fresh water. It does not taste salty. You find fresh water in most rivers, lakes, and streams. Let's find out how fresh water and salt water are different.

D 52

Science Idea Exchange

Collaborative Learning: Cooperative Learning

Assign specific children to gather and clean up materials. All children in the Activity group should have an opportunity to observe the salt and fresh water, record data, and share results. Also, each child in the group can be assigned a specific role:

- one who writes the words on tape and puts the tape on the cups;
- one who fills the cups with water;
- one who adds salt to one cup;
- one who adds the soap to each cup.

Science Background

Water in oceans is 3.5 percent salt, making ocean water denser than fresh water. Some inland lakes are salty and dense. The water in the northern half of Utah's Great Salt Lake is about 18 percent salt. The water in the Dead Sea is about 30 percent salt, making it the saltiest body of water on the earth.

Find out about salt water and fresh water.

You will need: 2 plastic cups water

 spoon salt masking tape

 piece of soap  marker

1. Write the words *fresh water* on a piece of tape. Write the words *salt water* on tape.
2. Put 1 tape on each cup.
3. Fill each cup half way with water.
4. Add 4 spoonfuls of salt to the *salt water* cup. Stir the water.
5. Observe the water in each cup. How does the water look and smell?
6. Put a piece of soap in each cup. Watch what happens.

Checkpoint
List two ways salt water and fresh water are different.

D 53

Safety Tip
Caution children not to taste the water.

Helpful Hint
Be sure the soap children use sinks in fresh water.

Observe and Listen
Pairs of children can describe fresh water and salt water to each other and list ways in which they are alike and different.

Ask for Evidence
Invite children to describe how the soap acted in each cup of water. (It floated in salt water and sank in fresh water.) Ask children to describe what could have caused the difference (the salt in the salt water).

Close
Check for Understanding
- As a follow-up to the **baseline assessment,** encourage children to revise their descriptions. Look for an understanding that fresh water has no salt or very little salt in it.
- **Answers to Checkpoint** Salt and fresh water look and smell different; soap floats in salt water.

Connecting Lessons
In the next lesson, children will discover that air surrounds the earth. ▶

Explorer's Activity Guide
Use Explorer's Activity Guide hands-on activity on page 159 to help children answer: "How are salt water and fresh water different?"

Teacher's Assessment Package
A **scoring rubric** to assess student performance is provided on page 82 of the Teacher's Assessment Package.

Activity Results

Your Ideas

_____

_____

_____

_____

_____

Lesson 7

Lesson Objective

Children learn that the earth is surrounded by air. They also learn about some characteristics of air.

Introduce

Invite Learning

Ask children to describe ways to show that their body contains air. Then present children with a drinking straw and a cup half filled with water. Ask for a volunteer to use the water and the straw to show that there is air in his or her body.

Make Connections

To **assess prior knowledge,** ask children if they can see, hear, feel, smell, or taste air. Children may have the idea that air does not exist because they can't see it. Invite children to tell or show how they know that air is all around them. Record their responses to use as a **baseline assessment.**

Teach

Ask for Evidence

Invite children to feel air from inside their body by blowing on their hands. Ask: *Is there air inside your body?* (yes) *How do you know?* (You can feel it on your hands.)

What is around the earth?

Air is all around the earth. You found air in the soil. Air is around and inside you. You cannot see air, but you can see what it does. You can feel air when it moves.

Moving air is wind. Wind makes trees bend and kites fly. It helps push sailboats across water. What else does wind do?

D 54

Science Idea Exchange

Science Background

The earth's atmosphere is made up of a mixture of gases (78 percent nitrogen, 21 percent oxygen, almost 1 percent argon, and smaller amounts of carbon dioxide and other gases). Air usually is invisible, odorless, and tasteless.

Science and Language Arts

Invite groups of children to act out the text of this lesson as a skit. Ask volunteers to take turns reading the text as the rest of the group uses hand and body movements to act out each sentence. Use the plastic bag as a prop.

Science and Music

The sound of a tuba or clarinet, for example, depends on the size of the column through which air is forced by the player. The sound of a drum or guitar depends on the size of the head or string creating the vibration. Invite children to draw their own musical instrument and show how it depends on air for its sound.

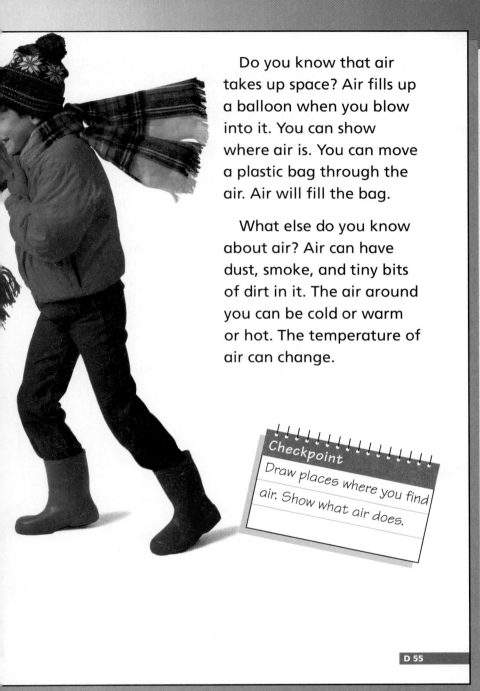

Do you know that air takes up space? Air fills up a balloon when you blow into it. You can show where air is. You can move a plastic bag through the air. Air will fill the bag.

What else do you know about air? Air can have dust, smoke, and tiny bits of dirt in it. The air around you can be cold or warm or hot. The temperature of air can change.

Checkpoint
Draw places where you find air. Show what air does.

Observe and Listen
Let children pantomime activities, such as flying a kite or walking into the wind, to demonstrate their understanding that the earth is surrounded by air. Listen as children try to guess the activity.

Act as a Consultant
Help children name characteristics of air and recognize that they can feel and hear air move though it is invisible, that air makes bubbles in water, that air can be warm or cold, and so on.

Helpful Hint
Provide small plastic bags for the activity described in the text.

Close

Check for Understanding
- As a follow-up to the **baseline assessment,** ask children if they wish to refine their responses, telling how they know air is all around them. Look for an increased understanding of the characteristics of air.
- **Answers to Checkpoint** Drawings should show air producing effects children discussed or have seen.

Connecting Lessons
In the next lesson, children will see that the sun heats air, soil, and water differently. ▶

Explorer's Activity Guide
Use Explorer's Activity Guide page 160 with this lesson to help children answer the text question, "What is around the earth?" with a hands-on activity.

Collaborative Learning: Cooperative Learning
Ask groups of children to list things that move in or through the air. Suggest they look out the windows for ideas. In each group, assign a recorder to write the list and a reporter to share it with the class. (Answers might include birds, insects, planes, clouds, rain, kites, flags, odors, sailboats, smoke, and trees.)

Special Education
Emphasize visual and tactile clues to the presence of air (bubbles, inflating a plastic bag, blowing on things, feeling air movement, hearing wind noises). Encourage children to blow on things and observe the movement of the object being blown upon.

Lesson 8

Lesson Objective

Children learn that the sun heats soil, air, and water at different rates. Skills: Organizing information, solving problems

Introduce

Invite Learning

Have children draw a picture or look at a magazine picture of an outdoor scene on a hot, sunny day.

Make Connections

To **assess prior knowledge,** invite children to circle the things in their picture that would feel hot. Some children may have the idea that sunlight heats things equally. Save the pictures to use as a **baseline assessment** in Check for Understanding.

Teach

Observe and Listen

- Have children work in pairs to interpret the illustration on pages D56–D57. One member of the pair should explain the illustration to his or her partner.
- Listen as the second member of the pair explains how the illustration shows that soil, water, and air warm up at different rates.

Let's Solve It!

Does the sun heat things the same way?

You know a lot about the earth and the air around the earth. Remember that the earth is heated by the sun. Let's find out if the sun heats air, soil, and water in the same way.

1. Look at the air, water, and soil. They were all the same temperature. Then they were put in the sun for 30 minutes.
2. Read the temperature on each thermometer. What is the temperature of the soil?

D 56

 ## Science Idea Exchange

Science Background

Because water warms and cools more slowly than land, large bodies of water often affect the temperature of nearby land. Temperature differences between a location near shore and locations farther inland can be significant. For instance, Chicago's official temperature is measured at O'Hare International Airport, 18 km (11.4 mi) from Lake Michigan. Wrigley Field, home of the Chicago Cubs baseball team, is only a few blocks from the lake. The temperature at the ballpark during a midsummer baseball game can be as much as 10°C (18°F) cooler than the official temperature at O'Hare.

Math/Science Connection

Help children use subtraction to find out how much the solar energy heated each substance in the pictures (soil, 15°C; water, 10°C; air, 5°C). Help children make a vertical or horizontal bar graph showing the temperature of soil, water, and air after 30 minutes.

3. Make a chart like this one.

4. Fill in the rest of the chart.

time	soil temperature	water temperature	air temperature
at start	25°	25°	25°
after 30 minutes			

Checkpoint

1. Where did you see the highest temperature after 30 minutes?

2. Does air, soil, or water heat up the most?

Ask for Evidence

Ask children to explain how the illustration shows that things get warm in the sun. (Temperatures got higher after 30 minutes in sunlight.) Have children explain how they know that soil, water, and air heat up differently. (After 30 minutes in sunlight, their temperatures are different.)

Close

Check for Understanding

● As a follow-up to the **baseline assessment,** return the pictures children examined in Make Connections. Ask children if there are other items in the picture they would circle or would now not circle. Look for an increased understanding that the sun heats land, air, and water at different rates.

● **Answers to Checkpoint** 1. Soil has the highest temperature after 30 minutes. 2. Soil heats up the most.

Connecting Lessons

In the next lesson, children will make posters to show the concepts they learned in this chapter. ▶

Explorer's Activity Guide

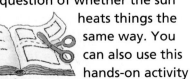

Use Explorer's Activity Guide page 161 to help children solve the question of whether the sun heats things the same way. You can also use this hands-on activity page to evaluate how well children understand the concept of this lesson.

Science Themes

By observing how sunlight heats substances at different rates, children develop their understanding of the themes of **systems and interactions** and **energy.**

Your Ideas

_____

_____

_____

_____

_____

*Chapter 3
Looking at the Earth* **D 57**

Lesson 9

Lesson Objective
Children make posters to show the concepts they learned in this chapter.

Introduce

Invite Learning
Review the **baseline assessment** activities you used in this chapter. Choose one or more to do again that you think will help children understand the chapter concepts.

Teach

Performance Assessment Activity
Children make a poster that shows the things that make up the earth.
Skills: Organizing information, summarizing

Materials (per group)
Module Kit Items: none
School Supplied Items: marker or crayon; posterboard *(1 sheet/child);* magazines; glue; scissors *(1/child)*

Helpful Hint
Provide magazines, such as travel and gardening periodicals, science magazines, or nature magazines with numerous outdoor scenes.

Chapter Review

What did you learn?

You learned about rocks, soil, and water. You learned how land looks in different places. You also learned that air is all around the earth. Now you can make a poster to show about the earth.

You will need: [ ] posterboard ✂ scissors
🖼 magazines 🖊 glue ✏ marker

Make a poster.
1. Draw a big circle on your poster.
2. Write the word *earth* at the top of the poster.
3. Look in magazines for pictures of things that make up the earth.
4. Cut out the pictures you find. Glue them inside the circle.
5. Write about your pictures at the bottom of the poster.

D 58

 Science Idea Exchange

Teacher's Assessment Package
Use the pages from the Teacher's Assessment Package at this time to promote **performance assessment** opportunities for your children.

Science Background
The earth's land, water, and air continually interact with one another, and a change in one affects others. For example, moving air (wind) causes ocean waves, which in turn transport sand on beaches and crash against the shore, wearing away rocky cliffs.

Save the Earth
Invite children to show their poster and point out their favorite part of the poster to the class. Ask children to imagine what that place might look like if people polluted the air, threw trash on the ground, or put garbage in the water. Ask children to list things they can do to keep the earth beautiful and healthful.

Observe and Listen

Before children make their poster, invite groups to use the literature selection *Begin at the Beginning* by Amy Schwartz (Harper & Row, 1983) to spur discussion of what makes up the earth. Have groups make a list of what they suggest that the book's character, Sara, could include in her painting.

Act as a Consultant

Help children identify what each picture on their poster shows—kinds of land, rocks, soil, water, or air.

Ask for Evidence

Review with children their questions from What Else Do You Want to Find Out? in the first chapter. Ask children which questions have been answered and how they think they can find the answers to questions that have not yet been answered.

Close

Check for Understanding

Answers to Share what you learned
1. Answers will vary, but children should point out pictures that look like places where they live. 2. Answers will vary with each child, but children should be able to explain why they chose a picture.

Share what you learned.

1. What pictures look like the part of the earth where you live?
2. What picture of the earth do you like the best? Tell why.

Explorer's Activity Guide

Use Explorer's Activity Guide page 162 as a hands-on activity to evaluate how well children understand the concepts covered in this chapter.

Managing Groups

Assign specific children to gather and clean up materials. Each child in the Chapter Review group should make a poster from magazine pictures and write about their pictures.

Activity Results

Children make a poster that includes pictures showing rocks, land, and water. Children's writing should include concepts found in this chapter.

People at Work

Nature of Work

Astronomers study the stars, planets, and other objects in the sky. They study the movements of these objects and look for new objects. Astronomers may predict when an object will appear in the sky. They can also determine what the sky looked like long ago.

Places of Work

Most astronomers work at universities, observatories, or planetariums. Some astronomers work with large telescopes far away from city lights. Others may work at public planetariums, helping people understand more about objects in the sky.

Training

Most work in astronomy requires college-level training in astronomy, physics, and computers.

Preparation

Interested children should study science, physics, math, and computer science. Children interested in the stars and outer space can read about the universe, keep a diary of what they learn and observe about the sky, and keep a record of the questions they have about objects in the sky.

A visit to a planetarium

At the planetarium you sit in a round dark room. You look up. What you see looks like the sky! You can see how the sun lights the moon. You can see different shapes of the moon. You can even see stars.

A person who studies the stars and planets is an **astronomer.** Stars and planets give off light. Telescopes help astronomers see the light from stars and planets.

 Science Idea Exchange

Examine the Career

Ask children what they think they would like about being an astronomer (it would be interesting to see lots of planets, it would be fun to use a telescope).

Explore Further

Children interested in learning more about astronomy might enjoy a visit to a planetarium. If that is not possible, you might consider inviting an astronomer from a nearby planetarium or college to your classroom. Before the visit, have children write down any questions they would like answered.

How does a telescope work?

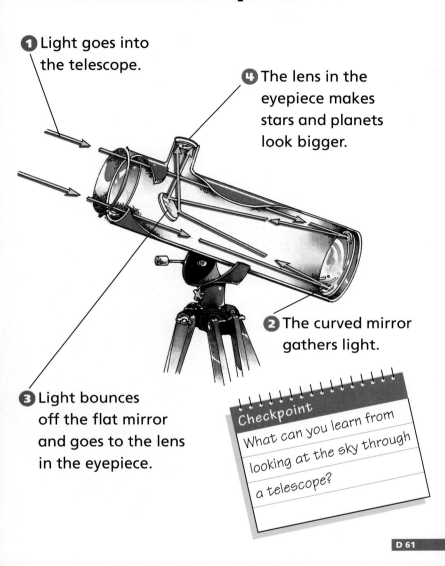

1 Light goes into the telescope.

4 The lens in the eyepiece makes stars and planets look bigger.

2 The curved mirror gathers light.

3 Light bounces off the flat mirror and goes to the lens in the eyepiece.

Checkpoint

What can you learn from looking at the sky through a telescope?

People at Work

Science Background

You may wish to share some of the following information about telescopes with children.

- An Italian scientist, Galileo, built the first refracting telescope for astronomical use. Despite his telescope's flaws, Galileo used it to view and draw the moon's craters and to discover the moons of Jupiter.
- The largest single-mirror telescope is at Mount Palomar Observatory in California. The mirror is about 5 m (16$\frac{1}{2}$ ft) in diameter.
- Building large mirrors and lenses is very difficult because flaws form in the glass and the glass bends under its own weight. In 1992, a telescope with a 10 m (33 ft) mirror was put into operation on Mt. Mauna Kea in Hawaii. It is made up of 36 separate six-sided mirrors.
- Most large telescopes collect light using a concave mirror, which is shaped like the mirror in a car headlight. After the light is collected, it is reflected by a plane (flat) mirror. The image produced by the plane mirror is magnified by a lens, like an eyeglass lens, in the eyepiece of the telescope.
- Many observatories and telescopes are located far from cities and towns so that the city lights do not interfere with astronomer's observations.

Discussion

Ask children how the discovery of the telescope might have changed the way earlier civilizations thought about objects in the sky.

Answers to Checkpoint

You can observe the surface of the moon. Stars and planets look bigger. You can also see stars and planets that aren't visible using your eyes alone.

Collaborative Learning: Small Groups

Have groups of three or four children build a model telescope. Children may use cardboard tubes from bathroom tissue and disks cut from colored paper. Then have group members explain what the parts do.

Module Review

Show What You Know

- You can use the first text paragraph to begin assessing what children know about the earth and sky. Children should be able to describe the appearance of the earth, the moon, the stars, and the sun. They may also explain why the sun and earth are important for life.
- Children can brainstorm a list of things they would like to tell others about their imaginary trip. Record their ideas on the chalkboard.

Plan Your Travel Project

Have children list their steps verbally or in writing before doing their travel projects. Ask how they will share their projects. Some children may decide to write, while others prefer oral presentations.

Assessment Projects

- **Make travel posters** Children's posters should include descriptive information about each of the places. Posters should have compelling images and language that encourage people to visit.
- **Talk with a reporter** Children may choose to work with a partner, with one person interviewing and the other responding to questions. They may set up a studio for the interview. You may wish to videotape the interviews.

Module Review

Show what you know.

Pretend you go on an imaginary trip. You travel to the moon, the sun, and other stars. You also visit different places on the earth. What do you see on your trip? What can you tell other people who want to take a trip like yours?

Plan your travel project.

1. Pick a project you would like to do.
2. How will you start your project?
3. How will your project look when you finish it?

Make travel posters.

Travel posters show places people can visit. Make travel posters about all the places you visited on your imaginary trip. Your posters can make people want to visit these places.

Science Idea Exchange

Develop a Project

Children may choose to do one of the projects in the book, or they may be able to develop other travel project ideas on their own.

Explorer's Activity Guide

For a **Home/School Connection,** use Explorer's Activity Guide pages 163–164. This letter home describes the concepts children have learned in this module and also provides a hands-on activity that the family can do together.

Using Multiple Intelligences (See page T5.)

The projects presented on these pages provide the opportunity for children to show their understanding of concepts using their strongest individual problem-solving abilities, or intelligences. The chart at right shows which of the seven intelligences are developed within each project and which chapter concepts each project assesses.

Talk with a reporter.

Pretend you are talking with a TV reporter. What questions can the reporter ask about all the places you visited on your imaginary trip. How can you answer the questions?

Write a travel guide.

Travel guides have words and pictures about places to visit. Make a travel guide about all the places you visited on your imaginary trip. Write about what people might see in these places.

Share what you know.

1. Share your project.
2. Which places would you like to visit? Why?
3. What part of your project did you like best?

D 63

Assessment Projects (cont'd.)

● **Write a travel guide** Children's travel guides may look like booklets or brochures, or they may be tape recordings with accompanying pictures.

Share What You Know

1. Encourage children to share their projects in a format that is comfortable for them: large group, small group, or one-on-one.
2. Children should offer specific examples of places they would like to visit and explain why these places appeal to them.
3. Encourage children to think about the form and content of their project. See if they can name one specific thing they liked best about doing it. They may identify parts of the process or the finished product. Ask them what they would do differently if they were to do their project again.

Performance Assessment

The module assessment projects can be used as performance assessment activities.

Travel Project

Project	Intelligence	Chapters Covered
Poster	visual/spatial	1, 2, 3
Interview	body/kinesthetic verbal/linguistic interpersonal	1, 2, 3
Travel Guide	verbal/linguistic visual/spatial	1, 2, 3

Family/School Partnership: Progress Report

Share with families their child's progress in the following areas:
● makes and records observations
● compares and contrasts objects
● classifies in more than one way
● experiments to solve problems
● asks questions and communicates information

Module D
Math/Science Connection

Test Your Rocks for Hardness

Review with children how they can sort rocks according to properties such as color, size, and shape. Explain that scientists use another way to sort rocks called the Rock Hardness Test (Moh's test). Explain to children that one substance is harder than another if it scratches the surface of that object. Be sure to point out that a mark that rubs off is not a scratch.

PROBLEM

Invite children to conduct a scientific experiment in which they compare and classify rocks. Their job is to test six rocks for their hardness. They can solve the problem by using their fingernail, a penny, and a marble to perform the Rock Hardness Test.

Materials (per group)
cover goggles, 6 rocks (*various kinds*), egg carton, masking tape, penny, marble, Rock Hardness Test sheet (*copy of chart shown here*), pencil

SOLVE THE PROBLEM

- Distribute an egg carton containing six different kinds of rocks to each group of children. Have the children label each rock with a number from 1 to 6. Children can use pieces of masking tape for labels and attach the labels in the appropriate position on the top inside cover of the egg carton.

- Help children do the Rock Hardness Test with each rock. First have children try to scratch rock sample 1 with their fingernail. Next have them try to scratch the rock with a penny. Then have children try to scratch a penny with the rock. Finally, have children try to scratch a marble with the rock.

- Have children record 1 point on their sheet if the rock can be scratched with a fingernail, 2 points if the rock can be scratched with a penny, 3 points if the rock scratches a penny, and 4 points if the rock scratches a marble. Direct children to continue until all six samples of rocks are tested on each scale.

- Have children total the number of points for each rock sample. Then have them sort the rocks from the least to the most hard, using the results of the Rock Hardness Test.

SCALE	SAMPLE 1	SAMPLE 2	SAMPLE 3	SAMPLE 4	SAMPLE 5	SAMPLE 6
1 pt. scratch with fingernail						
2 pts. scratch with penny						
3 pts. scratch a penny						
4 pts. scratch a marble						
total =						

Rock Hardness Test

Share the Solutions

Have the children in each group hold up their hardest rock and their softest rock. Encourage them to use their senses to observe how the rocks feel and look alike and different. Then discuss the following questions:

Why did some rocks score a higher number of points than other rocks?

How do the rocks that scored the highest number of points look and feel different from the rocks that scored the lowest number of points?

What is the point difference between your hardest and your softest rock?

EXTEND THE PROBLEM

- Have children in each group add the total points scored by their rocks.

- Help children use the hardness scale to test man-made materials such as a plastic cup, a magnet, and chalk for hardness. Help them calculate the totals for each sample. Have children sort the man-made materials from the least to the most hard.

Your Ideas

Contents

Observe and Listen

Invite children to imagine a world without birds. Have them describe to a partner how the world would be different if there were no birds. Encourage partners to work together to make a cutout of a bird. Have them list reasons that birds are important. Help them write their reasons on their cutout. Let children share their ideas with the rest of the class. You may wish to use yarn to hang the bird cutouts from the ceiling.

Act as a Consultant

Help children expand their ideas about why birds are helpful. Guide them to the realization that birds spread seeds. Birds also eat insects such as mosquitoes and are enjoyable to hear and see.

Raise Questions

Ask: *What kinds of birds do you see in your neighborhood?* Record responses. If children are not sure of the names of some birds, allow them to give descriptions of the birds they see. You may wish to have a field guide available so children can use the pictures to identify familiar birds. Take the children for a nature walk or allow time for them to birdwatch through the window.

Kids Did It

Kids Are for the Birds

Birds don't have an easy life! They need lots of food to live. Our class wanted birds to find enough food in our schoolyard. So we decided to make bird feeders.

We worked in teams. First, we decided what kinds of birds would use our feeders. Next, we learned about the birds. We read about what they eat. We found out whether they need feeders with perches. We found out other things we needed to know.

Science Idea Exchange

Explore Further

Provide commercial wild birdseed for children to examine. Have them group the different kinds of seed and identify them, if possible.

Discussion

Many species of birds are endangered. Some, such as the passenger pigeon and the dusky sparrow, have already died out. Others, such as the bald eagle and the bluebird, are present in far fewer numbers than they used to be. Invite children to give their own ideas about why some species of birds die out. Have them describe ways to preserve these birds.

Module A

Then we planned our feeders. They had to be the right size and shape for the birds. They had to hold the right kind of food. We also had to plan how to keep squirrels away.

Next, we made our bird feeders. When we were finished, we got together and shared them. It was fun to learn about different kinds of bird feeders. Finally, we put our bird feeders in different places around our school. Then we all became bird watchers!

You can do it.

Draw a picture of a bird feeder you would like to make. Tell about your bird feeder.

3

Science and Language Arts

You may wish to let children read through poetry books to find poems about birds that they would like to share with the class. Children may also enjoy recalling the nursery rhyme "The North Wind Doth Blow." Invite children to write a story or a poem about a bird they see at their bird feeder.

Science and Geography

Birds live nearly everywhere around the world. Show children pictures of particular regions and invite them to tell what they may know about the birds that live there. (Penguins live in cold southern regions such as Antarctica; parrots may be found in tropical rainforests in South America.) Children may wish to draw and attach a picture of a bird to the picture of the region the bird lives in.

Science and Music

Sharpen children's listening skills with birdsong recordings available in many libraries. Play the songs of birds that children hear in their neighborhood as well as exotic birdsongs. See if children can identify which birds sing which songs.

You Can Do It

Invite children to design their own bird feeder and to present their drawing to the class. Ask them to explain why they chose their design, what kind of food they would put into the feeder, where they would hang it, and what birds they expect to feed.

Collaborative Learning: Cooperative Learning

You might want children to work in groups to design bird feeders. Provide books so children can see several designs. Invite children to describe how they might keep unwanted animals such as squirrels from using the feeder. Ask children to discuss other problems they might need to solve.

Your Ideas

_____

_____

_____

_____

Kids Did It

Observe and Listen

Invite children to work in small groups to list some of the environmental conditions they are concerned about. Help children record their concerns on index cards. Share the concerns to stimulate conversation about ways to solve them.

Act as a Consultant

Attach tape to the back of each card prepared under Observe and Listen. Display the cards on the chalkboard. Invite volunteers to come to the chalkboard and sort the cards according to the type of problem or some other category. Let several volunteers sort the cards alphabetically. As children sort the cards, prompt them to include problems or solutions that may have been left out. Use questions such as: *What about air quality? Would you like to include disappearing animal habitats?* Act as moderator as the class discusses the categories.

Raise Questions

After children have shared their environmental concerns, ask: *What can you do about these conditions?* Help children narrow their focus to one or two problems. Ask: *How can the class work to reduce the amount of trash?* or *What can you do to protect wildlife habitats?* Shape the question to match children's concerns. Record their responses.

Kids Did it

Kids Save the Earth

Our class thinks the earth is a beautiful place! So we think it's important to take care of the earth. We wanted to share ways to help the earth. So our class made up an alphabet game!

First, we each picked a letter of the alphabet. Then we made big paper letters. Next, we thought of a word that starts with our letter.

4

 Science Idea Exchange

Explore Further

Invite children to make a collection of materials, such as polystyrene, that may cause environmental problems. Children may also include objects that are not harmful in themselves but that cause problems because of their volume, such as a week's supply of newspaper. Display the objects, with appropriate captions, in the classroom or in the school display case.

Discussion

You may wish to present pictures of endangered whales or eagles or photographs of floating garbage to the class. Engage children in a discussion about what they think will happen if we do not take steps to save the earth. Ask children to cite as evidence the activities and the things they have learned from their science class.

Module B

The word had to tell about a problem on the earth or a way to help the earth. Then we made a drawing about the word on our paper letter.

Finally, we all got together and shared our letters. We learned about ways to solve problems on the earth. Then we put our letters on our bulletin board. We invited other classes to see our ABC's About Our Earth. We were proud of what we had done!

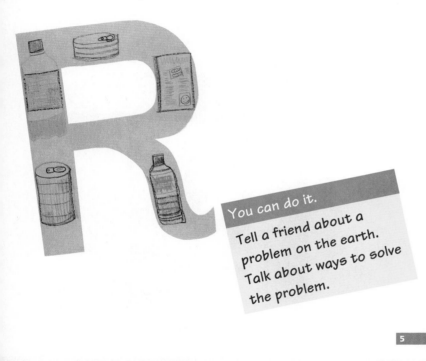

You can do it.

Tell a friend about a problem on the earth. Talk about ways to solve the problem.

5

Science and Social Studies

Earth Day, on April 22, is observed by people all over the world. Encourage children to plan a presentation suitable for Earth Day or any other day. Invite them to make a speech about environmental problems and what they can do about them. Encourage children to make a display of posters or collages that show problems and solutions.

Science and Language Arts

Suggest that children choose one problem or solution and write a class letter about it. Help them write a rough draft and then refine it. You may choose to send a final copy to a local official or legislator.

Science and Geography

Invite children to give their opinions on why it may be important that all countries work together to save the earth. Have them support their answer by showing, on a world map, how air and water pollution can travel across borders. Help children realize that a border is not a physical barrier.

You Can Do It

Environmental problems the children may list include acid rain, disappearing rainforests, and solid waste disposal. Solutions may include conservation of energy and recycling. Have children select a way to tell a friend about the problem, such as a letter, poster, or picture. Remind children to include their solutions to the problem.

Collaborative Learning: Small Groups

Divide the class into groups and invite each group to choose a letter and an environmental word or phrase beginning with the letter. Group members should trace a large letter from a stencil, cut out the letter, draw pictures to illustrate the word or phrase, and present the letter to the class.

Your Ideas

_____

_____

_____

_____

_____

Observe and Listen

Let children work in small groups. Invite them to lay a ball on a flat surface. Ask: *Will the ball move?* Then have children build a ramp by stacking two books and slanting a board or sheet of heavy cardboard so one end rests on the books and the other on the table. Invite volunteers to place the ball at the top of the ramp. Ask children to explain what pushed or pulled the ball down the ramp.

Act as a Consultant

- Encourage children to design a set of ramps to make the ball roll upward. Help children design a long, steep down ramp with a short up ramp at the end of it. Let them describe the motion of the ball as it starts down the steep ramp. Then have them describe the ball's motion as it moves up the short ramp.
- Suggest that children experiment with other objects to see what else will slide or roll down, then up, the ramps.

Raise Questions

Ask: *If the marble moves too quickly along the path, what could you do to slow it down?* (Children will likely say to make the ramp less steep. Someone may mention friction or making the surface rough.)

Kids Did It

Kids Make It Move

Our teacher gave our class a problem to solve. We had to move a marble. The marble was on a table. We had to move the marble to a bowl on the floor. So we invented machines to help us move the marble.

First, each team made a plan for its invention. Next, we collected things we needed to build our machines. We collected cardboard tubes and boxes. We collected straws, paper cups, and many other things.

6

 ## Science Idea Exchange

Explore Further

Invite children to embellish their machine with angles, turns, and open chutes. They can make elbow joints by cutting a *V* in a tube, bending the tube until the cut edges join, and taping the edges together. Children can also cut tubes in half lengthwise to make open chutes so they will be able to see the marble.

Discussion

Have children compare their machines to decide which is fastest, which takes the most push or pull, and which moves the marble the greatest distance. Discuss what children might learn from the activity and how it might be useful to them. Spark their imagination by mentioning wheelchair ramps and playground slides.

Module C

Then we built our machines and tested them. It was fun to watch how they worked! Finally our teams got together to share our inventions. Our class invented some very strange machines!

You can do it.

Invent a machine to move a marble. Share your invention with your classmates.

Science and Math

Experiment with objects of various weights that children can drop safely. Include at least two objects of the same weight, such as a flat sheet of notebook paper and a tightly crumpled sheet of notebook paper. Invite children to weigh or find the mass of each object using a simple balance scale. Allow children to take turns dropping the objects from the same height. Use a stopwatch to time each object's fall. Help children make a chart of their observations.

Science and Health

Invite children to wear leg weights as they move around the room. They should notice that when they wear the weights, it is harder to walk. When children remove the weights, their legs will move higher with less effort. Discuss how working with weights can help people develop muscle strength.

You Can Do It

Provide materials such as those shown in the illustration. Encourage children first to use only one object, such as a straw, to move the marble. Then have children choose a second object to use as part of their machine. Invite children to add one object at a time to their "Marble Mover." Allow children to rearrange the objects in their machine in any way they wish.

Collaborative Learning: Cooperative Learning

Groups of children will enjoy working together to invent their own "Marble Movers." Suggest that all group members plan their "Marble Mover." Then let the group assign a building task to each group member.

Your Ideas

_____

_____

_____

_____

Kids Did It

Observe and Listen

About two weeks before completing the module, build a small mound of firmly packed potting soil in a large pan. Plant grass seed on the mound. Set the pan in a sunny window and water as needed. When the grass has sprouted, build a similar mound without plants. Invite children to sprinkle small amounts of water gently over both mounds. Have them take turns describing what they observe. (More soil washes off the bare mound.) Allow teams to form explanations for their observations. Ask children to describe the appearance of the water that runs off each mound.

Act as a Consultant

Suggest that children pour gently, but with enough force to disturb the dirt on the bare mound. Direct their attention to what happens to the dirt. Help them compare this with what happens on the grassy mound. Invite children to pull the grassy mound apart and examine the plant roots. Lead them to an explanation of why the soil did not wash away.

Raise Questions

If possible, take children outdoors to find examples of erosion. If examples are not available, show photographs. Ask: *How can what you observed in the activity help you find a way to slow down soil erosion?*

Kids Did It

Kids Save Soil

Our new schoolyard was a dusty and muddy place to play. The ground was bare in some places. The soil in these places was blowing away. When it rained, the ground got muddy and soil washed away.

Our class wanted to help save the soil. So we made a map of the bare spots of land. Then we made a plan to take care of the bare land.

 Science Idea Exchange

Explore Further

Invite children to use two paint trays, grass seed, and a sprinkling can to explore how to limit soil erosion. Have children place 4 cups of soil in each tray and then plant grass seed in one tray. After the grass begins to grow, have them sprinkle water on each tray and measure the soil that slides to the bottom. Children should **infer** that grass helps hold soil in place.

Discussion

Lead children in a discussion about why soil conservation is important. Encourage children to draw two pictures to support their discussion. The pictures might show what happens when land is eroded by water or wind and how plants can slow erosion. Allow children to present their pictures and explain their ideas.

We found out that the roots of plants hold soil in the ground. Then the soil cannot be blown or washed away. So we decided to plant grass, flowers, and trees.

Each team picked a spot of land to care for. Our teams planted grass seeds and flower seeds. We planted flowers and trees. Soon colorful plants covered the bare ground.

You can do it.

Walk around your school or neighborhood. Find a place where the ground is bare. Tell what you could plant there.

9

Science and Social Studies

Children should conclude that trees and other plants protect against erosion. Encourage children to think of events and activities that change the land by destroying vegetation. Children may mention forest fires, housing developments, and industries such as mining.

Science and Health

Besides stopping erosion, trees and other plants have benefits for our health. Invite children to list other benefits of trees and other plants, such as providing shade and food. Help children understand that plants help air quality by giving off oxygen.

Science and Art

Show pictures of gardens to the class. Then provide seed catalogs for children to use to find plants for a bare spot. Encourage children to choose different kinds of ground covers and a variety of colors.

You Can Do It

Encourage children to search for an area near the school to take care of. Suggest that they think about why the area is in poor condition. Have them consider questions such as: How much light does the area get? What kind of soil is it? Do people walk across the area? Children can list plants and other materials they might use to help conserve the soil.

Collaborative Learning: Small Groups

Encourage groups of three to try the activity. Suggest that members share in these tasks:
• obtain permission;
• choose plants;
• plant the plants.
Remind children to make a schedule for caring for the plants.

Your Ideas

_____

_____

_____

_____

_____

Study Guide

Study Guide

Answer the questions. Use your own paper.

Chapter 1 Plants and Animals

A 4-5   1. Animals have special ____ parts.
   leaf   body   floating

A 6-7   2. Look at the picture. What part does the butterfly use to smell flowers?
   a. _____
   b. _____
   c. _____

A 8-9   3. Animals have ways of acting that help them ____ .
   stay alive   stay cold   stay small

   4. An animal hardly moves when it ____ .
   flies   hibernates   eats

A 10-11   5. A brown caterpillar would be hard to see on a ____ leaf.
   green   yellow   brown

A 12-13   6. A color or shape that makes an animal hard to see is called ____ .
   nectar   red   camouflage

A 14-15   7. Plant ____ take in water from the soil.
   leaves   roots   flowers

10

8. Look at the picture. Which plant parts make food the plant needs to live?

a.
b.
c.

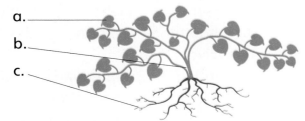

A 16-17 **9.** The thick ____ of the cactus hold water.

stems   leaves   seeds

A 18-19 **10.** Dandelion seeds are ____ through the air.

scattered   planted   grown

Chapter 2 Where Things Live

A 24-25 **1.** Plants and animals have special places where they ____ .

work   live   walk

A 26-27 **2.** Plants and animals live in many different kinds of ____ .

rocks   sunlight   habitats

A 28-29 **3.** A pond is one kind of ____ habitat.

dry   water   snowy

4. Green plants, ducks, and ____ might live in a pond habitat.

turtles   elephants   dogs

11

8. a. or b.

Lesson 7   pp. A16–A17
 9. stems

Lesson 8   pp. A18–A19
 10. scattered

CHAPTER 2

Lesson 1   pp. A24–A25
 1. live

Lesson 2   pp. A26–A27
 2. habitats

Lesson 3   pp. A28–A29
 3. water
 4. turtles

Study Guide

Study Guide

A 30-31   **5.** Animals get food, water, and ____ from their habitats.

insects   shelter   fur

6. A habitat gives plants ____ that they need to live.

nothing   some things   everything

A 32-33   **7.** Look at the pictures. Which of these is a good habitat for a cricket?

a.   b.   c.

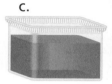

A 34-35   **8.** Zoo habitats are built to give each kind of ____ everything it needs.

cage   animal   tree

A 36-37   **9.** Which of these is in a habitat for koalas?

a tree   an apple   a pond

Chapter 3 Grouping Living Things

A 42-43   **1.** You can ____ things by how the things are alike.

smell   group   float

A 44-45   **2.** A rock is a ____ thing.

living   growing   nonliving

12

3. Birds and grasses are kinds of ____ .

plants   nonliving things   living things

A 46-47 **4.** Plants use ____ to make food they need.

animals   habitats   sunlight

A 48-49 **5.** A turtle belongs to a group of animals called ____ .

birds   fish   reptiles

6. Look at the pictures. Which animal belongs to a group called amphibians?

a.   b.   c.

A 50-51 **7.** Animals with body hair or fur are ____ .

turtles   mammals   fish

8. Birds have ____ on their bodies.

feathers   scales   fur

A 52-53 **9.** A ____ is an animal with no legs.

spider   worm   bee

10. Spiders have ____ legs.

four   eight   six

11. Insects have ____ main body parts.

three   six   eight

13

3. living things

Lesson 3   pp. A46–A47
  4. sunlight

Lesson 4   pp. A48–A49
  5. reptiles
  6. a.

Lesson 5   pp. A50–A51
  7. mammals
  8. feathers

Lesson 6   pp. A52–A53
  9. worm
  10. eight
  11. three

Study Guide

MODULE B

CHAPTER 1

Lesson 1   pp. B4–B5

  1. many places

Lesson 2   pp. B6–B7
  2. big and small

Lesson 3   pp. B8–B9
  3. yes

Lesson 4   pp. B10–B11
  4. meat
  5. a.

Lesson 5   pp. B12–B13
  6. names or teeth
  7. terrible lizard

Study Guide

Answer the questions. Use your own paper.

Chapter 1 Discovering Dinosaurs

B 4-5   **1.** Dinosaurs lived in _____ on the earth.
    cities   many places   buildings

B 6-7   **2.** What size were dinosaurs?
    only big   big and small   only small

B 8-9   **3.** Could some dinosaurs fit in a space the size of your classroom?
    never   no   yes

B 10-11   **4.** Dinosaurs with long sharp teeth ate _____ .
    leaves   meat   flowers

  5. Look at the pictures. Which kind of food did dinosaurs with big, flat teeth eat?

    a.   b.   c.

B 12-13   **6.** Dinosaur _____ tell how dinosaurs looked or acted.
    tails   names   teeth

  7. What does the word dinosaur mean?
    big animal   terrible lizard   fast runner

B 14-15 **8.** Did all dinosaurs run fast?

always   yes   no

Chapter 2 Dinosaur Detectives

B 20-21 **1.** Looking at ____ can tell about a person.

questions   dinosaurs   objects

B 22-23 **2.** Dinosaurs left behind ____ .

buildings   footprints   mud

B 24-25 **3.** A ____ can be a part or mark from an animal or plant.

shell   fossil   tool

B 26-27 **4.** Look at the pictures. Which fossil came from a plant?

a.   b.   c.

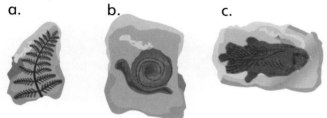

B 28-29 **5.** Fossils are ____ rocks and dirt.

on top of   buried in   never found in

B 30-31 **6.** Some dinosaur bones became ____ .

mud   rocks   fossils

7. Dinosaur fossils tell us about ____ .

dinosaurs   people   plants

15

Study Guide

Study Guide

B 32-33 8. Dinosaur ____ can fit together like puzzle pieces fit together.
  footprints   shapes   bones

B 34-35 9. Many fossils of dinosaur babies were found in ____ .
  trees   nests   lakes

10. People learned about dinosaurs and their babies from studying ____ .
  plants   mud   fossils

B 36-37 11. Fossils tell us about ____
  long ago   people   puzzles

12. Look at the pictures. Which animal lived at the time of the dinosaurs?
  a.   b.   c.

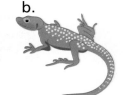 

Chapter 3 A Changing World

B 42-43 1. The world is always ____ .
  small   cold   changing

B 44-45 2. Kinds of animals are ____ when they no longer live on earth.
  extinct   harmed   endangered

16

3. Which of these may have made dinosaurs become extinct?

fossils   people   cold weather

B 46-47 **4.** Plants and animals may not get what they need when their ____ change.

names   habitats   fossils

5. Kinds of plants and animals may become ____ if they cannot get what they need.

extinct   bigger   polluted

B 48-49 **6.** Kinds of plants and animals are ____ when only a few of them are still living on earth.

extinct   fossils   endangered

B 50-51 **7.** Polluted water is ____ water.

clean   dirty   safe

B 52-53 **8.** Smoke can make air become ____ .

polluted   fresh   clean

B 54-55 **9.** Look at the pictures. Which picture shows a way to help protect animals?

a.   b.    c.

17

3. cold weather

Lesson 3   pp. B46–B47
  4. habitats
  5. extinct

Lesson 4   pp. B48–B49
  6. endangered

Lesson 5   pp. B50–B51
  7. dirty

Lesson 6   pp. B52–B53
  8. polluted

Lesson 7   pp. B54–B55
  9. a.

Study Guide

Study Guide

Answer the questions. Use your own paper.

Chapter 1 How Things Move

C 4-5   **1.** A strong wind can make a sailboat ____ .
  stay still   move   float

C 6-7   **2.** A push or a ____ is a force.
  pull   turn   boat

3. You use ____ when you pull an object.
  sound   light   force

C 8-9   **4.** Look at the pictures. Which picture shows a pull?
  a.   b.   c.

C 10-11   **5.** Which push will make a ball roll farther?
  strong push   weak push   no push

C 12-13   **6.** Which force will make a rubber band stretch the longest?
  no force   weak force   strong force

C 14-15   **7.** It takes ____ force to move a heavy object than it does to move a light object.
  less   more   weaker

18

8. Look at the pictures. Which pile of books would take the most force to move?

a.  b. c.

C 16-17 9. It is easiest to pull a heavy box over a ____ surface.

rough   bumpy   smooth

Chapter 2 Magnets

C 22-23 1. Two ____ can push and pull each other.
tables   metals   magnets

C 24-25 2. The ends of magnets are called north and south ____ .
poles   pushes   pulls

3. Two north poles held together will ____ .
push apart   pull together   not move

C 26-27 4. A magnet will pick up ____ .
a paper clip   an eraser   a paper

5. A magnet will not pick up ____ .
metal   paper clips   plastic

C 28-29 6. A ____ might have a magnet.
towel   toy   newspaper

19

8. c.

Lesson 7   pp. C16–C17
9. smooth

CHAPTER 2

Lesson 1   pp. C22–C23
1. magnets

Lesson 2   pp. C24–C25
2. poles
3. push apart

Lesson 3   p. C26–C27
4. a paper clip
5. plastic

Lesson 4   pp. C28–C29
6. toy

Study Guide

Study Guide

C 30-31   **7.** A magnet can ____ through paper.
freeze   pull   bounce

C 32-33   **8.** A weak magnet will pick up ____ paper clips than a strong magnet.
more   heavier   fewer

C 34-35   **9.** A battery and a wire can turn a nail into a ____ .
magnet   hammer   paper clip

Chapter 3 Moving and Machines

C 40-41   **1.** You can find ways to move ____ in your classroom more easily.
trees   hammers   objects

C 42-43   **2.** A ____ makes work easier.
plant   machine   tree

3. Look at the pictures. Which picture shows a machine?
a.   b.   c.

C 44-45   **4.** A ____ can help you move a wheelchair.
hammer   ramp   skateboard

Module C

C 46-47
5. A _____ is a lever.
seesaw wagon ball bearing

C 48-49
6. Ball bearings can make it easier to _____ things.
smell move stretch

7. Which of these are like ball bearings?
marbles blocks ramps

C 50-51
8. When you drink milk, you use your arm like _____ .
a lever a ramp a ball bearing

9. Which of these body parts is like a machine?
a.   b.   c.

C 52-53
10. Your bones and muscles help you _____ .
learn move see

11. _____ in your body help you twist.
Joints Arms Bones

C 54-55
12. Bones and muscles work _____ .
alone together slowly

13. Muscles change _____ when bones move.
size color taste

21

Study Guide

Study Guide

Answer the questions. Use your own paper.

Chapter 1   The Sun

D 4-5   1. Night sky and day sky are ____ .
   different   the same   both dark

D 6-7   2. The part of the earth that the sun is shining on has ____ .
   nighttime   daytime   rain

D 8-9   3. The ____ is bigger than the earth.
   sun   moon   cloud

D 10-11   4. The sun is made of hot ____ .
   rocks   water   gases

D 12-13   5. Plants need ____ to grow.
   darkness   sunlight   cold air

6. Look at the pictures. Which plant gets the sunlight it needs?
   a.   b.   c.

D 14-15   7. Plants that animals eat need ____ to live and grow.
   sunlight   clouds   moonlight

22

Module D

D 16-17 8. Energy that comes from the sun is called ____ energy.

warm   fast   solar

D 18-19 9. Plants and animals that died long ago changed into coal and ____ .

oil   air   water

Chapter 2 The Moon and Stars

D 24-25 1. Look at the pictures. Which picture shows things you can see in the night sky?

a.   b.   c.

D 26-27 2. Some stars look small because they are very ____ .

far away   close   dark

D 28-29 3. Long ago, people made up stories about groups of ____ .

moons   stars   dots

D 30-31 4. Groups of stars that seem to form shapes are called ____ .

animals   hunters   constellations

23

Study Guide

Study Guide

D 32-33   5. The moon has ____ light of its own.
   much   some   no

D 34-35   6. Look at the pictures. Which picture shows things that are on the moon?
   a.   b.   c.

   7. The moon has many holes called ____ .
   craters   oceans   stars

D 36-37   8. The different shapes of the moon are called ____ .
   craters   phases   circles

   9. The moon moves around the ____ .
   sun   earth   stars

Chapter 3 Looking at the Earth

D 42-43   1. You might dig through ____ when you dig in the earth.
   sand   hot gases   craters

D 44-45   2. You can find soil, and water on ____ .
   the stars   the sun   the earth

   3. You can ____ rocks by color.
   count   group   measure

24

D 46-47 4. You can find water, ____ , and bits of rock in soil.

oceans   wind   air

D 48-49 5. Land is ____ the same everywhere on the earth.

almost   not   always

D 50-51 6. Most of the water on earth is in ____ .

rain   oceans   streams

7. Water on the ____ can be found in lakes, rivers, oceans, and streams.

earth   moon   sun

D 52-53 8. People cannot drink ocean water because it is ____ .

cold   warm   salty

D 54-55 9. Moving air is called ____ .

space   wind   rain

10. Look at the pictures. Which picture shows what wind can do?

a.   b.   c.

25

Lesson 3   pp. D46–D47
4. air

Lesson 4   pp. D48–D49
5. not

Lesson 5   pp. D50–D51
6. oceans
7. earth

Lesson 6   pp. D52–D53
8. salty

Lesson 7   pp. D54–D55
9. wind
10. a.

Experiment Skills

Science Background

The steps described on these two pages represent a general procedure scientists use to solve problems. More specifically, the steps might include the following:

- **Make observations** You might observe something you cannot explain, and you become curious.
- **Identify problem** You identify the problem you want to solve, usually in the form of a question.
- **Collect information** You collect more detailed information about the problem, perhaps by making more observations, and record this information as data.
- **State hypothesis** You put your data and background knowledge together to come up with a hypothesis—a possible and testable explanation of the problem.
- **Test** You test your hypothesis by collecting more data. If possible, you collect more data by doing experiments.
- **Make conclusions** After analyzing the data, you make conclusions as to whether or not the data support your hypothesis. You might do more experiments to strengthen your hypothesis, or you might develop another hypothesis based on the data and then test it further.

These steps are traditionally labeled "The Scientific Method," though there is no single method that applies to every scientific problem. Rather, different combinations of these steps are used for different problems. Each combination can be a scientific method, forming and testing hypotheses about the natural world.

Using Scientific Methods

Almost every day scientists learn new things about the world. They try to find the answers to problems. Scientists use scientific methods to help them with problems. They use steps in their methods. Sometimes scientists use the steps in different order. You can use these steps to find answers too.

Explain the Problem

Ask a question like this. Does sun heat air?

26

Make Observations

Tell about the size, the color, or the shape of things.

Give a Hypothesis

Try to answer the problem. Think of different ideas. Then do an experiment to test your ideas.

Make a Chart or Graph

Write what you learn in your chart or your graph.

Make Conclusions

Decide if your hypothesis is right or wrong.

The following activity will give children practice using scientific methods.

- Tell children to pretend they are playing on the playground on a sunny afternoon. They notice the shadow of the flagpole is very long. But they remember other times when the shadow was short. Ask children to **explain the problem** they notice. (Answers will vary, but children should pose a question such as: When are the shadows of the flagpole longest and shortest during the day?)

- Ask children to **make more observations** about when the shadows are different sizes during the day.

- They should then **give a hypothesis** about how these shadows change during the day. (Hypotheses might include the idea that the shadows are longest in the early morning and late afternoon and shortest at noon.)

- To test their hypotheses, children can observe and measure the shadows of the flagpole throughout the day. Or they can do an experiment using an object, such as a crayon, stuck in the ground. They could then put a sheet of paper next to the crayon so that the shadow falls on the paper. Throughout the day, children can mark and measure the length of the shadow on the paper.

- Children should then **make a chart or graph** summarizing the information they collected.

- Based on the results in the charts, children should **make conclusions** as to whether or not the information supports their hypotheses. Ask children if they wish to change their hypotheses.

Helpful Hints

● Ask a group of children to make a safety poster listing safety tips for experiments or cardboard banners for each safety tip. Display the poster or banners in appropriate places throughout the room, such as over a sink or at work stations.

Safety in Science

Scientists are careful when they do experiments. You also need to be careful. Here are some safety rules to remember.

■ Read each experiment carefully.

■ Wear cover goggles when needed.

■ Clean up spills right away.

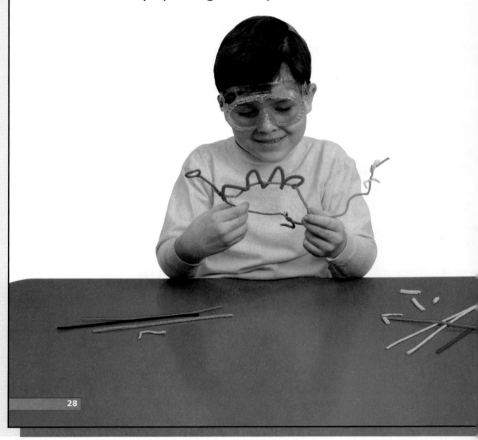

28

- Never taste or smell unknown things.

- Do not shine lights in someone's eyes.

- Clean up when you finish an experiment.

- Wash your hands after each experiment.

- Underscore the importance of each safety tip by asking children what could happen if each tip is not followed.
- Invite a scientist or high-school science teacher to your class. Ask him or her to discuss the importance of safety procedures in the classroom, in the laboratory, and in the field.

Experiment Skills

Purpose
Children will develop the skill of **collecting data** in an experiment that tests the kinds of food crickets like to eat.

Create Interest
Discuss with children the pets they have and the kinds of food their pets eat. Ask: *What kinds of animals have you seen that are similar to crickets?* (Answers will vary depending on each child's experience. Children may mention grasshoppers, butterflies, or other insects.) *What kinds of food do these animals eat? What kinds of food do you think crickets eat?* Explain to children that their answers are hypotheses that can be tested.

Materials (groups of 3)
shoe box with lid, cricket, sponge, small dish, water, small pieces of apple and cooked meat

Safety Tips
• Warn children not to eat any of the food used in the experiment.
• Direct children to wash their hands after handling the crickets and the food.

Experiment Skills

Experiment with Crickets

Sam catches a cricket in the basement. He knows that crickets eat apples. He wonders if a cricket might eat meat too.

Problem
Do crickets eat meat?

Give Your Hypothesis
Answer the problem.
Then do the experiment.

Science Idea Exchange

Collaborative Learning: Cooperative Learning
Each child in the experiment group should be assigned a specific task:
• prepare the box;
• be in charge of food and water;
• fill in the chart.
All children should make observations.

Alternate Experiment
Children may use small pieces of other kinds of food such as bread, cereal flakes, and lettuce instead of fruit and meat.

Follow the Directions

1 Make a chart like this one.

day	food that is left
1	
2	

2 Put the cricket in a box with air holes.

3 Give the cricket a bit of meat, a bit of apple, and some water.

4 Check the food each day for 2 days.

5 In your chart, write what food is left each day.

day 1   day 2

Tell Your Conclusion

Do crickets eat meat?

31

Helpful Hints

- Instead of doing the experiment, children may use the illustrations to test their hypothesis and reach a conclusion.
- Help children set up their charts. Ask: *What will you record in the chart?* (the kind of food the cricket did not eat each day) *What will this information tell you?* (the kind of food the cricket likes to eat)
- Children should dampen the sponge to provide water for the cricket.
- Point out that when children observe the food the cricket leaves, they are collecting the information needed to make conclusions about their hypothesis.
- After the experiment, you may want to release the crickets outside in a field or brush.

Answers to Tell Your Conclusion

Children should conclude that crickets eat fruit, but not meat.

Experiment Results

Crickets are herbivores. Thus, the cricket will prefer fruit to meat.

Your Ideas

_____

_____

_____

_____

_____

Purpose

Children will develop the skill of **making conclusions** in an experiment about fossils.

Create Interest

Discuss with children the experiences they may have had in finding objects buried in soil. Ask: *What kinds of objects have you found? What do they have in common?* (Answers will vary depending on each child's experience, but most of the objects will be of a hard substance.) *Do hard objects make better fossils than soft objects?* Explain to children that their answers are hypotheses that can be tested.

Materials (groups of 3)

2 small paper cups, clay, shell, cotton ball, plaster of Paris

Safety Tips

- Warn children not to put their hands near their mouth while working with clay or plaster.
- Direct children to wash their hands after handling the clay and plaster.
- Dispose of the remains of the experiment promptly.

Experiment with Fossils

The museum has more fossils of bones and teeth than other parts of dinosaurs. Rosa wonders if hard parts make better fossils than softer parts.

Problem

Do hard objects make better fossils than soft objects do?

Give Your Hypothesis

Answer the problem.
Then do the experiment.

32

 # Science Idea Exchange

Collaborative Learning: Cooperative Learning

Each child in the experiment group should be assigned a specific task:
- prepare the sample;
- break apart the sample;
- fill in the chart.

All children should make observations.

Alternate Experiment

Children may use other objects instead of, or in addition to, the shell and cotton. Have them try small flowers or leaves and chicken bones. Discuss conditions that help a good fossil to form.

Module B

Follow the Directions

1 Make a chart like this one.

what I used to make the fossils	what the fossils looked like
shell	
cotton ball	

2 Fill 2 paper cups half full of clay.

3 Put a small shell on the clay in 1 cup.

4 Put a cotton ball on the clay in the other cup. Fill both cups with plaster of Paris.

5 Let the plaster harden. Pull the cup and clay away from the plaster.

6 In your chart, draw how the fossils look.

Tell Your Conclusion

Do hard objects make better fossils?

33

Helpful Hints

- Instead of doing the experiment, children may use the illustrations to test their hypothesis and reach a conclusion.
- Point out that children should look at the impression left in the plaster and in the clay rather than the object itself.
- Help children set up their charts. Ask: *What will you record in the chart?* (what the fossils looked like) *What will this information tell you?* (which type of object, hard or soft, forms a better fossil)
- Point out that when children use the information on the chart, they are making a conclusion about their hypothesis.

Answers to Tell Your Conclusion

Children should conclude that hard objects make better fossils than soft objects.

Experiment Results

The shell makes a much clearer imprint in the clay and plaster than the cotton ball.

Your Ideas

_____

_____

_____

_____

_____

Experiment Skills

Purpose
Children will develop the skill of **testing a hypothesis** in an experiment about magnets.

Create Interest
Allow children to use magnets and to observe how the magnets affect objects around them. Ask: *What kinds of objects does a magnet attract?* (Answers will vary depending on each child's experience, but many will suggest metal.) Demonstrate that magnets attract paper clips. Ask: *Will two magnets together attract more clips than one?* Explain to children that their answers are hypotheses that can be tested.

Materials (groups of 2)
box of paper clips, 2 magnets of the same kind

Safety Tip
Warn children not to put clips or magnets into their mouth.

Experiment Skills

Experiment with Magnets

Mary spills paper clips on the table. David offers to help pick them up. Mary wants to use a magnet. David thinks two magnets will make the job easier.

Problem
Are two magnets stronger than one?

Give Your Hypothesis
Answer the problem.
Then do the experiment.

34

Science Idea Exchange

Science and Art
Children may enjoy making magnet pictures. Dip sheets of construction paper in melted paraffin and let them dry. Have children wear cover goggles and place magnets under the paper while you sprinkle iron filings on top. Tap the paper to allow patterns to form. In a sunny window, the wax will melt slightly to encase the filings.

Alternate Experiment
Children may be interested in trying magnets of different shapes or sizes. They may also compare the number of clips picked up by each team. Even magnets of the same size do not necessarily have the same strength.

Module C

Follow the Directions

1 Make a chart like this one.

number of magnets	number of clips
1	
2	

2 Put paper clips on the table.

3 Use 1 magnet to pick up the paper clips. How many do you pick up? Write the number in the chart.

4 Use 2 magnets to pick up the clips. How many do you pick up? Write the number in your chart.

Tell Your Conclusion

Are 2 magnets stronger than 1 magnet?

- Instead of doing the experiment, children may use the illustrations to test their hypothesis and reach a conclusion.
- After describing the experiment, point out that testing a hypothesis is done by collecting more information about the problem. Ask: *How does this experiment test the hypothesis?* (Observations made in the experiment will show whether the hypothesis is supported.)
- Help children set up their charts. Ask: *What will you record in the chart?* (how many clips one magnet attracts and how many clips two magnets attract) *What will this information tell you?* (whether two magnets together attract more clips than one magnet)

35

Answers to Tell Your Conclusion

Children should conclude that two magnets are stronger than one.

Experiment Results

Provided magnets are of the same strength, two magnets will pick up more paper clips than one magnet, though not necessarily twice as many clips.

Your Ideas

_____

_____

_____

_____

_____

Purpose
Children will develop the skill of **making conclusions** in an experiment about heat from the sun.

Create Interest
Encourage children to discuss their observations about what happens to things that have been left out in the sun. They may have noticed that sand, sidewalks, or metal toys get hot when they sit in the sun during warm weather. Ask: *Do you think the sun can heat water?* Explain to children that their answers are hypotheses that can be tested.

Materials (groups of 3)
2 plastic cups, cold water, 2 alcohol thermometers

Safety Tips
- To prevent falls, have children wipe up spills immediately.
- Caution children to handle thermometers carefully and not to touch glass or liquid if a thermometer breaks.
- Remind children not to look directly at the sun.

Experiment with the Sun and Heat

Dan wants to swim. His mother says the water is too cold. She tells Dan to swim later when the water is warm. Dan wonders if the sun heats the water.

Problem
Can the sun heat water?

Give Your Hypothesis
Answer the problem.
Then do the experiment.

36

Science Idea Exchange

Collaborative Learning: Cooperative Learning
Each child in the experiment group should be assigned a specific task:
- fill the cups;
- place the cups outside;
- record the observations.
All children should observe results.

Alternate Experiment
You may choose to use other containers, such as small juice cans or paper cups, instead of plastic cups. Children may notice that the difference in temperature is greater when water is placed in metal containers.

Module D

Follow the Directions

1 Make a chart like this one.

water	temperature
cup in sun	
cup in shade	

2 Fill 2 cups with cold water.

3 Put 1 cup in a sunny place. Put the other cup in a shady place.

4 Wait for 2 hours.

5 Measure the temperature of each cup.

6 Write the temperatures in your chart. Circle the cup that has warmer water.

Tell Your Conclusion

Can the sun heat water?

37

Helpful Hints
- Instead of doing the experiment, children may use the illustrations to test their hypothesis and reach a conclusion.
- After describing the experiment, ask: *What is the same about the two cups?* (Both contain the same amount of water.) *What is different about the two cups?* (One is in the sun; the other is in the shade.) Point out that the difference in their position may cause a difference in the results. Explain that there is only one difference in the experiment—sunlight or lack of sunlight. Any difference in the temperature of the water is probably due to this difference.
- Some children may need help in comparing the heights of the two lines. Remind them that the higher the temperature, the higher the line. Be sure that all children in each group observe the thermometers.
- Be sure that the water used to fill the cups is the same temperature.

Answers to Tell Your Conclusion
Children should conclude that the sun can heat water.

Experiment Results
The line is higher for the thermometer that sat in water heated by the sun.

Your Ideas
_____

_____

_____

_____

_____

A amphibian, p. A49. a group of animals that lives on land and in water. Frogs and toads are amphibians.

antenna, p. A7. one of the feelers on the heads of insects. The butterfly used its antennas to smell flowers.

B ball bearings, p. C48. balls that turn freely so that work is made easier. Ball bearings help the wheels of a car spin.

battery, p. C34. something that stores electricity. Large batteries make cars start.

bird, p. A49. a group of animals with wings, feathers, and two legs. Most birds can fly.

bone, p. C52. hard part of the body. Bones move when muscles pull them.

C cactus, p. A16. a plant that grows in hot dry places. A cactus grows in the desert.

camouflage, A12. color or shape of an animal that matches the place where the animal lives. A chipmunk's camouflage makes it hard to see in the woods.

caterpillar, p. A10. an insect that looks like a furry or colorful worm. A fuzzy caterpillar crawled on a branch.

clay, p. D42. soil that is easily shaped when wet and hard when dry. Bricks are made from clay.

coal, p. D18. a black rock that gives off heat when it is burned. Coal comes from plants that died millions of years ago.

constellation, p. D30. a group of stars that form a pattern. The Big Dipper is a constellation.

crater, p. D34. a hole in the ground shaped like a bowl. The surface of the moon is covered with craters.

cricket, p. A32. an insect that makes noise by rubbing its wings together. The cricket chirped all night.

D desert, p. A16. a dry habitat that is usually sandy and without trees. It was sunny and hot in the desert.

dinosaur, p. B4. animal that lived millions of years ago. I read a book about dinosaurs.

diorama, p. B36. a scene that shows a group of animals and plants against a modeled background. Joey's diorama of the desert looked so real.

E **electricity,** p. C34. a kind of energy. Electricity makes the lights work.

endangered, p. B48. might become extinct. We should protect endangered animals.

energy, p. D16. the power to do work. Light, heat, and electricity are kinds of energy.

extinct, p. B44. no longer lives on the earth. Dinosaurs are extinct.

F **fish,** p. A49. a group of animals covered with scales that live in water. I like to watch the fish swimming in the tank.

float, p. A18. to be held up by air, water, or other liquid. A hot air balloon will float in the sky.

force, p. C7. something that makes something else move. A push is a force.

fossil, p. B24. a part or a print of a plant or animal that lived long ago. She studied the dinosaur fossil.

fuel, p. D18. anything you can burn that gives heat or power. Wood is a fuel.

G **gas,** p. D10. something that is not solid or liquid and has no shape of its own. The air we breathe is made of several gases.

globe, p. D33. a small, round copy of the earth. A globe has a map of the earth drawn on it.

group, p. A42. to gather a number of persons or things together. The teachers grouped all the second graders together.

H **habitat,** p. A26. a place where living things live. The bird has a nest habitat.

hatch, p. B34. to come out from an egg. Two chickens hatched today.

hibernate, p. A9. spend the winter resting or sleeping. Bears hibernate all winter.

I insect, p. A30. a small animal with six legs and three body parts. Bees are insects.

J joint, p. C52. the place in the body where two bones are joined. Your knee is a joint.

K koala, p. A36. a small gray animal that looks like a bear. Koalas live in Australia.

L lever, p. C46. a bar used for lifting They used a lever to lift a rock.

living, p. A44. having life; something that grows. Animals and plants are two kinds of living things.

lizard, p. B12. a long reptile. The lizard ran over my foot.

M machine, p. C42. something that applies force to make work easier. My new bicycle is a machine.

magnet, p. C22. something that pulls pieces of metal to it. Nails will stick to a magnet.

mammal, p. A49. a group of animals usually covered with hair or fur. Cats are mammals.

model, p. A54. a small copy of something. A globe is a model of the earth.

moon, p. D32. the brightest thing in the night sky. Sunlight shining on the moon makes it shine.

muscle, p. C52. a part of the body that helps the body move. Leg muscles help you run.

N **nectar,** p. A6. sweet liquid found in flowers. Bees make nectar into honey.

nonliving, p. A44. something that does not have life. A book is a nonliving thing.

O **oil,** p. D18. a thick liquid that comes from under the ground. Oil is a fuel.

P **phases,** p. D37. the shapes of the lighted part of the moon. Michi drew the different phases of the moon.

plant, p. A47. any living thing that can make its own food from sunlight, air, and water. Trees are plants.

pole, p. C24. the end of a magnet. Magnets have north and south poles.

polluted, p. B50. made dirty and harmful. The children couldn't swim in the lake because the water was polluted.

pond, p. A28. water with land all around it. A pond is smaller than a lake.

protect, p. B54. to keep something safe. Mother birds protect their babies.

R **ramp,** p. C44. a slope that connects two levels. I pushed the box up the ramp.

reptile, p. A49. a group of animals with dry, rough skin. Snakes are reptiles.

rot, p. B26. become spoiled. The apples started to rot.

rough, p. C18. an uneven surface, not smooth. Sandpaper feels rough.

scale, p. A50. the thin, hard pieces covering some fish, snakes and lizards. The scales on a fish are interesting.

scatter, p. A18. to throw a little bit here and there. The birds scattered the bird seed.

shell, p. B26. the hard, outside covering of some animals. Turtles have shells.

shelter, p. A30. something that covers something else from weather or danger. When it rained, everyone ran for shelter.

skeleton, p. B33. the bones of the body that support it and give it shape. You cannot see your skeleton.

smooth, p. C18. an even surface; not bumpy. The ice was so smooth that Bonnie was able to skate very fast.

soil, p. A27. dirt, the top layer of the earth. Marisa dug a small hole in the soil.

solar energy, p. D16. energy that comes from the sun. Many homes are heated with solar energy.

spider, p. A30. a very small animal with eight legs. I watched the spider spin its web.

star, p. D26. a tiny light in the night sky. A star is made up of hot, glowing gases.

stem, p. A14. the part of a plant that holds up leaves above the ground. The plant has a thin stem.

T **trunk,** p. A15. the main stem of a tree. The children leaned against the trunk of the big oak tree.

V **valley,** p D48. the low area between mountains or hills. Rivers often run through valleys.

W **web,** p. A56. a net of tiny threads made by a spider. The spider's sticky web helps it catch its food.

wheel, p. C43. a kind of machine. Wheels help make a skateboard move easily.

wildlife, p. A38. plants or animals not grown or tamed by people. It is a good idea to have parks for wildlife.

Acknowledgments

Outside Credits

Interior Design
Kym Abrams Design, Inc.
The Quarasan Group, Inc.

Unless otherwise acknowledged, all photographs are the property of Scott, Foresman and Company. Page abbreviations are as follows: **(T)** top, **(C)** center, **(B)** bottom, **(L)** left, **(R)** right, **(INS)** inset.

Module A
Photographs
Front & Back Cover: Background: Patti Murray/EARTH SCENES Children's Photos: Michael Goss for Scott, Foresman and Company.

Page A2 John Shaw/Tom Stack & Associates **A3** Anna E.Zuckerman/Tom Stack & Associates **A5** Robert Lankinen/ The Wildlife Collection **A4(BL)** Don & Pat Valenti **A4(BR)** John Cancalosi/DRK Photo **A4-5(T)** Larry R.Ditto/Bruce Coleman, Inc. **A6** John Shaw/Tom Stack & Associates **A8-A9(T)** Jeff Foot/Bruce Coleman, Inc. **A8(B)** Mary Clay/ Tom Stack & Associates **A9(TR&B)** E.R.Degginger/ANIMALS ANIMALS **A12** Charlton Photographs **A13(T)** William E.Ferguson **A13(CL)** E.R.Degginger **A13(CR)** Marcia W.Griffen/ ANIMALS ANIMALS **A13(B)** Michael Fogden/DRK Photo **A14** Robert Frerck/Tony Stone Worldwide **A16** James Tallon **A18** David Cavagnaro/ Peter Arnold, Inc. **A24(L)** Tom Bean/DRK Photo **A24-A25(T)** Tom Bean/DRK Photo **A24-A25(B)** Margot Granitsas/The Image Works **A25(T)** Cameramann International Ltd. **A25(B)** Tom Bean/DRK Photo **A26-A27** Anna E.Zuckermann/Tom Stack & Associates **A28(T)** George I.Bernard/ANIMALS ANIMALS **A28(C)** Ray Richardson/ANIMALS ANIMALS **A28(B)** Ralph A.Reinhold/ANIMALS ANIMALS **A29(T)** Patti Murray/ANIMALS ANIMALS **A29(B)** E.R.Degginger **A34(T)** Rudi VonBriel **A34(B)-A35(B)** Esao Hashimoto/ANIMALS ANIMALS **A35(TL)** Ron Austing/Photo Researchers, Inc. **A36** Brian Parker/Tom Stack & Associates **A46(TL)** Aaron Haupt/David Frazier Photolibrary **A46(TR)** Stephen J.Krasemann/DRK Photo **A46(B)** Robert A.Tyrell/Oxford Scientific Films/ANIMALS ANIMALS **A47** John D.Cunningham/Visuals Unlimited **A50** Van Welsen/Tony Stone Worldwide **A52** David M.Dennis/Tom Stack & Associates **A53(TL)** E.R.Degginger **A53(R)** Hans Pfletschinger/Peter Arnold, Inc.

Illustrations
Page A7 Laurie O'Keefe **A15** Cindy Brodie **A20-21** Don Charles Meighan **A30-31** Erika Kors **A38-39** Nancy Lee Walter **A44-45** Renee Daily **A48-49** Kim Mulkey **A56-57** Don Charles Meighan **A61** Mike Eagle

Module B
Photographs
Front & Back Cover: Children's Photos: Michael Goss for Scott, Foresman and Company.

Page B2(T) Alex Kerstitch/Visuals Unlimited **B2(C)** Kjell B.Sandved/Visuals Unlimited **B20-B21(T) & B20(B)** Bruce Selyem/Museum of the Rockies, Montana State University **B21(TR)** Scott Berner/Visuals Unlimited **B21(C)** British Museum of Natural History **B21(BR)** Bruce Selyem/Museum of The Rockies, Montana State University **B26** William E.Ferguson **B27(T)** Alex Kerstitch/ Visuals Unlimited **B27(B)** Kjell B.Sandved/Visuals Unlimited **B28** Phil Degginger **B32** American Museum of Natural History, New York City Neg.2143 **B48(T)** Wendy Smith/Bob Rozinski/Tom Stack & Associates **B48(B)** Marty Stouffer/ ANIMALS ANIMALS **B49(TL)** Kerry T.Givens/Tom Stack & Associates **B49(TR)** William E.Ferguson **B49(B)** Gerald & Buff Corsi/Tom Stack & Associates **B56-B57** Gregory G.Dimijian, M.D./Photo Researchers, Inc. **B60** David R.Austen/Stock Boston

Illustrations
Page B2 Raymond E. Smith **B4-5** Robert Masheris **B6-7** Raymond E. Smith **B10** Ka Botzis **B12-13** Robert Masheris **B14-15** Cecile Duray-Bito **B16-17** Cecile Duray-Bito **B22** Ka Botzis **B30-31** Cecile Duray-Bito **B34-35** Ka Botzis **B36-37** Raymond E. Smith **B38-39** Sharron O'Neil **B42-43** Ronald C. Lipking **B44-45** Roberta Polfus **B46-47** Edward Brooks **B52** Rondi Collette **B61** Mike Eagle

Module C
Photographs
Front & Back Cover: Background: Holt Confer/DRK Photo Children's Photographs: Michael Goss for Scott, Foresman and Company.

Page C2(B) William E.Ferguson **C42** William E.Ferguson **C46** E.R.Degginger **C60** Courtesy, Huffy Bicycles

Illustrations
Page C4-5 Rondi Collette **C8-9** Yvette Banek **C18-19** Linda Hawkins **C28-29** Meryl Henderson **C36-37** Lisa Pompelli **C40-41** Cindy Brodie **C52-53** Vincent Perez **C57** Vincent Perez **C61** Mike Eagle

Module D

Photographs

Front & Back Cover: Background: E.R.Degginger   Children's Photos: Michael Goss for Scott, Foresman and Company.

Page D3(B) Tom Bean/DRK Photo   **D4-D5** Joseph A.DiChello
D6-D7(T) Lawrence Migdale/Stock Boston
D6-D7(B) Mike J.Howell/Stock Boston   **D10** NASA
D16 Bob Daemmrich/Stock Boston   **D26-D27** Dennis DiCicco
D32 E.R.Degginger   **D34** NASA   **D36-D37** Dennis DiCicco
D48 Stephen J.Krasemann/DRK Photo   **D49** Tom Bean/DRK Photo
D50-D51(T) Telegraph Colour Library/FPG
D50-D51(B) Larry Ulrich/DRK Photo
D51(TR) Scott Berner/Visuals Unlimited
D51(BR) Stan Osolinski/Tony Stone Worldwide
D60 Alan Carey/The Image Works

Illustrations

Page D3 Pam Hohman   **D14-15** Rondi Collette
D18-19 Raymond E. Smith   **D20-21** Lisa Pompelli
D24-25 Diana Philbrook   **D28-29** Pam Hohman
D38-39 Nan Brooks   **D56-57** Linda Hawkins
D61 Mike Eagle

Back Matter

Photographs
Page 9 Bob Daemmrich/The Image Works

Illustrations
Pages 10-25, 38-46 Precision Graphics

CONTENTS

ACKNOWLEDGMENTS

Unless otherwise acknowledged, all photographs are the property of ScottForesman. Page abbreviations are as follows: (T) top, (C) center, (B) bottom, (L) left, (R) right, (INS) inset.

Photographs

Scope and Sequence grid: Page FM 6–KB: Herb Segers/Animals Animals 1B: Thomas Howland/Grant Heilman 2A: John Shaw/Tom Stack and Assoc. 4A: NOAO 6A: The Adler Planetarium of Astonomy Collection 6C: Bruce Selyem/ Museum of the Rockies   Page FM7– KD: R. Starkweather/Westlight 1D: Joseph A. DiChello 3D: Courtesy Ford Motor Co. 4D: Stephen Dalton/Photo Researchers 4E: Tony Stone Images 4F: Michael and Patricia Fogden 5D: Bettman Archive 6D: Kjell Sandved/ Visuals Unlimited   Page A1c (B) Norbert Wu/Tony Stone Worldwide   Page B1c (T) Joe McDonald/Visuals Unlimited   Page C1c (BL) Mickey Gibson/Animals Animals Page D1c (Both) NASA

Illustrations

Scope and Sequence grid: Page FM6–4C: Joe Le Monnier 6B: Biomedia   Page FM7–2D: Pam Homan 3E: Carl Kock 3F: Ron Becker   Page A1g (B) Stan Tusan   Page A1h (T) Yoshi Miyake Page A63a (B) Ruth Brunke   Page A63b (T) Ruth Brunke   Page B1d (B) Yoshi Miyake   Page B1g (B) Susanne DeMarco   Page B1h (T) Yoshi Miyake   Page B63a (C) Ruth Brunke   Page C1g (B) Ruth Brunke   Page C1h (T) Yoshi Miyake Page C63b (C) Ruth Brunke   Page D1c (B) Yoshi Miyake   Page D1d (L) Yoshi Miyake   Page D1g (B) Ruth Brunke   Page D1h (T) Yoshi Miyake Science Idea Exchange icons Steve Mach

MULTICULTURAL EDUCATION IN *DISCOVER THE WONDER*

Great care has gone into making *DISCOVER THE WONDER* accessible to *all* students, no matter what their learning styles, cultural heritages, or native languages. Through content, illustrations, learning strategies, and special features, this program encourages every student to participate in the process and excitement of science.

CONSTRUCTIVIST, HANDS-ON SCIENCE

DISCOVER THE WONDER follows a constructivist and hands-on approach to science. This teaching/learning approach recognizes that students construct meaning by building on prior knowledge. The Teacher's Edition provides suggestions that invite students from all cultural backgrounds to share their diverse personal experiences. Look for the heading Make Connections in the lesson plan for strategies you can use to assess prior knowledge.

The Pupil's Edition and the Teacher's Edition provide many hands-on activities that allow second-language learners to learn a concept by doing rather than by reading. Each chapter in *DISCOVER THE WONDER* begins with a Discover Activity. This activity provides a common "starting point" for students with diverse background knowledge about a topic. The Teacher's Edition provides suggestions for using the Discover Activity to help your students think about and share what they already know about a topic.

Many opportunities for cooperative learning are provided in *DISCOVER THE WONDER* Teacher's Edition and other program components. Cooperative learning activities allow students of different ethnic and cultural backgrounds to work collaboratively and learn from each other. A small-group setting builds self-esteem because it allows each individual to contribute something special to enhance the learning of the group.

OPPORTUNITIES FOR ALL STUDENTS TO LEARN SCIENCE

DISCOVER THE WONDER's assessment program recognizes the uniqueness of the individual. The Module Performance Assessment is based on Howard Gardner's theory of multiple intelligences. This theory, discussed on page T5 of the Teacher's Edition, recognizes that learning takes place in a cultural setting and that students learn in at least seven different ways. Each Module Assessment provides a menu of optional projects for students to choose from. The projects provide the opportunity for *all* students to show understanding of science concepts using their strongest individual problem-solving abilities, or intelligences. In addition, the Module Event in the Teacher's Edition provides opportunities for students to use their various intelligences.

DISCOVER THE WONDER offers many nontraditional assessment options for the culturally diverse classroom. Portfolio Assessment opportunities in the Teacher's Edition, Teacher's Assessment Package, and Explorer's Activity Guide can be used to document an individual student's development over time. Portfolios can provide you with evidence of your students' different learning styles and their preferred learning modes. In the Teacher's Assessment Package, you will find additional assessment options to choose from. Performance Tasks, Student Drawings, and Open-Ended/Oral Questions provide multiple ways for your students to show what they know.

DISCOVER THE WONDER also provides a concept map in the Teacher's Edition for every chapter. These organizers can help you provide visual overviews of chapter concepts for those students who are visual learners.

OPPORTUNITIES FOR APPRECIATING CULTURAL DIVERSITY

Special features in the Teacher's Edition enhance multicultural understanding. Science Across Cultures, for example, highlights science contributions of diverse cultures and showcases how nations collaborate in scientific endeavors. Multicultural Connections in the Science Idea Exchange provide suggestions for appreciating cultural diversity that you can share with students.

DISCOVER THE WONDER presents a balanced view on issues in science. The authors and multicultural reviewers provided guidance for presenting a multicultural rather than a Eurocentric point of view on science issues. For example, the topic of rainforest destruction is presented with sensitivity to the viewpoint that clearing a rainforest has economic benefits for certain groups of people.

INTEGRATED SCIENCE

DISCOVER THE WONDER makes connections among the sciences, which are treated as separate subjects in traditional science programs. This approach is particularly important at the upper-grade elementary level, where students with special needs are sometimes denied access to "difficult" disciplines such as physical science. An integrated science program is by nature nondiscriminatory. It involves all students in a balanced curriculum of life, earth, and physical sciences.

A Constructivist, Hands-on Approach To Science

Maureen Allen
Irvine Unified School District, California

A building contractor who sets out to build a house usually knows how it should look and has plans to follow. The contractor lists materials needed, establishes a time line, surveys materials available, and gets whatever else is needed. Before beginning, the contractor checks that the foundation can be built properly. Later, the design may be modified to accommodate structural changes.

Developing, or constructing, a teaching unit can resemble this procedure. The goals and objectives for the students are clearly defined and visualized. Just as the contractor surveyed the materials available, a teacher who uses the constructivist approach may survey the students to learn what they already know about the topic. A teacher can also find out what students already know by allowing them to engage in an exploration activity. The teacher finds out what students want to know by asking them to think of questions they would like to have answered. The teacher gains new insights and, before building a layer of learning on a poorly built foundation, can work out any misconceptions students may have.

If the teacher does not learn what students already know about a topic, the class may repeat things they already know or try to build on knowledge they do not have. They will miss opportunities to connect with previous learning and to build foundations for future learning.

Just as a contractor may modify the design, a teacher may alter lesson plans and provide activities to meet students' needs and to help them construct new understanding of a topic. These adjustments may detour from the prescribed unit or text, but they can ensure construction of a solid foundation.

By now you may be thinking that the constructivist method does not seem very different from what you already do in your classroom—and you are absolutely right! It is not a new method, but rather a new way to combine several good practices.

The following components are usually included in the constructivist approach:

- **Invitation** to learn is made to students in a variety of ways.
- **Exploration** allows students to formulate questions and discover new things that can guide future learning.
- **Explanation** allows students to begin to understand the topic and to design with the teacher a plan to find out the answers.
- **Take Action** phase allows for transfer of new knowledge to the students' real world.

DISCOVER THE WONDER follows the constructivist approach. At the beginning of each chapter, the Discover Activity is an invitation to learn. This hands-on, minds-on activity engages students and allows them to explore the topic. The teacher can observe the students' readiness and understanding and can proceed accordingly. Students explore and investigate the topic in activities in lessons that follow, and eventually construct explanations. Reviews at the end of lessons, chapters, and modules give students the opportunities to take action, using their new knowledge in cognitively appropriate activities.

In the constructivist approach to learning, teachers facilitate learning by providing appropriate activities, questions, and classroom environments so students can construct their own understanding of concepts.

Teachers who provide cooperative or small-group learning situations provide another vehicle for students to construct their own knowledge bank. Students can listen to others reason while working in cooperative groups.

You can use the following practices to help your students construct their understanding of a concept:

- Find out what students already know about a topic.
- Provide an activity so they can explore the topic.
- Obtain a list of the questions they would like to answer.
- Cluster similar questions and decide as a class which to answer.
- Design a plan to find the answer for each question.
- Work in cooperative groups to answer the questions.
- Share the answers students find and stress the thinking and rationale behind them.
- Transfer the new knowledge to a new situation or to one that allows it to be utilized.

The constructivist approach to learning provides opportunities for assessment. Beginning a unit of study by asking students to write what they know about the topic provides baseline data. The tests or products of a unit can then be compared to the baseline.

Students must construct knowledge for themselves. It cannot be merely transmitted from the teacher. When you ask how students know what they know, you begin to reach underlying concepts, ideas, or misconceptions in their minds that can interfere with the understanding of a new concept. The teacher is no longer the sole deliverer of knowledge, but rather the facilitator of learning.

COMPREHENSION IN READING

Robert A. Pavlik

Cardinal Stritch College, Milwaukee, Wisconsin

BEYOND READABILITY LEVELS

When you select a new textbook, prepare the next week's lessons, or make up the next day's assignments, your main concern is not the readability level of your science text. Experienced teachers know readability level does not indicate the concept difficulty or interest appeal of a text. It tells only the average word length and sentence length in selected samples.

Underlying the readability level is the assumption that students find reading easier if words are smaller and sentences shorter. Yet students enjoy learning long, scientific names of dinosaurs and other living things. Using primarily short sentences can result in choppy text and text that is hard to comprehend. A student's reading level does not indicate his or her ability or inability to read and comprehend a particular text.

Today, more and more teachers are abandoning or limiting the use of readability levels when they select and use textbooks. Textbook authors and editors are also questioning and limiting the use of such "tools." They know that using readability levels as guides for writing and editing can lead to a dry, stilted writing style.

The authors and editors of *DISCOVER THE WONDER* maintained an awareness of readability levels. However, they applied other criteria to achieve the standards that teachers and students require of science textbooks.

SCIENCE KNOWLEDGE, NOT JUST SCIENCE FACTS

Far too many science textbooks merely define or describe the objects and processes that relate to many science topics. You will know you are looking at such a text if the verbs in most sentences are "is called," "are called," "is," "are," "was," and "were." Overuse of these verbs indicates content that focuses mostly on factual knowledge, rather than on explanations and important ideas.

As you and your students use *DISCOVER THE WONDER,* you will find that explanations and narrations far outnumber definitions and descriptions. Most sentences have verbs that involve actions. The explanations and narratives provide in-depth science knowledge. The text gives reasons for and significant evidence about events and processes. It provides insights into unusual or surprising facts and ideas. Multicultural connections are included, which increase understanding of the effects of science on people, and personal connections relate science to the students' real world.

This depth of science content builds the background knowledge your students need to do the critical thinking and application activities found throughout *DISCOVER THE WONDER.*

ONLY ESSENTIAL SCIENCE VOCABULARY

Many science textbooks identify too many words as key words. Up to 80% of science words may be used only on the page where they are introduced. Students are too often tested on words that are not important enough to be used more than once in the text!

In *DISCOVER THE WONDER,* only words and phrases most essential for science concepts and processes are highlighted. These key words are used often throughout the text.

ADVANCED USE OF VISUALS

The advanced use of visuals in *DISCOVER THE WONDER* improves students' ability to learn from visual representations of scientific objects and processes. Phrases, statements, or questions in the text direct students to the purpose, features, or importance of the visuals. A special, two-page visual/verbal presentation in each chapter shows classifications, cycles, cause-effect relationships and other visually oriented material that is most effectively presented this way.

ACTIVE, NARRATIVE WRITING STYLE

The active writing style in *DISCOVER THE WONDER* engages students' interests, activates background knowledge, and promotes critical thinking. The question or declarative sentence that opens each lesson helps students activate background knowledge and provides a meaningful setting for the lesson's content. The active voice in most sentences clarifies cause and effect relationships. Participatory sentences build background knowledge and complement hands-on activities. Questions help students make connections between reading and experiences, interact with visuals, summarize what they read, and predict outcomes while reading. Judicious use of "you" promotes students' identification with the knowledge and uses of science.

DISCOVER THE WONDER fulfills the criteria for meaningful, well-written texts for teaching and learning science.

MULTIPLE INTELLIGENCES IN SCIENCE

Robert A. Pavlik

Cardinal Stritch College, Milwaukee, Wisconsin

NEW DEFINITION OF "INTELLIGENCE"

Howard Gardner of Harvard University challenges the longstanding definition of "intelligence" as a fixed, general ability for problem solving. Instead, Gardner defines intelligence

". . . as the capacity to solve problems or to fashion products that are valued in one or more cultural settings." (Howard Gardner, Thomas Hatch, "Multiple Intelligences Go to School," *Educational Researcher,* Vol. 18, Nov. 1989, p. 5)

His definition is developmental and sensitive to the contexts or cultures for learning and communicating meaning.

SEVEN WAYS TO BE "SMART"

Gardner encourages us to ask, answer, and act on "How are our students smart?" not "How smart are our students?" His emphasis is on the ways students can solve problems and create and communicate meaning. All students can be smart in at least seven ways:

- **Body/Kinesthetic Intelligence** involves using one's understanding of one's body and its functions, as shown by an athlete, a dancer, and a mime.
- **Interpersonal Intelligence** involves using one's understanding of the goals, strengths, sources of strength, weaknesses, and strategies of others to interact with them in mutually satisfying ways, as shown by a teacher, a friend, a leader, a politician, and a salesperson.
- **Intrapersonal Intelligence** involves using one's understanding of one's self to guide how one thinks and acts, as shown by an adviser, a counselor, a philosopher, and one's self.
- **Logical/Mathematical Intelligence** involves recognizing and using logical reasoning and notational language, as shown by an accountant, a detective, a judge, a mechanic, and a scientist.
- **Musical/Rhythmic Intelligence** involves using one's understanding of music and rhythm skillfully, as shown by a choir member, a conductor, and a musician.
- **Verbal/Linguistic Intelligence** involves using one's understanding of the structures, functions, and nuances of language, as shown by an author, an editor, a poet, a speaker, and a translator.
- **Visual/Spatial Intelligence** involves visualizing objects, actions, and ideas and changing one's perception of reality, as shown by an architect, an artist, a magician, a painter, a surgeon, and a tour guide.

Traditional curriculum, instruction, and assessment have emphasized mostly the logical/mathematical and verbal/linguistic intelligences. The more students know about other ways that they are smart, the more successful and the higher their self-esteem will be both during and beyond their school years. The activities found throughout *DISCOVER THE WONDER* provide many ways for students to express and develop their various intelligences. Many other features—such as Let's Solve It and visual/verbal lessons in the Pupil's Edition, the variety of helpful suggestions in the Teacher's Edition, and the Explorer's Activity Guide—provide further opportunities for your students to show how they are smart.

USING PROJECTS TO DEVELOP MULTIPLE INTELLIGENCES

In the Teacher's Edition for the Module Review, a chart identifies the intelligences involved in optional projects suggested. A similar chart is also provided for the Module Event. Guide students at the beginning of the year to choose a project that uses their strongest intelligence. Later in the year, encourage them to try projects that require other intelligences. For those projects, they can work collaboratively with other students who are strong in those areas of intelligence.

ACHIEVING ENGLISH PROFICIENCY

Although students who are native speakers of English may experience some difficulty with new terminology and concepts, students who are non-native users of the language are more prone to difficulties. Regardless of their first language, students for whom English is their second language often exhibit some of the following behaviors:

- They seem to communicate effectively on an interpersonal level with other students in class and appear to follow and understand classroom activities, but they do not completely comprehend the activities.
- They seem withdrawn and uninterested, rarely voluteering answers to questions or participating in class.
- They have trouble following both oral and written directions, especially if the directions include references to more than one task at a time.
- They seldom finish reading the text material and have difficulty answering comprehension questions.
- They are reluctant to write and, when required to do so, they make frequent grammar and usage errors. They also show difficulty with the conventions of written English, such as punctuation, spelling, and capitalization.

In working to help students overcome these difficulties, teachers should avoid the common mistake of equating a lack of English proficiency with lower cognitive or intellectual ability. The non-native user of English who appears to lack aptitude or motivation is probably experiencing a linguistic problem. Such students may be academically quite capable and motivated, but they lack the language skills to reason, hypothesize, make predictions, and form and defend logical arguments *in English.* These students have not fully developed what linguist James Cummins calls Cognitive Academic Language Proficiency (CALP) skills. These skills are crucial to the comprehension of abstract concepts expressed in abstract language. Proficiency in language is acquired for non-native users of English, just as it is for native users, by continuous exposure to and experience in the language.

For the non-native user it is essential to make the language a functional tool that expresses concepts clearly. Students might know the meaning of words and might understand the grammar, but idioms, metaphors, and figurative language may be incomprehensible to them. Words with multiple meanings, such as *table,* words that sound the same, such as *to, too,* and *two,* and words that are rarely used except in activity and test directions, such as *match, paragraph,* and *conclusion,* will be confusing for the non-native user of English.

Language is acquired through meaningful communication, by engaging in an exchange of information in a variety of low-anxiety settings. In the classroom this communication should involve surrounding the learners with language they can understand and devising tasks to use the newly acquired language.

You will find that language development activities and features designed to build academic language proficiency and to enhance science instruction for all students have been integrated into the Pupil's Edition and Teacher's Edition of *DISCOVER THE WONDER.* These activities and features are especially valuable for the student not yet proficient in English.

Although the specific needs of different students, the scope of the subject matter, and the ratio of second-language learners to proficient students in a classroom will vary, the following strategies can help create a nonthreatening, low-risk environment while simultaneously making the content more accessible to students.

- **Group work**
  Allowing students to work in small, mixed groups of less proficient and more proficient students promotes peer recognition and support. Students have opportunities to practice expressing ideas without risking language errors in front of the class and the teacher and to hear and interact in English. The teacher can monitor students' progress and provide guidance in a less threatening manner.
  In the *DISCOVER THE WONDER* Teacher's Edition, the Collaborative Learning activity suggestions provide the opportunity for students to engage in group interaction in a low-anxiety setting. Students with more advanced skills can help their peers who are newer to the language.

- **Visual cues**

  Multiple forms of input are desirable. Words, especially spoken words, can confuse the less proficient student, and they do not allow for review. Write on the chalkboard key terms, vocabulary, and names. As the words are used in discussion, point them out on the chalkboard. This provides students with a "handle" to hang onto in a stream of words.

  Whenever possible, make use of pictures, photographs, maps, and charts to reinforce or visually enhance the topic. In *DISCOVER THE WONDER* visual representations of scientific objects and processes reinforce and expand students' understanding of the content. Phrases, statements, or questions in the text direct students to the purpose or importance of the visuals.

- **Clear speech**

  Teachers of students who are at low levels of linguistic competence in English are encouraged to use a slower but natural speech rate. Speak audibly and clearly to help students hear the differences between words that sound alike. Use direct forms of speech, and avoid passive verb forms and contractions. Talk in shorter sentences and use ample repetitions.

- **Positive feedback**

  Students need to know when they are right or even partly right. Focus on the content of responses rather than the form. Do not correct grammatical or usage errors in front of the class. This can be so embarrassing for students that their further participation is stifled. One way to deal with such errors is to acknowledge the contribution and then repeat the complete answer using the language correctly.

- **Voluntary participation**

  Ample opportunity to participate in class discussions is important for less proficient students, but verbal participation should not be forced. Students should be encouraged in a noninsistent way to share their ideas.

- **Build on the familiar**

  Integrate students' cultural background and multicultural experiences into discussions whenever possible. This practice recognizes students' cultural identities and enriches the entire class.

  The Discover Activities in *DISCOVER THE WONDER* provide students with a common experience at the beginning of the content material. These activities utilize and focus prior knowledge to increase the students' comprehension of new material.

- **Body language**

  The use of gestures, demonstrations, and pantomime can help make English more comprehensible. Be demonstrative, gesturing with your hands, arms, or whole body. In other words, be a ham! Your students will enjoy the fun, and they will understand more too.

TEACHING SAFETY IN THE CLASSROOM

Dr. Jack A. Gerlovich, Science Education Safety Consultant/Author
Des Moines, Iowa

Activities throughout *DISCOVER THE WONDER* reinforce and extend science concepts using materials and procedures that are inherently safe. *Discover the Wonder* teaches that safe procedure is part of sound scientific inquiry. Students who use this program learn not only how to safely investigate the topics at hand; they also develop safety habits that will serve them well in future scientific endeavors.

How does *Discover the Wonder* accomplish this task? First and foremost, by performing the activities in the text, students learn that simple, safe materials can be used extensively to investigate science concepts. Second, cover goggles are listed and shown in activities wherever appropriate. Third, the Teacher's Edition includes safety tips for the various student activities and teacher demonstrations that appear throughout the program. Following is a list of the most general of these tips for the elementary science classroom. If followed from the start, these guidelines should be easily assimilated into classroom procedures by teachers and students alike.

- The proper use of cover goggles that meet American National Standards Institute (ANSI Z87.1) standards should be demonstrated to students. Cover goggles should be worn whenever the potential for eye injury exists; for example, when heating any substance, when using any chemicals including "ordinary" substances such as vinegar, and when using glassware. Even relatively safe items such as rubber bands and balloons can cause eye injury and warrant the use of goggles.

- To prevent student interference with each other and to assist the safe exit of students from the room in case of an emergency, teachers should try to assure that rooms are not overcrowded, that students understand exit procedures, and that aisles are kept uncluttered.

- Teachers should periodically conduct simulations with students for dealing with foreseeable emergencies. Examples might include exiting the room due to an emergency, coping with a fire, aiding someone who has been splashed by a substance, and helping a fall victim.

- Prior to using any equipment or substances, teachers should be certain they understand the proper function and hazards associated with the use of those items. This information should be communicated to the students.

- Always use rounded safety scissors.

- All equipment should be properly stored. The more dangerous items should be kept under lock and key.

- Whenever possible, plastic items should replace glass. If glass containers are essential, temperature- and break-resistant glassware should be selected.

- To prevent slipping and falls, any liquids spilled on tile or hardwood floors should be wiped up immediately.

- If the teacher cannot satisfy himself or herself that all foreseeable dangers have been reduced to an acceptable level, the activity should be altered or eliminated.

Teachers should be aware of all applicable federal, state, and local regulations and relevant guidelines from professional organizations which apply to the activities being performed. Examples would include Occupational Safety and Health Administration (OSHA) standards for workplace safety; state laws relating to cover goggles; local fire department requirements regarding the use of open flame, fire extinguishers, and fire blankets; and National Science Teachers Association (NSTA) suggestions regarding overcrowding. Refer to the following materials for other information about classroom safety.

Downs, G., et al.
Science Safety for Elementary School Teachers, 1983. Iowa State University Press, Ames, Iowa 50010.

Gerlovich, J., and Hartman, K.
Safe Science Teaching: A Diskette for Elementary Educators, 1990, Jakel, Inc. 585 Southfork Dr., Waukee, Iowa 50263.

COOPERATIVE LEARNING

What Is Cooperative Learning?

Cooperative Learning is an instructional strategy that dramatically increases social and academic learning by providing a setting in which students collaborate on academic tasks. In *DISCOVER THE WONDER,* cooperative learning strategies are used to engage all students in the hands-on activities that make doing science such a worthwhile experience.

What Are the Benefits of Cooperative Learning?

Many studies show that the benefits of cooperative learning are concrete and long-lasting. These findings indicate that:

1. Academic achievement is increased. The achievement gap between high and low achievers is narrowed.

2. Self-esteem is enhanced. The "our group" feeling includes and validates each group member. Each person in the group plays a meaningful role—a role that is important for the entire group's success.

3. Language skills are developed more rapidly. This is especially true for second-language learners who feel more comfortable speaking and contributing in a small group setting.

4. Good work skills are developed. Employers today insist that their workers think critically and work together cooperatively. Both skills are important outcomes of cooperative learning.

Is Cooperative Learning Group Work?

In *DISCOVER THE WONDER,* cooperative learning is not just group work. Social skills, such as the need to speak quietly and to listen to others is emphasized. All students are given specific responsibilities within the group. Students are held accountable for those responsibilities as well as for their academic learning.

How Are Cooperative Learning Groups Formed?

There are two basic ways to form cooperative learning groups—random and balanced. Random grouping can be achieved by counting off, grouping by rows, and so on. Balanced grouping is achieved by placing together high, medium, and low-achieving students, equal numbers of boys and girls, and special education students with regular education students. In *DISCOVER THE WONDER,* we suggest and support groups of four students for each hands-on activity—the best combination of students for cooperative learning success.

How Do I Assess Work Done in Cooperative Learning Groups?

In *DISCOVER THE WONDER,* students should be held accountable for their assignments whether they work individually or in cooperative learning groups. Accountability, a basic element of cooperative learning, can be accomplished in the following ways:

1. Students can work cooperatively to learn the assigned material and then can be tested individually.

2. Students can earn a group score. For group scoring, the accountability criteria must be established before the group work begins.

3. Individual scores can be averaged within each group and each member of the group can receive the average score.

4. You can use the *DISCOVER THE WONDER* Activity Rubrics for each formal activity as a guide for assessing each student's work in the group. These Activity Rubrics are located in the *Teacher's Assessment Package.*

PORTFOLIO ASSESSMENT IN SCIENCE

James E. Marshall and Adrienne L. Herrell
California State University, Fresno

While much has been written about the use of portfolios in documenting children's growth in reading, writing, and mathematics, portfolios are especially appropriate in science education. Because of the need to document children's growing science content knowledge as well as their ability to use science processes such as observing, classifying, communicating, measuring, inferring, predicting, and experimenting, portfolios are invaluable in assessing your students in science.

The portfolio is not simply a collection of items documenting representative work, best accomplishments, and growth over time. The science portfolio is much more; it serves many purposes:

- It involves students in assessment and encourages reflection on learning.
- It allows the teacher to assess the learning that is taking place in the classroom and to plan appropriate lessons and activities.
- It serves as a vehicle for helping parents to better understand the importance of both content and process in science education.
- It aligns science instruction and assessment by taking advantage of the opportunity to document students actually "doing science" instead of simply answering low-level questions about science.

BASELINE ASSESSMENT

With current emphasis on constructivist learning, portfolios become exceedingly useful. One of the most important parts of constructivism is to begin instruction based on your students' level of understanding. This requires that students be preassessed on the upcoming topic to bring to the surface prior knowledge and attitudes. These preassessments, often called baseline assessments, direct instruction by revealing students' current conceptions, attitudes, interests, and skills. They can be as simple as a question posed to the class or as complex as an activity that results in a student-generated product. Baseline assessments permit students to periodically reflect on their prior conceptions as they construct new understandings. Whether oral or written responses, drawings, or models, these baseline assessments become potent additions to students' portfolios, when compared with subsequent activities and products, because they vividly illustrate growth in science literacy. *DISCOVER THE WONDER* Teacher's Edition provides opportunities for baseline assessment in the lesson plans. Before doing an activity, invite your students to make predictions about the activity results. Your students can place their written predictions in their portfolios for periodic review and updating.

CONTENTS OF A PORTFOLIO

There is no prescription for what items should be in a portfolio. Obviously, items should demonstrate growing content knowledge, but equally important, items should demonstrate the student's science process skill abilities and even his or her attitudes toward science. Even the student's ability to communicate through writing, drawing, drama, and speaking can be documented. Simply, the portfolio documents content that is learned, skills that are mastered, and attitudes that are displayed.

The following is a sample of items to consider for a portfolio:

- videotaped presentations
- audiotaped interviews
- student testimonials, taped or written
- test scores and answer sheet
- photos of experiments or constructions
- individual or group work
- performance tasks
- written work in the student's primary language
- lists of books read
- pictures drawn
- data collected
- graphs
- concept maps
- copies of awards/prizes
- personal journal excerpts

DISCOVER THE WONDER Teacher's Edition provides numerous specific suggestions for portfolio items. Look for portfolio ideas under Assessment Options on the Module and Chapter Planning Guides. Again, these are just suggestions. You and your students may find many more items that illustrate progress as well as best accomplishments.

SELECTING ITEMS FOR THE PORTFOLIO

Involving students in the assessment of their achievement and growth is one of the greatest advantages of portfolio assessment. The selection process is very individual, with each student, under the guidance and recommendations of the teacher, determining what materials to include to tell the "story" of the science they learned and how they learned it. The process encourages students to reflect on their own work, to consider new ideas and their connections to each other and to prior knowledge, and to confront their feelings and attitudes about the discipline.

However, studies by teachers have shown that students need guidance in the selection and reflection process. Strategies such as using class discussions and peer consultation, as well as sharing examples of what other students have selected for their portfolio, can help students think about their work and its significance.

MAINTAINING THE PORTFOLIO
While all portfolios will not look alike, teachers need to decide on a container appropriate for the types of items students will be selecting and on available classroom storage. Many early childhood teachers (K-2) are using large posterboard folders sewn together with yarn, decorated by the children and stored either flat in a closet or upright in a rack on the counter. Other teachers are using letter-size file folders with accordion sides (which can be expanded from 1-3 inches) and storing them in crates or special drawers in the classroom file cabinet. Regardless of the container, the contents need to be arranged in a useful manner so both student and teacher can easily review and update the items.

To make the portfolio meaningful for those who read and review it, the teacher can set guidelines for the student to maintain the portfolio, such as:

- include organized table of contents
- identify who selects each item
- date all work to document growth over time
- provide written descriptions/titles of all drawings, graphs, photos, etc.
- provide a written reflection on the contents of the portfolio

EVALUATING THE PORTFOLIO
While the individual items without the portfolios can certainly be graded by the teacher, the richness of portfolio assessment lies not in the grade on each item but instead on the opportunity to display the unique strengths and interests of each student. The focus of portfolio evaluation should be on the broad picture of each student's growth in science content and process over time. This broad focus is possible because the portfolio can provide indications of:

- representative work over the evaluation period
- attitudes toward science based on item selection and reflection
- science process skills based on performance samples
- ability to cooperate with others based on group work

- learning styles and preferred learning modalities
- communication skills based on writing samples or tapes

Because the student is involved in selecting items for the portfolio, it is natural for the student to also be involved in presenting the portfolio for review. Teachers are typically planning portfolio review presentations to correspond with each grading period. A variety of formats are possible:

- individual conferences with the teacher and/or parent
- sharing with small groups of peers and the teacher
- formal presentations to parents, teachers, and administrators
- formal presentations to small groups of peers and invited community members
- presentations to invited middle- or high-school students

In all cases, peers, parents, administrators, older students, or community members evaluate the portfolio and its presentation by providing oral feedback and/or responding to a rating scale typically developed by groups of teachers. The Teacher's Assessment Package of *DISCOVER THE WONDER* provides a useful generic rubric to aid in this holistic scoring of student portfolios.

The guidelines that the students and teachers used in preparation for their presentations should be shared with the evaluators as they provide a context for assessing the portfolio presentation. Most importantly, feedback, whether oral or on a rating scale, should reflect the broadest desired outcomes of the science program.

Scope and Sequence
Grade 2

Module	**A** Living Things
Chapter	**1** Plants and Animals **2** Where Things Live **3** Grouping Living Things
Module Themes	• scale and structure • systems and interactions • diversity

Grade Concepts

Physical Science
Different forces and energy can affect matter.

• Color and camouflage

Chapter 1

Earth Science
The position of the sun and the earth in space affects the energy that the earth receives from the sun and causes changes on the earth.

• Animals live in different climates

Life Science
Living things have characteristics that help them survive in their particular habitat.

• Characteristics of animals • survival behaviors of animals • water storage in plants • seed dispersal • habitats • classification of living things

Chapters 1, 2, 3

Health/Human Body
The human body has systems that work together.

Technology/Society
People can use scientific knowledge to make work easier and to help other living things.

• Pollution can change habitats

Science Process/History
Scientific inquiry involves many processes such as classifying, comparing, observing, and modeling.

• Classifying living things • comparing lack of water on different plants • drawing conclusions about living things

Chapters 1, 3

B Changes Over Time	**C** Making Things Move	**D** The Earth and Sky
1 Discovering Dinosaurs **2** Dinosaur Detectives **3** A Changing World	**1** How Things Move **2** Magnets **3** Moving and Machines	**1** The Sun **2** The Moon and Stars **3** Looking at the Earth
• diversity • scale and structure • patterns of change	• systems and interactions • energy	• systems and interactions • energy • modeling
• How pollution harms plants *Chapter 3*	• Force • strength of force • force and mass • magnets and poles • electromagnets • simple machines • motion • electricity • friction *Chapters 1, 2, 3*	• Sun as energy source • how sunlight heats air, water, and land • moon reflects sunlight • colors and heat absorption *Chapters 1, 3*
• Formation of fossils *Chapter 2*		• Day and night • positions of the sun and the earth in space • coal and oil as stored energy from the sun • constellations • phases of the moon • air, water, and land on earth • soil *Chapters 1, 2, 3*
• Characteristics of dinosaurs • diet of dinosaurs • classification of dinosaurs • fossils • extinct and endangered species • habitat loss *Chapters 1, 2, 3*		• Living things need sunlight *Chapter 1*
• Need for unpolluted air *Chapter 3*	• Skeletal system • muscular system *Chapter 3*	
• Helping endangered animals survive *Chapter 3*	• Machines make work easier • use of magnets • conserving electricity • machines affect the environment *Chapter 3*	• Using the energy from the sun • garbage and the environment *Chapter 2*
• Making a model of a fossil • measuring dust and dirt in air • classifying dinosaurs • making inferences *Chapter 2*	• Measuring and comparing forces • showing how machines reduce force needed • making a model of an arm • observing effects of electrical charge *Chapters 1, 3*	• Comparing melting rate of ice in sun and shade • demonstrating how moon craters form • classifying rocks • comparing fresh and salt water • predicting moon phases *Chapters 1, 2, 3*

MATERIALS LIST FOR ACTIVITIES

Quantities are based on a class size of 32 students working in groups of 4. Items keyed with a diamond (•) are available in the Module Equipment Kit for that module. Each Module Equipment Kit contains at least the minimum amount of each keyed item. To find out additional information about an item, refer to either the activity page number in this Teacher's Edition or the *Equipment Kit Teacher's Guide* from your Module Equipment Kit. Cover goggles are available in a separate Safety Kit. For more information about other equipment kit configurations, call 1-800-554-4411.

2A Living Things

Item	Minimum Amount Needed (for 8 groups)	Activity Page Number
Consumable Items		
• Card, index	128	A58
• Clay, modeling	16 sticks	A54
• Cotton ball	32	A19
Crayons	8 boxes	A5, A37, A40, A43
• Cricket	16	A32
• Cricket food	as needed	A32
• Cup, clear plastic, 10 oz.	8	A27
Glue	8 bottles	A25, A37, A54
Leaves, dried	16 or more	A32
Magazine (See Activity)	8	A25, A45
Netting (See Activity)	8 pieces	A32
• Paper, construction	32 sheets	A19, A37
• Paper, construction, brown	16 sheets	A10
• Paper, construction, white	16 sheets	A10, A54
Paper, drawing	128 sheets	A5, A40, A43, A51
Paper, wrapping, brown	8 large sheets	A10
Paper, writing	96 sheets	A22, A25, A40
• Pebble	1 1/2 cups	A27
Pencil	32	A22, A25, A40, A51, A58
Picture of an insect	8	A54
• Pipe cleaner, green, 12"	248	A37, A54
• Pipe cleaner, white, 12"	200	A37, A54
Plant, fern	8	A17
Plant, jade	8	A17
Plant, small potted	8	A27
Shoe box	16	A32, A37
• Soil	16 cups	A27, A32
Twigs	16 or more	A32
Water	4 liters	A17, A27, A32
Nonconsumable Items		
Book with pictures of animals	8	A5
• Dropper, plastic	8	A32
Cover goggles	32	A37, A54
• Feather	8	A51
• Hand lens	8	A51
Jar lid	8	A32
• Scale, fish	8	A51
Scissors	32	A25, A37, A43, A45, A54
Timer	8	A10
Watering can	8	A17

2B Changes Over Time

Item	Minimum Amount Needed (for 8 groups)	Activity Page Number
Consumable Items		
• Bag, paper, small, #3	8	B21
• Birdseed	4 cups	B55
• Button	32	B5
• Card, index	56	B11, B18
Cardboard strip, 5 cm x 50 cm	8 strips	B24
Carton, milk	8	B55
• Clay, modeling	24 sticks	B5, B23, B29
Clay shoe print	8	B24
Container for plaster of Paris	8	B24
• Dowel, 1/8" x 4"	8	B55
Marker	8	B11
Newspaper	8 sheets	B29
Paper, construction	136 sheets	B5, B40, B58
Paper, white	240 sheets	B5, B18, B43, B58
Pencil	32	B5, B43, B58
• Petroleum jelly	1/2 cup	B24, B53
• Pipe cleaners, 12"	72	B18, B33
Plant cutting	16	B50
• Plaster of Paris	8 cups	B24
• Plastic slide	8	B53
• Plastic wrap	16 sheets	B23
• Sand	4 cups	B29
Shoe box	8	B18
• Stick, craft	32	B5, B18
• String	about 3 meters	B55
Tape, masking	32 strips	B8, B24
Towel, paper	8	B53
Vinegar	about 1 liter	B50
Water	about 6 liters	B24, B50
• Yarn, blue, 3-oz. skein	32 meters	B8, B11
Nonconsumable Items		
Container for vinegar	8	B50
Container for water	8	B24, B50
Cover goggles	32	B18, B33, B50, B55
Crayons	8 boxes	B18, B40, B43, B55, B58
• Cup, clear plastic, 10 oz.	24	B29, B50
Dinosaur model	8	B18
• Hand lens	8	B53
• Knife, plastic, heavy duty	8	B24
• Meter stick	8	B8
Object, small (See Activity)	about 32 different objects	B21
• Paintbrush	8	B29
Scissors	32	B5, B40, B55
Shoe	8	B23
• Spoon, plastic, heavy duty	8	B29

• *Items included in the Module Equipment Kit*

2C Making Things Move

Item	Minimum Amount Needed (for 8 groups)	Activity Page Number
Consumable Items		
Balloons, long	8	C54
Battery, D-cell	8	C35
Card, index	16	C26
Cardboard	8 sheets	C30
Cardboard	16 strips	C54
Crayons	8 boxes	C20, C38, C58
Fastener, paper	8	C54
Glue	8 bottles	C5, C20
Magazine	16	C20
Marker	8	C26
Paper, construction	32 sheets	C58
Paper, large (See Activity)	8 sheets	C20
Paper, mural	8 large sheets	C14
Paper, unlined or drawing	112 sheets	C5, C13, C30, C38, C58
Paper, wax	8 1-meter sheets	C41
Pencil	32	C13, C38, C47, C58
Plastic wrap	8 sheets	C30
Rubber band, #72	32	C13, C14, C45, C48
Rubber band, #82	8	C35
Stick, craft	8	C5
String	32 meters	C14, C17, C45, C48
Tape, masking	about 5 meters	C11, C47
Water	4 liters	C5
Yarn, blue, 3-oz. skein	16 meters	C26
Nonconsumable Items		
Ball	24	C41
Baseball bat	16	C41
Block, wood	8	C5, C30
Board, masonite	8	C45
Book (See Activity)	24	C14, C17, C41, C45, C47, C48
Box, cardboard	8	C41
Can, soup or juice	8	C11
Chair, small	8	C45
Clay, modeling	1 stick	C5
Cloth, cotton	8 pieces	C30
Container for water	8	C5
Cover goggles	32	C13, C14, C26, C35, C45, C48, C54
Lid, screw type, metal	8	C48
Magnet, bar, alnico	16	C23, C26, C30, C33
Magnet, ceramic, cylinder	8	C33
Magnet, horseshoe, 3"	8	C33
Marble, 5/8"	80	C41, C48
Nail, 20d	8	C35
Objects, magnetic/nonmagnetic	160	C26
Pan, plastic, 8 qt.	8	C5
Paper clips, #1	80	C30, C33, C35
Rug	8	C17
Ruler, metric	8	C13, C14, C47
Scissors	32	C20
Skateboard	8	C41
Wire, insulated	about 5 meters	C35

2D The Earth and Sky

Item	Minimum Amount Needed (for 8 groups)	Activity Page Number
Consumable Items		
◆ Aluminum foil	1 roll	D17, D49
◆ Bag, sandwich	40	D43
◆ Battery, D-cell	16	D5, D30, D33
Box, cardboard	8	D17
◆ Card, index	80	D40
◆ Chalk	32 pieces	D25
◆ Clay, brown	8 sticks	D49
◆ Clay, green	8 sticks	D49
Crayons	8 boxes	D22
Glue	8 jars	D58
Ice cube	16	D11
Magazine	8	D58
Marker	8	D22, D43, D53, D58
◆ Paper, construction, black	40 sheets	D25, D30
Paper, drawing	128 sheets	D22
Paper, white	8 sheets	D46
Paper plate	16	D9, D49
◆ Pebble	4 cups	D49
Pencil	8	D22, D30, D40
Plant	16	D12
◆ Plastic wrap	8 sheets	D17
Posterboard	32 sheets	D58
Potato, small (2")	8	D17
Rocks, assorted	96	D49
◆ Salt	1 1/2 cups	D53
◆ Sand	12 cups	D35, D49
◆ Soap, bar	16 pieces	D53
Soil, schoolyard	8 cups	D43
◆ Soil, vacant lot	4 cups	D46
◆ Tape, masking	about 4 meters	D5, D43, D53
Tape, transparent	1 roll	D17, D22
◆ Toothpicks	32	D46
Towel, paper	16	D46
Water	about 5 liters	D12, D46, D53
Nonconsumable Items		
◆ Ball, golf	8	D5, D33, D35
Clock or watch	8	D11
Container for water	1	D46, D53
Cover goggles	32	D30, D46
◆ Cup, plastic, 10 oz.	16	D53
◆ Flashlight	8	D5, D30, D33
◆ Globe, inflatable	8	D33
◆ Hand lens	8	D46
◆ Marble	8	D35
◆ Pan, foil, large (See Activity)	8	D35
◆ Pan, pie, aluminum	16	D11
Rocks, assorted	4 cups	D45
◆ Ruler, metric	8	D9
Scissors	32	D58
◆ Spoon, plastic	8	D46, D53
Watering can	8	D12